Applying AutoCAD®

A Step-By-Step Approach

for AutoCAD Release 10
on MS-DOS®, UNIX®, and Macintosh®II computers

by
Terry T. Wohlers
WOHLERS ASSOCIATES

GLENCOE/McGRAW-HILL
A Macmillan/McGraw-Hill Company
Mission Hills, California

Send all inquiries to:
Glencoe/McGraw-Hill
15319 Chatsworth Street
P.O. Box 9509
Mission Hills, CA 91395-9509

ISBN 0-02-677087-3 (Work-Text)
ISBN 0-02-677088-1 (Instructor's Guide)
ISBN 0-02-677089-X (Diskette)

3 4 5 6 7 8 9 10   93 92 91 90

Except where otherwise credited, all CAD drawings within this book were developed with AutoCAD by the author and plotted using a Houston Instrument pen plotter. The AutoCAD images on the front cover were produced with the Bell & Howell Color Digital Imager (CDI) IV film recorder. Landscape rendering courtesy of Greg Jameson, LANDCADD, Inc. Engine drawing courtesy of Joe Schubeck, Eagle Engine Manufacturing. Golden Gate Bridge and Sydney Opera House renderings courtesy of Gary V. Thomas, Autodesk, Inc. Photos on back cover courtesy of Houston Instrument, Apple Computer, Inc., CalComp, and Compaq Computer Corporation.

Dedication

To my lovely wife, Diane, for supporting me throughout the development of this book. And to our son, Chad, for his patience.

Acknowledgments

The author wishes to thank the staff at Glencoe Publishing Company for their hard work and dedication to this book. A very special thanks to Trudy Muller, Director of Technical Education, and Mike Kenny, Editorial Director.

Thanks to all of the people at Autodesk, Inc., who took part in making this book possible. A special thanks to Dr. Joseph Oakey, Manager of the Education Department at Autodesk.

The author also wishes to thank the following organizations for their contributions to this book: Apple Computer, Inc., Bell & Howell Quintar Division, CAD Studio, CalComp, Chase Systems, Compaq Computer Corporation, Control Systems, Eagle Engine Manufacturing, Houston Instrument, LANDCADD, SymSoft, and Synthesis, Inc.

Advisory Board

Table of Contents

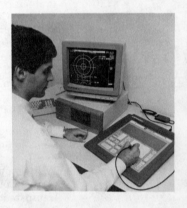

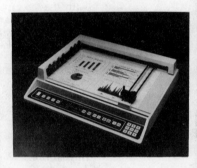

(cont'd. next page)

(Cont'd. from previous page)

Illustrations in front matter provided by the following:

IBM Corporation (p. iv); Houston Instrument (pp. v, viii, and xi); CalComp (pp. vi and ix); Compaq (p. vii); Apollo Computer, Inc. (p. x); Sequoia Creative, Inc. (p. xii); Apple Computer, Inc. (p. xiii).

Introduction

Applying AutoCAD®: A Step-By-Step Approach is a work-text based on the AutoCAD® computer-aided drafting and design package, Release 10. It is designed primarily for new users of AutoCAD, though experienced users also will find it to be a helpful aid for reference and review. Through step-by-step instruction, the book takes students from the beginning to the advanced level. Along the way, they are encouraged to experiment, to create, and to learn firsthand the power and versatility of AutoCAD.

Applying AutoCAD is not restricted to one discipline. Rather, it serves all areas which require methods of drafting, design, and engineering, such as architecture, civil engineering, mapping, landscaping, mechanical and structural engineering, electricity/electronics, facilities planning, and interior design. Less common but potentially very productive areas include theater set and lighting design, museum display design, graphic arts, and even archaeology.

Applying AutoCAD is fully compatible with personal computers running the **MS/PC-DOS®** operating system. Ten major versions of the AutoCAD software run on MS/PC-DOS machines; AutoCAD is installed on this type of computer more than any other. Appendices E-H offer special assistance in using MS/PC-DOS with AutoCAD.

The AutoCAD commands and functions presented in *Applying AutoCAD* are also compatible with the **Apple Macintosh® II** version of AutoCAD. Macintosh II users should first read Appendix I, "Apple Macintosh II Version of AutoCAD." This appendix discusses the unique features of the Macintosh II. If you are using the Mac II version of AutoCAD, ignore any references to MS/PC-DOS commands and functions that may be made in the book.

If you are using another operating system supported by AutoCAD, such as **DEC VMS®** or a **UNIX®** variation, you will also find *Applying AutoCAD* useful in learning how to apply the wide range of commands and functions found in AutoCAD.

Format

The contents of this book are formatted in a straightforward, simple-to-use manner so that instructors, regardless of their background, can easily adapt the book to their existing courses. The book's structure in fact lends itself to picking and choosing units and problems as instructors see fit. Therefore instructors should by no means feel obligated to use the entire work-text to accomplish their course objectives.

For educators beginning a new course using AutoCAD, the book provides an excellent base for developing the course. The units are sequenced in the best order for learning AutoCAD, so instructors are encouraged to use the book's outline as their course outline.

The book contains enough exercises for an entire semester course. Some instructors have used the earlier editions for both introductory and advanced courses. The instructor can adjust the pace and assignments according to the level of the learner group and to the number of hours the students receive on the AutoCAD workstations.

Features

- Fifty clearly-defined units guide students in their progress from basic to advanced levels. Progress is easy to see and review is simple.

- In addition to the fundamentals of AutoCAD, the book presents advanced topics of special interest, including
  - symbol libraries
  - attributes and bills of materials
  - isometrics
  - 3D modeling using surfaces of revolution, ruled surfaces, tabulated surfaces, Coons surface patches, and basic 3D polygon meshes
  - X, Y, Z point filters
  - User Coordinate Systems (UCSs)
  - Dynamic View facility
  - screen, tablet, and icon menu development and customization
  - AutoLISP applications and programming
  - parametric programming
  - DXF and IGES translations
  - slide shows and slide libraries
  - digitizing and plotting
  - hard disk organization, use of batch files, and system management
  - Extended AutoLISP, use of extended memory and I/O page space, and virtual (RAM) disk setup
- Notations in margins correlate every topic to the *AutoCAD Reference Manual* to easily expand students' instruction through individual reading.
- Hint sections throughout the units help students effectively tap the full power of AutoCAD.
- Questions and problems at the end of each unit ensure mastery of AutoCAD.
- Optional problems section challenges and motivates advanced students.
- Useful appendices on topics such as disk formatting, producing backup copies, and reconfiguring AutoCAD help students organize AutoCAD.
- "AutoCAD at Work" vignettes help students understand how AutoCAD is used in business and industry.
- As a bonus, a tablet menu template has been included in the book (Unit 42). In addition, step-by-step instructions teach students how to create their own.

Optional Diskette

An optional companion diskette is available for use with *Applying AutoCAD*. The diskette contains more than 30 useful files. For example, AutoLISP routines (including the special parametric program) and menu files presented in the book are contained on the diskette, saving you the time and effort of accurately entering them manually.

If you want to experiment with DXF and IGES files created by other CAD systems, several are contained on the diskette so that you can see how they import to AutoCAD. Also available on the diskette are several drawing files, including prototype drawings, for use with many of the exercises presented throughout *Applying AutoCAD*. These files save you drawing preparation time when completing the exercises.

The diskette also contains a sample slide show as well as a program that enables you to create a bill of materials. For additional information, contact the address listed on page ii of this book.

To the Student

By following the step-by-step exercises in this book, you will learn to use AutoCAD to create, modify, store, retrieve, and manage AutoCAD drawings and related files. For review and practice, questions and problems have been provided at the end of each unit. In addition, there is a section of more challenging problems following Unit 50.

In order to derive the full benefit of this book, you should be aware of the following:

- *Notational conventions.* Computer keyboards differ. In this book, you will find many references to the RETURN key. On your keyboard, this key may be marked ENTER, NEXT, etc. Likewise, you will find references to the CTRL (control) key. On some keyboards this key is labeled with a different name.

In the step-by-step instructions, user input is in **boldface** type. For example, the instruction "enter the **LINE** command" means that you should either type the word LINE on the keyboard or select it from a screen or tablet menu. Command names are usually shown in uppercase letters, but you can type them in either upper- or lowercase letters.

On the computer screen, AutoCAD default values are displayed within < > . You can select the default value by simply pressing the RETURN key or the space bar.

- *ACAD.DWG prototype drawing.* As you work with AutoCAD, you will learn of the AutoCAD defaults and how these modes and settings are stored in AutoCAD's default prototype drawing called ACAD.DWG. If/when you want to learn more about these default modes and settings, turn to Appendix K, which contains details on the ACAD.DWG prototype drawing.

- *End-of-unit questions.* The questions at the end of each unit are intended to help you review the material in the unit and to expand your knowledge. Therefore, in order to answer some of the questions, you may need to work on the computer or refer to the *AutoCAD Reference Manual*.

About the Author

Terry Wohlers is president of WOHLERS ASSOCIATES, a consulting and training firm located near Denver, Colorado. The firm provides strategic planning and market research to vendors, planning and management assistance to engineering managers, and hands-on AutoCAD training to end-users.

Formerly with Colorado State University, Mr. Wohlers pioneered one of the nation's first university courses on AutoCAD. Since then he has conducted more than 40 seminars and workshops on CAD for practicing professionals throughout the United States and Europe.

The author of more than 80 articles and books on engineering office automation, Mr. Wohlers is contributing editor of such publications as *Computer Graphics World* and *Architectural & Engineering Systems*. His "Peak Efficiency" column appears monthly in *CADENCE*, a popular magazine devoted entirely to AutoCAD.

Mr. Wohlers is currently chairman of the National Computer Graphics Association (NCGA) Section for MicroCADD. He is also an affiliate faculty member at Colorado State University and holds M.S. and B.A. degrees in industrial sciences and technology.

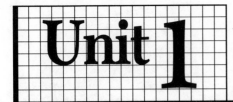

Unit 1   En Route We Pass the Main Menu

■ **OBJECTIVE:**

To understand the purpose of the AutoCAD Main Menu and the components found in the Drawing Editor and to learn the function of the SAVE, END, and QUIT commands

AutoCAD's Main Menu is the starting point through which you will always pass prior to applying AutoCAD. Therefore it is important for you to understand it.

The AutoCAD Drawing Editor is where you spend 95 percent of your time with AutoCAD. The Drawing Editor allows you to create, change, view, and plot drawings. It is therefore necessary for you to understand the purpose of each component found in the Drawing Editor.

■ *Taking a Look Around* _____

1 Start AutoCAD, and you will find yourself in the Main Menu.

HINT: _____
AutoCAD is started by entering **ACAD**. If you need assistance with logging onto the proper drive or directory and starting AutoCAD, see Appendices G and H at the back of this book.

```
Main Menu

    Ø.   Exit AutoCAD
    1.   Begin a NEW drawing
    2.   Edit an EXISTING drawing
    3.   Plot a drawing
    4.   Printer Plot a drawing

    5.   Configure AutoCAD
    6.   File Utilities
    7.   Compile shape/font description file
    8.   Convert old drawing file

Enter selection:
```

2 Select option 1, "Begin a NEW drawing," and press **RETURN**. The computer will ask you to name the drawing. Type **STUFF** and press **RETURN**.

*The numbers in this column correspond to sections in the *AutoCAD® Reference Manual*. Refer to these sections if you would like additional information about the topics covered in *Applying AutoCAD*. For example, if you would like to learn more about the Main Menu, turn to Sections 1.3 and 2.5 of the *Reference Manual*.

AutoCAD® Reference Manual *
1.3, 2.5
1.3, 2.6
2.5.1

CAUTION:

If you are storing your drawing on a floppy diskette, NEVER REMOVE THE DISKETTE FROM THE DRIVE WHILE YOU ARE IN THE DRAWING EDITOR. If you do, you will damage your drawing file.

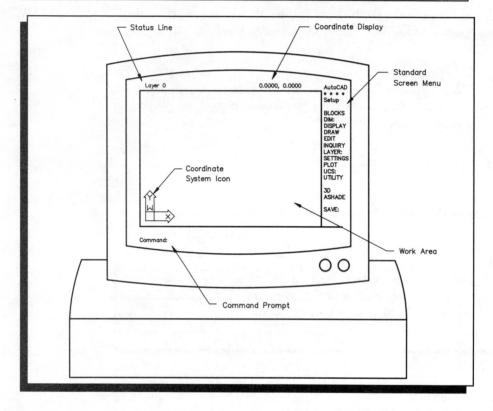

You should now be in the AutoCAD Drawing Editor.

At the right of the screen, you'll find the root page of the standard screen menu. Note each of the items found in this menu.

Notice the prompt line at the bottom of the screen. Keep your eye on this area. This is where you will receive messages from AutoCAD.

At the top of the screen is the status line. The status line tells you the name of the current layer, the status of various AutoCAD modes, and the coordinates of the screen crosshairs (coordinate display).

The rest of the screen is the work area.

Let's see how the screen changes when we enter information.

③ Using your pointing device (mouse or digitizing tablet), select **DRAW** from the root page of the screen menu and watch what happens.

2.6.2

. 8.10

4 Next, select one of the Draw commands, such as **LINE**. Notice that the prompt line has changed:

Command: LINE From point:

---

5 You have just entered the LINE command. AutoCAD is asking you to tell it where you want the line to start. In Unit 2, you'll actually draw some lines. For now, cancel by pressing **CTRL** (control key) and **C** simultaneously.

6 Select the **LAST** option and notice where it takes you.

7 Next, select the **AutoCAD** option found at the top of the screen menu.

8 Now select another item from the root page of the standard screen menu and step through the submenus as you did above.

NOTE:

In Appendix R you'll find the primary screen menu hierarchy.

9 Review Appendix R and then further experiment with moving from one screen submenu to another.

NOTE:

Selecting a menu item which ends with a colon (as in LAYER:) will enter this command as well as display a submenu.

Selecting a menu item whose name is all UPPER CASE, but *without* a colon, will display only a submenu.

Subcommands and command options are generally lower case or mixed case (as in "color" or "Color") and work properly only when picked in response to the appropriate prompts.

10 Enter the **END** command when you are finished. (Either type it and press RETURN or select END from the UTILITY submenu.)

The END command will store your drawing contents on the disk and will take you back to the Main Menu. (In this case, you are storing an empty file named STUFF.)

11 After the Main Menu appears, you can exit AutoCAD by choosing option **0**, "Exit AutoCAD."

SAVE, END, and QUIT Commands _____

There are various ways of storing your drawing to disk and/or exiting the Drawing Editor. They are described below.

SAVE — will save your work but will *not* exit you out of the Drawing Editor.

3.3

END — will save your work and *will* exit you out of the Drawing Editor.

3.2.1

QUIT — will exit you out of the Drawing Editor but will *not* save your work.

3.2.2

You will have the opportunity to practice these commands in the upcoming units.

What If I Enter the Wrong Command? _____

2.6

As you work with AutoCAD, you will be entering commands either by selecting them from menus or typing them at the keyboard. Occasionally you might accidentally select the wrong command or make a typing error. It's easy to correct such mistakes.

If you catch a typing error *before* you press RETURN . . .   use the backspace key to delete the incorrect character(s). Then continue typing.

If you select the wrong command from the standard screen menu . . .   you can usually get back to the "Command:" prompt if you press the space bar once or twice;

OR

enter CTRL C (press the control and C keys at the same time).

If you type the wrong command . . .   enter CTRL C to return to the "Command:" prompt.

Questions

1. Explain the overall purpose of the Main Menu.

_____

_____

2. Describe the purpose of the first two Main Menu options:

   0. Exit AutoCAD _____

   _____

   1. Begin a NEW drawing _____

   _____

3. Briefly describe the function of the following screen menu options:

   LAST _____

   DRAW _____

   AUTOCAD _____

   LINE: _____

4. Briefly explain the basic function of the AutoCAD "Command:" prompt line.

   _____

   _____

5. Explain the purpose of the following AutoCAD commands:

   SAVE _____

   END _____

   QUIT _____

6. With regard to screen menu items, what does a colon (:) after the menu item indicate?

   _____

   _____

Problems

Select the following submenus from the root page of the screen menu. Then select the commands indicated and list the options available under each command. The first problem has been completed as an example.

ROOT PAGE

MENU ITEM	COMMAND	AVAILABLE OPTIONS
1. DRAW ⟶	POLYGON ⟶	Edge
		I-scribe
		C-scribe
2. DRAW ⟶	CIRCLE ⟶	_____
		_____
		_____
		_____
		_____
3. EDIT ⟶	CHAMFER ⟶	_____
		_____
		_____
4. EDIT ⟶	ERASE ⟶	_____
		_____
		_____
		_____
		_____
		_____
		_____
5. EDIT ⟶	COPY ⟶	_____
		_____
		_____
		_____
		_____
		_____
		_____

AUTOCAD® AT WORK

Computer-Aided Design and Drafting: A Brand-New Medium

"We were both working for large architectural firms in Texas. We looked at each other one day and said, 'We're not getting any younger—let's start our own company.' " When the two-person Houston, Texas, firm of Buday Wells, Architects, first opened its doors in 1983, partners Richard Buday (quoted above) and Dwayne Wells brought in a microcomputer with word processing and accounting software—they knew it would enhance the efficiency of general office practices. What they didn't know, however, was that their micro could also function as a primary design tool.

"Armed with a vision of the future," says Richard Buday, "we went out looking for an affordable CAD system, although we had no idea at the time that micro-based CAD systems even existed. When we met a consultant who showed us CAD software running on a PC, we were amazed. Nearly all the benefits of mainframe CAD—boilerplating, cutting and pasting, revising—were there. We could draw, rotate, duplicate, and mirror images to any size and scale."

The partners installed AutoCAD on their microcomputer, adding a graphics card and a D-size flatbed plotter. "Learning to draw on CAD," Buday notes, "was like learning how to use a brand-new pen. After you get past that awkward stage of learning how to hold the pen, it becomes an extension of your hand and an extension of your thinking process.

"We started out using it as an electronic draftsperson; we would design manually and then copy the designs into the computer to print them. But as a two-person firm, we had more work than we could handle, so we soon began using the computer for design too. The computer became our great equalizer—we began producing as if there were four or five people in our office rather than just two."

Now the firm (which has grown to five people) uses the computer for all its designing and drafting, producing plans with a productivity ratio of two to three times that of work done manually. "The bottom line result," says Buday, "isn't that we go home any sooner—we still work 12-hour days. The difference is that we do more in the same amount of time. Because CAD can duplicate any element of a design, we're not wasting time on repetitive work.... The key to making any CAD program efficient is building into it as much of your working habits and techniques as you can. The more you build into your computer, the less you have to do by hand."

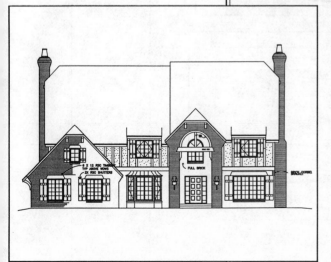

Courtesy of Rodger A. Brooks, Architect

Unit 2

The Line Forms Here

■ OBJECTIVE:

To apply the LINE, MULTIPLE, and POLYGON commands, the pull-down menus, and several AutoCAD shortcuts

The LINE command is the most often used AutoCAD command simply because most drawings contain lines. There are a number of ways to produce these lines. Some ways are simple; others can be a bit confusing. The following exercise uses the simplest approach to producing lines since you are probably new to the system.

The POLYGON command allows fast creation of regular polygons. A regular polygon is one with sides of equal length.

■ *Drawing Lines with a Pointing Device*

1 Load AutoCAD and select option **2**, "Edit an EXISTING drawing," from the Main Menu.

2 In reply to "Enter NAME of drawing:" enter **STUFF**.

3 After you find yourself in the Drawing Editor, select the **LINE** command from the screen menu.

4 With your pointing device, draw two of the polygons shown here.

HINT:
After you've completed one polygon, press **RETURN** or the **space bar** to end the LINE command. To construct the next polygon, bring up the LINE command again by pressing RETURN or the space bar. This will activate the previously used command—a real shortcut and timesaver.

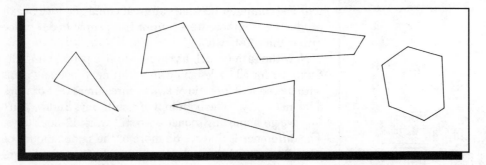

5 Create more polygons using the LINE command.

HINT:

To automatically close a polygon and terminate the line command, type the letter C and press RETURN (or select "close" from the screen menu) prior to constructing the last line of the polygon. Press RETURN or the space bar to reactivate the LINE command.

MULTIPLE Command

3.9

The MULTIPLE command is available to achieve multiple entries of a command. For example, "Command: MULTIPLE LINE" will cause AutoCAD to automatically repeat the LINE command until a cancel (CTRL C) is issued.

1 Type **MULTIPLE LINE** and press **RETURN**.

2 Create several polygons.

Notice the LINE command remains entered.

3 Enter **CTRL C** to cancel the LINE command.

4 Practice drawing additional polygons using the automatic close feature as well as the other shortcuts just described.

LINE Undo Option

4.1.1

From time to time, it's necessary to back up or undo one or more of the line segments. Suppose you have drawn three lines in creating a polygon, and you're about to enter your fourth point when you realize the third line you drew is incorrect. The easiest and fastest way of correcting this is to select the Undo option from the screen menu or type U (short for Undo) and press RETURN.

1 Enter the **LINE** command.

2 Create three connecting line segments of any length and orientation.

3 Type **U** and press **RETURN**.

Your last line segment should disappear.

4 Continue to enter **U** until all the line segments are gone.

POLYGON Command _____

The POLYGON command enables you to create regular polygons with anywhere from 3 to 1024 sides. Let's try a pentagon.

1 Select the **DRAW** submenu from the screen menu.

2 Select **next**, located near the bottom of the screen menu.

This displays the remaining DRAW menu items.

3 Select **POLYGON** from the menu.

_____ NOTE: _____

Typing the POLYGON command at the "Command:" prompt is an alternative to the preceding three steps. If you are a fast typist, you may prefer to do this.

4 Type **5** in reply to "Number of sides:" and press **RETURN**.

5 With your pointing device, pick a point in an open area on your screen. This will be the center of your polygon.

AutoCAD now wants to know if you want to create a polygon inscribed within or circumscribed about a circle.

6 Select **I-scribe** from the screen menu or type **I** and press **RETURN**.

7 With your pointing device, move your screen crosshairs around the center of your polygon.

8 Pick a point, or enter a numeric value, such as .5, at the keyboard.

9 Draw several more regular polygons using the remaining two options provided by the POLYGON command.

Pull-Down Menus _____

AutoCAD also provides pull-down menus, as shown in the following illustration. However, certain display devices do not support AutoCAD's advanced user interface and consequently do not support the pull-down menus.

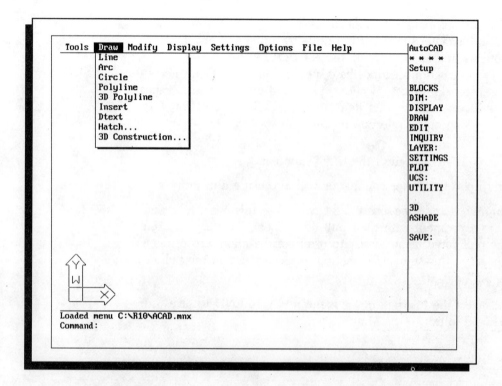

1. Using your pointing device, move the crosshairs to the top of the screen.

A menu bar will appear if your computer display device supports the pull-down menus and if the "status line" is configured. If the status line is present but the menu bar does not appear, skip this section. Enter **END** to save your work and to exit to the Main Menu. If the menu bar does appear, then continue.

2. On the menu bar, pick the **Draw** menu and review its contents, but do not pick one of its items at this point.

3. Move the pointing device and pick other pull-down menus and review their contents.

NOTE:

Appendix S illustrates all of the items found in each pull-down menu.

4. Return to the **Draw** menu and select the **Line** menu item.

5. Draw a line and press **RETURN** when you are finished.

Notice the LINE command automatically reenters at the "Command:" prompt. This is characteristic of certain pull-down menu items. Their operation appears similar to applying the MULTIPLE command. Technically, the instructions behind these special pull-down menu items use the "Auto" and "Single" object selection modes and are designed to repeat indefinitely until you pick another item or press CTRL C. See Unit 4 for more information on object selection modes.

6 Enter **CTRL C** to cancel the LINE command.

Picking menu items that enter commands will also cause a cancel.

As other commands and functions are introduced in this book, take the opportunity to experiment with their pull-down menu counterparts. You may find the pull-down menus easier to use than the main screen menu. However, not all of the AutoCAD functions are contained in the pull-down menus.

7 Last, select the **File** pull-down menu and pick **END** to save your work and to exit to the Main Menu.

Questions

1. Describe the purpose of Main Menu option 2.

   _____

   _____

2. Explain the relationship between your pointing device and the screen crosshairs.

   _____

   _____

3. What is the fastest and simplest method of reentering the previously entered command?

   _____

4. What is the fastest method of closing a polygon when using the LINE command?

   _____

5. Describe the purpose of the MULTIPLE command.

   _____

6. Explain the use of the LINE Undo option.

   _____

7. Explain the use of the LINE Continue option.

   _____

8. How is the operation of using the Line pull-down menu item different than selecting LINE from the standard screen menu or typing it?

   _____

   _____

9. Explain each of the following POLYGON command options.

   Edge _____

   I-scribe _____

   C-scribe _____

How to Save Your Problems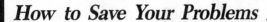

Most units of this work-text conclude with some problems for you to complete. You'll probably want to save your problems, so start a new file for each one. Code the file by unit and problem number. For example, for the problems in this unit:

1. Select option 1 from the Main Menu.
2. For the first problem, call the file **PRB2-1**.
3. When you are finished with that problem, enter **END** to save it and return to the Main Menu.

Now you are ready to start PRB2-2. Repeat Steps 1 through 3 for each problem you do.

Problems

Using the LINE and POLYGON commands and your pointing device, draw each of the following objects. Don't worry about exact sizes, but do try to make them look as much like the ones below as possible. Practice the shortcuts and various options covered in this unit.

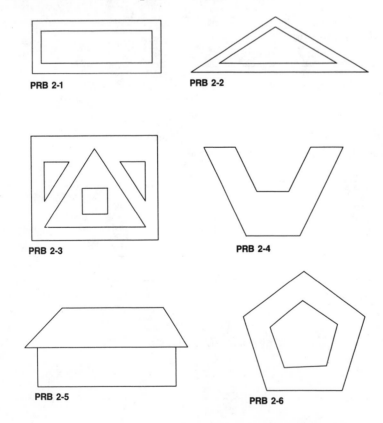

PRB 2-1

PRB 2-2

PRB 2-3

PRB 2-4

PRB 2-5

PRB 2-6

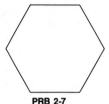

PRB 2-7

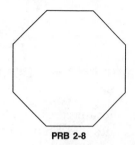

PRB 2-8

AUTOCAD® AT WORK

CAM (Computer-Aided Monster) *

New York City lies in ruins, destroyed by an earthquake. Even worse, the temblor has awakened a giant beast. Eyes flashing, lips snarling, he roars with anger as smoke and flames surround him. King Kong is on the rampage.

The scene is witnessed by a group of visitors who have come to view the wreckage. Fortunately, they are safe in their specially built tour trams—or are they? As the trams cross a suspension bridge, the thirty-foot ape shakes the bridge's cables. Kong's huge jaws open, showing the visitors menacing yellow fangs and enveloping them in his steamy breath.

The visitors, however, manage to escape. They always do, for the ruined city is actually a set on the Universal Studio lot in Hollywood, and Kong is a mechanical and electronic marvel designed and built by Sequoia Creative Inc. to terrify and delight tourists.

To create the monster, the special-effects company used metal, plastic, fur, paint—and AutoCAD. Using the AutoCAD computer drafting package saved time and money. After the designer finished drawing a main part, a detail drafter used that drawing as the basis for his work. This avoided having to start a new drawing for each piece. Also, the ability to draw plans quickly and accurately reduced the number of revisions needed during construction.

AutoCAD's accuracy and the skills of Sequoia Creative's staff paid off. Originally, an audience distance of eighty feet was planned so that imperfections in the monster would not be seen. The final result, however, was so realistic that the tour trams now pass within six feet of Kong, almost close enough to shake hands with this furry celebrity!

*Based on a story in *CADalyst* magazine, Vol. 3, No. 5.

Courtesy of Sequoia Creative, Inc.

Unit 3 And Around We Go

AutoCAD®
Reference
Manual

■ OBJECTIVE:

To apply the CIRCLE, ARC, ELLIPSE, DONUT, and DRAGMODE commands

The purpose of this unit is to experiment with the AutoCAD commands that allow you to produce arcs and circular objects.

The following race car is typical of the extent to which drawings utilize round and curved lines. Later, you may wish to create a simplified version of this car.

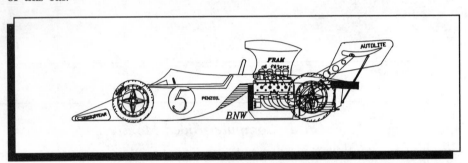

AutoCAD Drawing Courtesy of BNW, Inc.

■ *CIRCLE Command* _____

4.3

AutoCAD makes it easy to draw round and curved lines. For example, to draw wheels, follow these steps.

1. Load AutoCAD and proceed into the Drawing Editor by beginning a new drawing. Name it **CAR**.

2. Select the **CIRCLE** command from the DRAW submenu contained in the screen menu at the right of your screen.

3. Select the **CEN,RAD:** option.

4.3.1

4. Draw the larger (outer) circle of the wheel first. Use your pointing device to pick the center point and then the radius. AutoCAD will complete the circle. Don't worry about exact location or size.

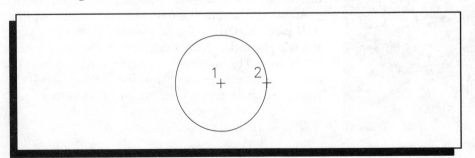

5 Next, draw the smaller circle, again by selecting **CEN,RAD** from the screen menu and picking the center point and the radius.

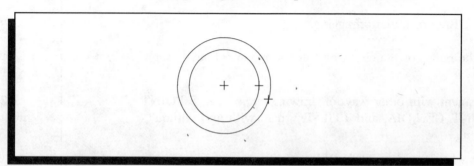

6 Now enter **DRAGMODE**. Select it from the SETTINGS submenu or type it.

6.14

Note the prompt line that appears on the screen. If DRAGMODE is <On> or <Auto>, type **OFF** to turn it off. If DRAGMODE is <Off>, enter either **ON** or **Auto**.

7 Now draw the second wheel, again using the CIRCLE CEN,RAD option.

What is the difference between drawing the circles with DRAGMODE ON (or Auto) and drawing them with DRAGMODE OFF?

NOTE:

As you have seen, dragging allows you to visually move, rotate, or scale an object. Not every command supports dragging. The *AutoCAD Reference Manual* will state whether or not a command supports dragging.

2.7.5

DRAGMODE ON enables dragging for every command that supports it. To initiate dragging within a command, enter DRAG. If the DRAG request is embedded in the menu item—as is the case with the CEN,RAD option— you do not need to enter DRAG.

DRAGMODE Auto enables dragging for every command that supports it, without having to enter DRAG.

When DRAGMODE is OFF, no dragging of objects can occur, even when DRAG is embedded in menu items.

To learn more about how dragging works, try the following.

8 With DRAGMODE ON, draw a circle as before.

Now, let's draw another circle, but this time . . .

9 . . . .instead of selecting the CEN,RAD option from the screen menu, press the **space bar**.

10 Pick a center point for the circle. Note what happens when you move the crosshairs. The circle does not drag.

11 Enter **DRAG** to initiate dragging.

12 Pick the radius of the circle, or enter a numerical value, such as .75.

13 Experiment with other ways of drawing circles, *i.e.*, 2 POINT, 3 POINT, CEN,DIA, and TTR. Try them with and without dragging.

4.3.2
through
4.3.5

Can you drag when using the CEN,DIA option?

ARC Command _____

4.4

Now let's focus on the ARC command. (If you need to clear the screen, see Unit 4 for instructions on how to use the ERASE command.)

1 Enter the **DRAGMODE** command and the **Auto** option.

2 Select the **ARC** command from the DRAW submenu contained in the screen menu at the right of your screen.

3 Select the **3-point** option and produce several different arcs.

4.4.1

Let's experiment with other methods of creating arcs.

1 Select the **S,C,E** (start point, center, endpoint) option from the menu.

4.4.2

2 Specify three consecutive points: start, center, and end.

3 Select the **S,C,A** (start point, center, included angle) option.

4.4.3

4 Specify a start point and center point.

5 Then enter a number (positive or negative) up to 360. The number specifies the angle in degrees.

6 Try the **S,E,R** (start point, endpoint, radius) option.

4.4.5

7 Simply enter three consecutive points. Remember, you may enter a numerical value for the radius.

**AutoCAD®
Reference
Manual**

⑧ Experiment with the remaining ARC options. What do the following options specify?

S,C,E = _____ Start, Center, End _____

S,C,A = _____

S,C,L = _____

S,E,A = _____

S,E,R = _____

S,E,D = _____

C,S,E = _____

C,S,A = _____

C,S,L = _____

Next, let's produce the following curved line, which is really a series of arcs.

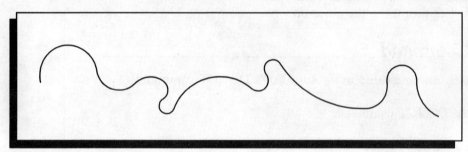

① Make sure DRAGMODE is set to Auto or On.

② Enter the **ARC 3-point** option and draw an arc.

③ Pick the **continue** option (CONTIN:) found in the ARC submenu.

④ Create the second arc segment.

Notice it is tangent to the first.

⑤ Repeat Steps 3 and 4 until you are finished.

■ *ELLIPSE Command* _____

4.6.5

① Make sure DRAGMODE is set to Auto.

② Select the **ELLIPSE** command from the DRAW submenu and specify a first point as shown in the following illustration.

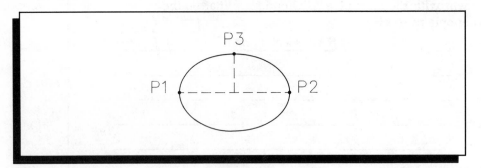

3 Specify the second point directly to the right of the
first point.

4 Move your crosshairs and watch the ellipse develop. Pick a
point, or enter a numeric value, and the ellipse will appear.

5 Experiment with the ELLIPSE command by constructing
additional ellipses using the other options.

DONUT Command

4.6.4

Solid-filled donuts can be created using AutoCAD's DONUT command.

1 Enter the **DONUT** command.

2 Specify an inside diameter of **.75**...

3 ... and an outside diameter of **1.3**.

Your crosshairs should now be locked onto an outline of a donut ready to be
dragged and placed by its center.

4 Place the donut anywhere on the screen by picking a point.

5 Move your crosshairs away from the new solid-filled donut and
notice the prompt line at the bottom of your screen.

6 Place several donuts on your screen.

7 Press **RETURN** when you're finished.

That's all there is to the DONUT command.

8 Store your work and exit the Drawing Editor by entering the
END command.

Time Out for a Discussion on Storing Your Drawings

Until now, you may have been storing your AutoCAD drawing files in the main AutoCAD hard disk directory. This directory will eventually grow large and too cumbersome to review your files. Therefore it is not a good practice to continue storing files in this fashion. Two other, and much better, alternatives are explained here.

1) Create a directory under your main AutoCAD directory. Its name should reflect the files you plan to store in it. For example, you could call it by your first name, such as Frank or RaNae. This would then become your personal directory for storing AutoCAD-related files.

NOTE:

Refer to Appendix G for steps in creating and using hard disk directories.

2) The second option is to store your AutoCAD drawings on a formatted floppy diskette. This is easy to do, and it also keeps your main AutoCAD directory clean of user files. Two disadvantages, though, are that floppy drives operate more slowly than hard disk drives and floppy diskettes have less capacity than hard disks.

If you use this second option, you must specify the drive prior to the name of your drawing (*e.g.*, **A:CAR**, if the drive you use is "A" drive).

If you are already using one of these methods, that's good. If you are not, consider one of them before your main AutoCAD directory of files becomes too large (more than 100 or so files).

The units in this book are *not* written specifically to either of these storage options. This leaves it up to you to choose the option best for you. Once you have decided, use this option to override the way drawings are created and retrieved in this book. If you don't, they will be stored in the main AutoCAD directory.

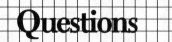

Questions

1. When drawing circles, arcs, and ellipses, what happens when the DRAGMODE command is set to Auto?

_____

_____

2. What happens when the DRAGMODE command is Off?

_____

_____

3. Briefly describe the following methods of producing circles.

   2-point _____

   3-point _____

   CEN,DIA _____

4. In what AutoCAD submenu are the ARC and CIRCLE commands found?

_____

5. What function does the ARC CONTIN option serve?

_____

_____

6. When specifying an angle in degrees, what direction does a negative number specify: clockwise or counterclockwise?

_____

7. Explain the purpose of the DONUT command.

_____

_____

8. Describe two procedures for storing AutoCAD files.

_____

_____

_____

Problems

Using the commands you've just learned, complete the following drawings. Don't worry about text matter or exact shapes, sizes, or locations, but do try to make your drawings look similar to the ones below.

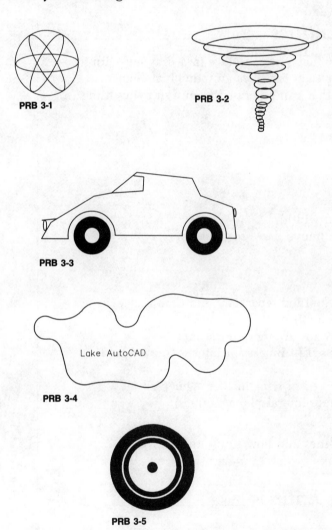

PRB 3-1

PRB 3-2

PRB 3-3

Lake AutoCAD

PRB 3-4

PRB 3-5

23

Unit 4 — Now You See It . . .

■ OBJECTIVE:

To apply the ERASE, REDRAW, and OOPS commands and object selection options

As you use AutoCAD, you will often need to delete all or part of a drawing. This unit shows you how.

First, a Word about Entities

1.2.1

An entity is a predefined element that you can place in a drawing with a single command. AutoCAD treats each entity as an individual element. For example, the smallest object that can be erased from a drawing using the ERASE command is an entity.

AutoCAD uses 14 types of entities:
   Lines
   Points
   Circles and Arcs
   Dimensions
   Traces (solid lines of a specified width)
   Polylines (a connected series of line and arc segments of a
      specified width)
   Solids (solid filled areas)
   Text (words, numbers, etc.)
   Shapes (small objects that can be filed separately and then added to
      drawings; shapes are seldom used)
   Blocks (objects formed from groups of other entities)
   Attributes (text information stored in Blocks for later extraction and
      reporting purposes)
   3D Polylines (3D objects composed of straight line segments)
   3D Faces (3D triangular or quadrilateral plane sections)
   3D Meshes (3D polygon meshes)

You'll learn more about these entities and how to use them as you complete the exercises in this book.

Erasing and Restoring Entities

1 Load AutoCAD and Begin a New Drawing. Call it **MISTAKES**.

NOTE:

As explained in the previous unit, you may prefer to store your files in a personal directory or diskette. If you choose to use a directory, enter the name of the directory before the name of the drawing; for example, DIANE\MISTAKES. (See Appendix G for information on how to create directories.) If you choose to use a diskette, enter A:MISTAKES, if your formatted diskette is contained in drive A. (See Appendix E for information on formatting diskettes.)

AutoCAD® Reference Manual

2 Using the LINE and CIRCLE commands, draw the following box and circle at any convenient size and location.

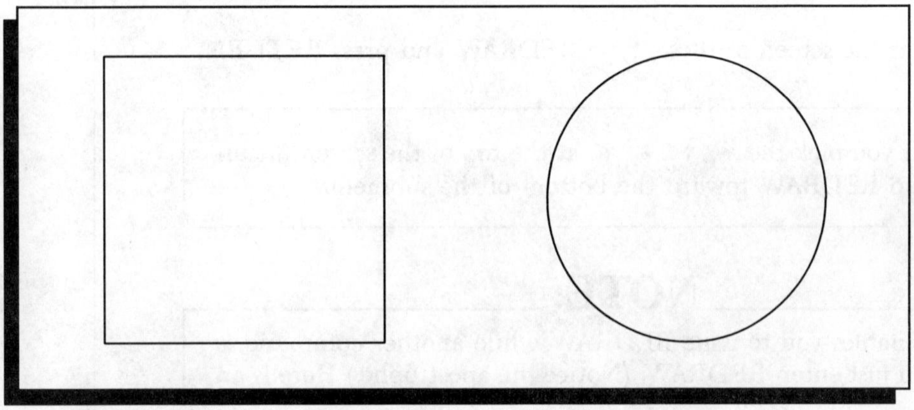

3 Select **ERASE** from the EDIT submenu at the right of your screen. 5.1.1

AutoCAD asks you to "Select objects:". Notice that your crosshairs have changed to a small box. The box provides a larger pointer for selecting objects.

4 Select **Window** from the screen menu (or type **W** and press **RETURN**). 2.9

5 Place a window around the square you created. To do this, imagine a box or rectangle surrounding the entire figure. Move the crosshairs to any corner of the imaginary box and pick a point. Then move the crosshairs to the opposite corner and pick a point. The object must lie entirely within the window.

Notice what happens. The object to be erased is highlighted with broken lines as shown in the following illustration.

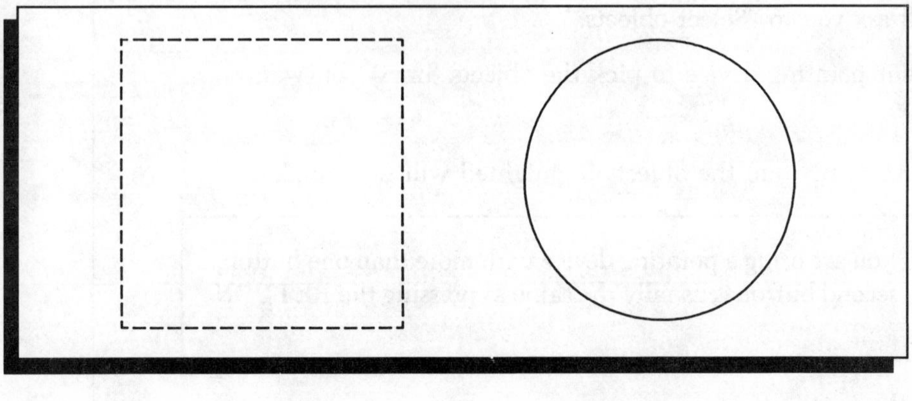

6 Press **RETURN** to make it disappear.

Now the lines are gone, but the "blips" (construction points) remain.

7 To clear the screen of these, type **REDRAW** and press **RETURN**.

6.8

HINT:
> If you pick the ＊ ＊ ＊ ＊ at the top of the screen menu, you will find REDRAW toward the bottom of the submenu.

NOTE:

AutoCAD enables you to issue REDRAW while another command is entered. You just enter 'REDRAW. (Notice the apostrophe.) Here is an example:

> Command: LINE
> From point: 'REDRAW

After REDRAW is performed, the following appears:

> Resuming LINE command.
> From point:

This operation is called the transparent use of the REDRAW command. Try it.

What if you erased an object by mistake and you want to restore it?

8 Enter the **OOPS** command.

5.1.2

What if you want to select single entities, such as individual line segments?

1 Enter **ERASE**. (Do not use the Erase item contained in the Modify pull-down menu for this exercise.)

AutoCAD will ask you to "Select objects:".

2 Use your pointing device to pick the objects (lines) you want to erase.

3 Press **RETURN** and the objects highlighted will be erased.

HINT:
> If you are using a pointing device with more than one button, pressing the second button is usually the same as pressing the RETURN key.

Now let's try the Last option.

1 Issue **OOPS** to restore the original figures.

2 Enter the **ERASE** command.

3 Select **Last** from the screen menu. (Or type **L** and press **RETURN**.)   5.1.1

The last object you drew should be highlighted.

4 Press **RETURN**.

If you reenter ERASE and Last, entities will be erased in the reverse order from which they were created.

Now let's try a new object selection procedure.

1 Enter **OOPS** to restore the original figure, or if necessary, recreate the objects.

2 Enter the **ERASE** command.

3 Place a window around the square, but do not press RETURN yet.

4 Type **R** and press **RETURN**, or select the **Remove** option from the menu.   2.9

Notice that the prompt line changes to "Remove objects:". You can now remove a line or lines from your erase window. The line(s) you remove will *not* be erased.

5 Remove one of the lines by simply picking one with your pointing device.

Note that the line you picked is no longer broken.

To restore the "Select objects:" prompt. . .

6 . . . type **A** for Add and press **RETURN**, or select **Add** from the screen menu.   2.9

Notice that your prompt line changes back to "Select objects:".

7 Now use your pointing device to select the circle or one of the lines in the square.

8 Press **RETURN** to make the highlighted lines disappear.

So you see, you can select and remove objects as you wish until you are ready to perform the operation. The objects selected are indicated by broken lines. These procedures work not only with the ERASE command but also with all commands that require object selection, such as MOVE, COPY, MIRROR, ARRAY, and many others.

9 Enter **OOPS** to restore the figures to the screen.

There is another way of backing up or undoing objects you have selected. Let's try it.

1 Enter the **ERASE** command.

2 Pick two lines from your square, but do not press RETURN.

Two lines should now be broken.

3 Type **U** and press **RETURN**, or select the **Undo** option from the screen menu.   2.9

Notice what happened to the last line you selected.

4 Select the **Undo** option again.

So you see, you can back up one step at a time with the Undo option.

The Crossing option is similar to the Window option, but it selects all objects within and crossing the window boundary.   2.9

1 Enter **ERASE** at the keyboard or from the standard screen menu.

2 Type **C** and press **RETURN**, or select **Crossing** from the screen menu, and pick a point in the center of the screen.

3 Move your crosshairs to form a box and notice that it is made up of broken lines.

4 Form the box so that it crosses over at least one entity on the screen and press the pick button in reply to "Other corner:".

5 Press **RETURN**.

Single Option _____   2.9
                                                          B.4.13

1 Select the **Erase** item from the **Modify** pull-down menu.

The single (SI) object selection option is embedded in this menu item.

2 Select one of the lines on the screen.

The Single option causes the command to execute immediately, without pause for further interaction.

3 Pick another line.

Auto Option

The Auto option enables you to apply the Window and Crossing options without the need to enter them.

1 Select **Erase** from the pull-down menu.

The Auto (AU) option is also embedded in this menu item, as you can see.

2 Pick a point in the center of the screen.

3 Move your pointing device to the right, and then up or down to form a box.

If you were to pick a second point, you would erase all objects that lie entirely within this box. This is equivalent to the "Window" option.

4 Move your pointing device to the left of the first point, and then up or down to form another box.

Notice the box is made up of broken lines. If you were to pick a second point, you would erase all objects that lie within or cross the box. This is equivalent to the "Crossing" option.

5 Pick a point.

6 Experiment further with this object selection procedure.

7 Enter **END** to save your work and to exit the Drawing Editor.

Questions

1. After you enter the ERASE command, what does AutoCAD ask you to do?

   _____

2. What command is used to delete the construction points?

   _____

3. How do you place a window around a figure during object selection?

   _____

   _____

4. If you erased an object by mistake, how can you restore it?

   _____

   Will this method work if you drew something else after erasing the object?

   _____

5. How can you retain part of what has been selected for erasure while remaining in the ERASE command?

   _____

6. What is the fastest way of erasing the last object you drew?

   _____

7. Describe each of these object selection options.

   Window   = _____

   Last   = _____

   Previous = _____

   Crossing = _____

   Remove   = _____

   Add   = _____

   Undo   = _____

Problem

To gain skill in using the object selection options and the ERASE command, try the following exercise. **Do not** enter the Erase item from the pull-down menu for this particular problem.

1. Load the drawing called **STUFF**.

2. Enter the **ERASE** command and use the various options to accomplish the following:

    • Place a window around polygon *a*.
    • Pick two of polygon *b*'s lines for erasure.
    • Use the Crossing option to select polygons *c* and *d*.
    • "Remove" one line selection from polygon *c* and one from polygon *d*.
    • Pick two lines from polygon *e* for erasure but then "Remove" one of the lines so it won't be erased.

3. Now press **RETURN**.

4. Enter **REDRAW**.

You should have nine entities (line segments) left on the screen.

5. Enter **OOPS** to restore your drawing to its original form.

HINT:
If you run into difficulties, type **QUIT** and discard the changes you've made. This will take you back to the Main Menu and you can again load **STUFF**.

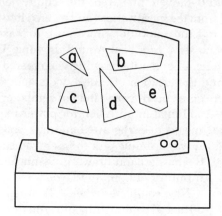

AUTOCAD® AT WORK

Using CAD to Design a Computer Center*

The Center for Computer-Integrated Engineering and Manufacturing (CCIEM) at the University of Tennessee's College of Engineering provides students, faculty, and staff with access to several state-of-the-art computer-aided design/computer-aided engineering (CAD/CAE) systems. In addition, the Center provides local industries with technical assistance in CAD/CAE, CIM (computer-integrated manufacturing), robotics, and artificial intelligence research and development.

In June of 1984, the process of specifying the design and layout of this multi-vendor computational facility was initiated. The proposed facility was to occupy space previously designated for classrooms and consisted of about 2,800 sq. ft. The design had to maximize the space available and provide for future growth of the facilities. Steven R. Foster, manager and coordinator of CCIEM, recognized that the task could best be handled on a CAD system, and AutoCAD was selected for its features and moderate cost.

The design of the CCIEM facility included a number of steps, each step providing information to the next to build up the database. Information required to design the facility included specifications for hardware, a raised floor, workstations, air conditioning, lighting, power, fire protection, and security. As bid data were prepared, the requirements for the equipment were captured from the specifications and entered into the graphics database.

The first step in the renovation process was to make a 3D drawing of the existing layout to serve as a background drawing. Using the background drawing as a base, a composite drawing was created containing the raised floor system and the location of access doors and ramps.

Symbols were developed for each item of computer equipment to be used in the facility. Additional information for power requirements and device description was included in the attribute data assigned to each symbol. It was a simple task to insert the equipment symbols into the background drawing. Symbols were also used for the furniture, simplifying layout.

Now completed, the CCIEM represents one of the most advanced computer facilities on the University of Tennessee campus. It offers a pleasant, comfortable environment in which to conduct research and development. Additionally, as the Center grows it will be possible to utilize an up-to-date set of plans maintained in the CCIEM centralized database to change the configuration of the Center.

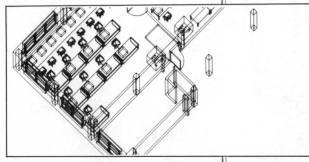

*Based on a story in *CADENCE* magazine, Vol 2, No. 1.

 **Obtaining Help**

■ OBJECTIVE:

To obtain help when using AutoCAD commands

Working with AutoCAD is easy as long as everything goes smoothly, but sometimes you get stuck on how to use a certain command. Help is available, and this unit will show you how to get it.

■ *HELP Command*

3.1

1 Load AutoCAD and select option 2 from the Main Menu. Type **STUFF** and press **RETURN**.

2 After the drawing is on the screen, enter **HELP** or **?**.

You will receive the following prompt:

```
Command name (RETURN) for list):
```

At this point you can type in the name of a command to obtain instructions on how to use that command. Or you can press RETURN to get a list of AutoCAD commands. Let's try both.

3 Type **MOVE**. (Don't forget to press **RETURN**.) You should get a screen that looks like this:

```
The MOVE command is used to move one or more existing drawing
entities from one location in the drawing to another.

Format:  MOVE  Select objects:  (select)
               Base point or displacement:
               Second point of displacement:  (if base selected above)

You can "drag" the object into position on the screen.  To do this,
designate a reference point on the object in response to the "Base
point..." prompt, and then reply "DRAG" to the "Second point:" prompt.
The selected objects will follow the movements of the screen
crosshairs.  Move the objects into position and then press the
pointer's "pick" button.

See also:  Section 5.2 of the Reference Manual.

Command:
```

Note the mention of the *Reference Manual* in the above screen. This is the same guide that is referred to in the marginal notations throughout *Applying AutoCAD*.

4 Turn to Section 5.2 of the *Reference Manual*. This section describes EDIT and INQUIRY commands. Note that section 5.2.1, "MOVE Command," includes detailed information that is not provided when using the HELP command on the computer.

5 Press **RETURN**.

You will again get the message "Command name (RETURN for list):".

6 Press **RETURN** to see a partial list of commands.

```
AutoCAD Command List   (' = transparent command)

APERTURE        CHANGE          DIVIDE          EXPLODE         IGESOUT
ARC             CHPROP          DONUT           EXTEND          INSERT
AREA            CIRCLE          DOUGHNUT        FILES           ISOPLANE
ARRAY           COLOR           DRAGMODE        FILL            LAYER
ATTDEF          COPY            DTEXT           FILLET          LIMITS
ATTDISP         DBLIST          DVIEW           FILMROLL        LINE
ATTEDIT         DDATTE          DXBIN           'GRAPHSCR       LINETYPE
ATTEXT          'DDEMODES       DXFIN           GRID            LIST
AXIS            'DDLMODES       DXFOUT          HANDLES         LOAD
BASE            'DDRMODES       EDGESURF        HATCH           LTSCALE
BLIPMODE        DDUCS           ELEV            'HELP / '?      MEASURE
BLOCK           DELAY           ELLIPSE         HIDE            MENU
BREAK           DIM/DIM1        END             ID              MINSERT
CHAMFER         DIST            ERASE           IGESIN          MIRROR

Press RETURN for further help.
```

Notice the transparent commands—those that can be entered while another command is in progress.

7 Press **RETURN** again to see the remaining AutoCAD commands.

```
    AutoCAD Command List   (' = transparent command)

MOVE           PRPLOT          ROTATE          STRETCH         UNITS
MSLIDE         PURGE           RSCRIPT         STYLE           'VIEW
MULTIPLE       QTEXT           RULESURF        TABLET          VIEWPORTS
OFFSET         QUIT            SAVE            TABSURF         VIEWRES
OOPS           REDEFINE        SCALE           TEXT            VPOINT
ORTHO          REDO            SCRIPT          'TEXTSCR        VPORTS
OSNAP          'REDRAW         SELECT          TIME            VSLIDE
'PAN           'REDRAWALL      'SETVAR         TRACE           WBLOCK
PEDIT          REGEN           SHAPE           TRIM            'ZOOM
PLAN           REGENALL        SHELL/SH        U               3DFACE
PLINE          REGENAUTO       SKETCH          UCS             3DMESH
PLOT           RENAME          SNAP            UCSICON         3DPOLY
POINT          'RESUME         SOLID           UNDEFINE
POLYGON        REVSURF         STATUS          UNDO

At the "Command:" prompt, you can enter RETURN to repeat the last command.

Press RETURN for further help.
```

⑧ Press **RETURN** again and you will see tips on entering coordinates.

⑨ Press **RETURN** again and you will see tips on selecting objects.

①⓪ Return to the Drawing Editor by pressing the flip screen function key (**Fl**).

There is another very useful way of obtaining help.

① Enter the **MOVE** command.

② Type **'HELP** or **'?** (note the leading apostrophe) and press **RETURN**.

As you can see, this procedure allows you to obtain help in the middle of a command, when you're most likely to need it. When you press RETURN, the command resumes.

③ Exit the Drawing Editor by entering **QUIT**. (Obtain HELP if you're unsure how to use QUIT.)

35

Questions

1. How do you obtain a listing of all AutoCAD commands when you are in the Drawing Editor?

   _____

   _____

2. Suppose you have entered the MIRROR command. At this point, what is the fastest way of obtaining AutoCAD screen help on the MIRROR command?

   _____

   _____

3. How do you return to the graphics screen after obtaining help?

   _____

4. How is the information in the *AutoCAD Reference Manual* different from the screen help information?

   _____

   _____

5. After entering HELP or ? at the "Command:" prompt, a list of AutoCAD commands is displayed. What other information does this command display?

   _____

   _____

Problems

1. Obtain AutoCAD screen help on each of the following commands and state their general purpose.

   REDRAW _____

   QUIT _____

   GRID _____

   SNAP _____

   AXIS _____

   REGEN _____

2. Locate each of the above commands in the *AutoCAD Reference Manual* and read what it says about each of them.

AUTOCAD® AT WORK

Aloha, CAD

New technologies create new ways of doing business. For the Texas-based Tandy Corporation, owner of electronics manufacturer and retailer Radio Shack, and Facilities Data Management Corporation (FDM), a two-person architectural firm in Kailua, Hawaii, CAD software has made it possible to work together in different states—without exchanging paper documents.

FDM prepares the architectural, mechanical, and electrical drawings for new and remodeled Radio Shack stores in Hawaii. Construction designs are passed between Tandy headquarters in Fort Worth and FDM's offices on floppy diskettes rather than on bulky paper drawings, with each company contributing revisions to copies of original drawings. Redrawing—bane of the architect's existence—has been virtually eliminated.

The design cycle begins with Robert Hartman, FDM's president and principal architect. He visits the site (usually a shopping mall) of a proposed store and measures the space. FDM then makes a shell drawing of the existing space (known in real estate terms as a loft space drawing) using AutoCAD software.

When Hartman has finished the shell drawing, he copies it from his microcomputer's hard disk onto a floppy and then sends the diskette off to Tandy in Fort Worth. Tandy's architects, running AutoCAD on their own computers, call up the drawing file, which will serve as a base layer, and add layouts for lighting, power requirements, and such fixtures as displays and shelves. With the CAD program, the layouts can be drawn, viewed, and printed out as separate layers, or stacked in any combination like transparencies.

With the Tandy requirements now drawn in, FDM adds the remaining architectural details—doors, partitions, floor coverings, special ceiling treatments, and written instructions for the building contractor.

Next, the disk goes to Syntech, an engineering consulting firm in Honolulu. There, the drawing file is copied onto a hard disk shared by two microcomputers. That way, one CAD operator can work on the electrical plans while another works on the mechanical plans.

When their work is finished, Syntech prints out hard copy of the electrical and mechanical plans for submission to the Honolulu Building Department for permit processing. The floppy disk, now complete with all architectural and engineering layouts, is returned to FDM and then sent to Tandy for the corporation's final approval. Once the building permit has been received, construction begins.

Tandy and FDM are considering speeding up the design process still further. "The next step is electronic transfer via modem," says Hartman. "That could cut the project design time (which currently averages three to four weeks) down to a week or less."

```
        TYPICAL FDM/RADIO SHACK TITLE SHEET
                FILE NAME: TRS-SHT
              CAD NOTES TO OPERATOR
   THESE NOTES ARE ON LAYER 40 - DO NOT PLOT THEM!


FOR EACH RADIO SHACK STORE:      HARTMAN'S PLOTTER IS A
                                 HOUSTON INSTRUMENTS DMP-42
   CHANGE STORE NAME             PLOTTING LIMITS ARE 21.5" X 30.5".
   STORE NUMBER                  PLOTTING THIS SHEET AT
   SHEET NUMBER                  PLOT ORIGIN 0,0,0,0 WILL
   DATE                          LEAVE A BLANK RIGHT HAND
                                 MARGIN APPROX 4" WIDE,
PLOT AS FOLLOWS:                 USING 24" X 36" CUT SHEET PAPER.


   LAYER 4 - BLUE - FINE POINT BLUE INK
   LAYER 2 - RED - FINE POINT BLACK
   LAYER 3 - YELLOW - FINE POINT BLACK
   LAYER 5 - WHITE - #2 PEN, BLACK
   LAYER 6 - WHITE - #3 PEN, BLACK

   ORIGIN POINT IS 0.0,0.0
   SCALE IS 1=1
```

Courtesy of Radio Shack, a division of Tandy Corp., and Autodesk, Inc.

Unit 6 — Becoming a Keyboard Artist

AutoCAD®
Reference
Manual

■ OBJECTIVE:

To enter coordinates using the absolute, relative, and polar methods

So far, you have used only the pointing device to enter coordinates. Another method is to use the keyboard to specify coordinates. This method allows you to draw lines of any specific length and angle.

AutoCAD uses a Cartesian coordinate system. (See the illustration below.) The *origin* is the point where the values of X and Y are both zero. On the computer screen, the origin usually is located at the lower left corner. AutoCAD calls this system the *World Coordinate System* (WCS). Temporary coordinate systems whose origins are specified by the user are also available in AutoCAD. They are called *User Coordinate Systems* (UCS) and are explained fully in Unit 36.

1.2.1

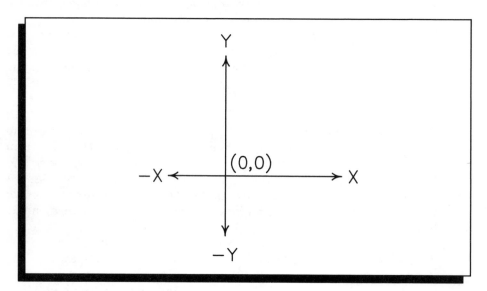

A point is expressed as an (x,y) coordinate pair. For two-dimensional (2D) drafting, all work can be done using (x,y) coordinates. If your work involves three-dimensional (3D) modeling, the Z-axis can be added to locate 3D points using an (x,y,z) coordinate triple. The Z-axis is perpendicular to the plane defined by the X and Y axes. Refer to Units 34-39 for details on how to apply AutoCAD's 3D capabilities.

■ Methods of Entering Points

Consider the following three ways to specify coordinates when using the LINE command.

Absolute Method

2.7.1.1

Example: LINE From point: 2,3   This will begin the line at absolute
           To point: 5,8   point 2,3 and end it at 5,8.

Relative Method

Example: LINE From point: 2,3
        To point: @2,0

This will draw a line 2 units in the positive X direction and 0 units in the Y direction from point 2,3. In other words, the distances 2,0 are relative to the location of the first point.

Polar Method

Example: LINE From point: 2,3
        To point: @4<60

This will produce a line segment 4 units long at a 60-degree angle. The line will begin at point 2,3.

The polar method is useful for producing lines at a precise angle. Note the following illustration. If you specify an angle of 120 degrees, in which direction will the line slant?

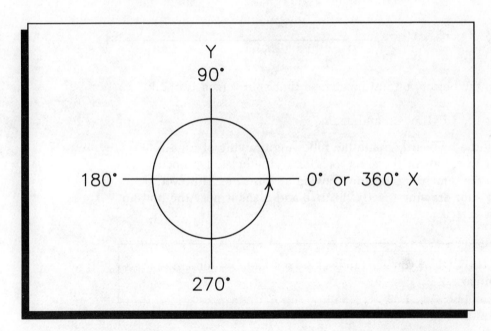

1 Load AutoCAD and Begin a New Drawing. Name it **GASKET**.

2 Enter the **LINE** command and input the following sequence to produce a drawing. Don't forget to press **RETURN** after each entry.

Command: LINE From point: **4,3**
To Point: **@3,0**
To Point: **@2.5<90**
To Point: **C**

What object was produced by entering these instructions?

NOTE:

In Unit 12, you will learn to use editing commands such as MOVE, COPY, and MIRROR. Absolute, relative, and polar coordinate specification can be combined with these commands and others. As an example, consider the last step in the following sequence.

Command: MOVE
Select Objects: (select a line)
Select Objects: (press RETURN to terminate the selection set)
Base point or displacement: (pick end of line)
Second point of displacement: @3.25<45

If you enter the @ character without anything else at the "Command:" prompt, you will specify the same point as the last point entered. Try it.

Creating a Gasket

1 Erase the object you just created so that your screen is blank.

2 Enter the **LINE** command again.

3 Using the keyboard, create the following drawing of a gasket. Don't worry about the exact location of the holes. Do not try to place the dimensions on the drawing at this time. However, do make your drawing exactly this size and place it near the bottom of the screen.

HINT:

Use Undo if you need to back up one step but remain in the LINE command.

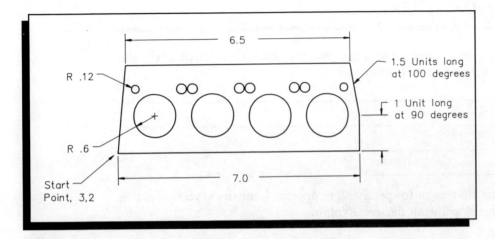

③ Enter **REDRAW** to delete the construction "blips."

④ Enter **END** to save your drawing and return to the Main Menu.

AUTOCAD® AT WORK

Making Music with AutoCAD

Father Kevin Waters is an acclaimed musical composer, scholar, and author living in the Spokane, Washington area. He uses AutoCAD and a package called AutoMusic to create music. AutoMusic, developed by SPOCAD (Spokane, WA), is a library of over sixty musical figures including whole to sixteenth notes and rests, time signature numbers, a range of accidentals such as sharps and flats, dynamic markings, and more.

Father Waters explained that the AutoCAD and Auto-Music combination provides the "opportunity to quickly and inexpensively produce publisher quality print of scores for conferences, classroom work, and distribution to bands, choirs, and orchestras. Furthermore," he added, "it gives you the flexibility to reduce or enlarge the size of copy, so it can be used for many purposes." Father Waters also likes the ability to edit and duplicate repetitive measures.

With over seven published works and eight premiers to his credit, Father Waters has written music for the liturgy, theater, chamber ensemble, and symphony orchestra. He is currently involved in the preparation of a full-length opera titled *Edith Stein*.

Courtesy of SPOCAD

Questions

1. Briefly describe the differences between the absolute, relative, and polar methods of point specification.

   _____

   _____

   _____

   _____

2. Is there an advantage to specifying endpoints from the keyboard rather than with the pointing device? Explain.

   _____

   _____

3. What is the advantage of specifying endpoints with the pointing device rather than the keyboard?

   _____

   _____

4. Why is entering absolute points impractical much of the time when completing drawings?

   _____

   _____

5. How can you back up one step if you make a mistake in specifying LINE endpoints?

   _____

Problems

For each of the following drawings, list exactly what you would enter when using the LINE command to produce the drawings. Try to incorporate all three methods—absolute, relative, and polar—to enter the points. After completing all of the blanks, enter the sequence into your computer.

1. Command: LINE From point: _____

   To point: _____

   To point: _____

   To point: _____

   To point: _____

   To point: _____

   To point: _____

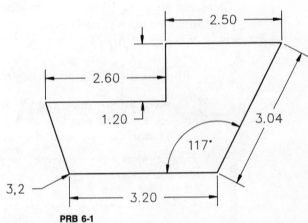

PRB 6-1

2. Command: LINE From Point: _____

   To point: _____

   To point: _____

   To point: _____

   To point: _____

   To point: _____

   To point: _____

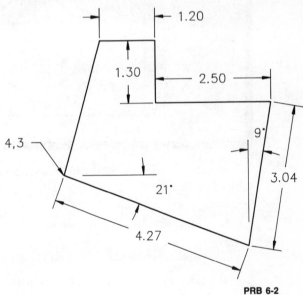

PRB 6-2

Unit 7 Grabbing Points

**AutoCAD®
Reference
Manual**

8.7

■ OBJECTIVE:

To apply the Object Snap feature and the APERTURE command

This unit covers the powerful Object Snap capability and shows how to size the target box for use with Object Snap.

■ *Using Object Snap* ───────────────

There will be times when you will want to automatically "grab" a specific point in your drawing, such as an endpoint of a line or the center of a circle. With AutoCAD's Object Snap feature, you can do both, and more.

1 First, load AutoCAD and Begin a New Drawing. Name it **OBJSNP**.

2 To get ready for using the Object Snap feature, draw the following object. Omit all numbers and, at this point, ignore the words. Don't worry about exact sizes and locations.

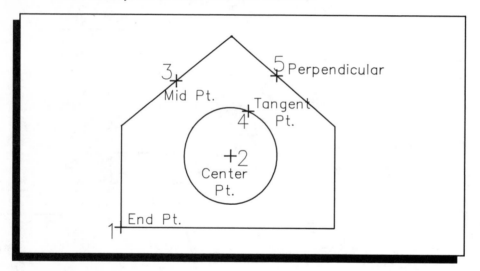

When you are finished with the above drawing, let's practice using the Object Snap feature.

8.7.1

1 Enter the **LINE** command.

2 Now enter the Object Snap mode called **END** and press **RETURN**.

You should now have what AutoCAD calls a target box at the center of the crosshairs.

3 Move your crosshairs/target box so that it touches the horizontal or vertical line near point 1, and pick it.

**AutoCAD®
Reference
Manual**

NOTE:

The crosshairs do not have to lie exactly on point 1. The crosshairs can be away from point 1 as long as the target box touches the line and is closer to point 1 than to the other endpoint of the line.

This begins to illustrate the power and accuracy of Object Snap. Let's experiment with another Object Snap mode.

4 In response to the "To point:" prompt on the screen, type **CEN** and press **RETURN**. "Cen," by the way, is short for "center."

5 Move your crosshairs/target box and pick any spot on the circle.

Your line should have snapped to the center of the circle.

HINT:

Instead of typing the Object Snap modes, you can select them from the Object Snap submenu, found by picking the * * * * from the top of the screen menu. Or, you may select the Tools pull-down menu, which has similar contents. Pressing the third button on your pointing device will also display this menu.

8.7.2

The following is a list of all the Object Snap modes. Note that endpoint and center are included in the list.

Select from either menu ...	Or type ...
CENter	CEN
ENDpoint	END
INSert	INS
INTersec	INT
MIDpoint	MID
NEArest	NEA
NODe	NOD
PERpend	PER
QUAdrant	QUA
QUICK,	QUICK
TANgent	TAN
NONE	NONE

During the following steps, pick the modes from the screen menu.

6 Snap to point 3 by picking **MIDpoint**.

7 Snap to point 4 by picking **TANgent**.

⑧ Snap to point 5 by picking **PERpend**.

Your drawing should now look like the following. If it doesn't, try it again.

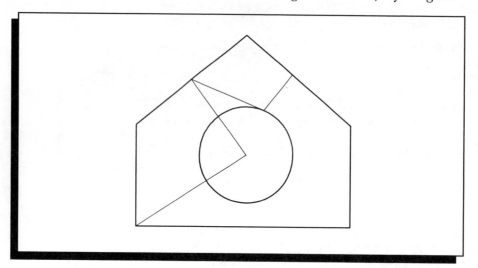

⑨ Experiment with each of the remaining Object Snap modes.

NOTE:

Even though the Object Snap submenu may seem convenient, some of the time you may choose to type the modes as you need them. Additionally, if you are using AutoCAD's tablet menu, consider picking the Object Snap modes from it. See Unit 43 for details on using the standard AutoCAD tablet menu.

APERTURE Command

8.7.5

Now let's practice changing the size of the target box.

① Enter the **APERTURE** command.

You can now choose any size from 1 to 50 pixels. A pixel is a picture element on a screen. All the images you see on the computer screen are made up of these tiny dots called pixels.

② Enter 5 for the aperture size.

③ Use one of the Object Snap modes to see the new size of the target box. It should now be half its original (10-pixel) size. The smaller size may help you be more precise in your point selection.

④ Change the target box size to 15 pixels.

5 Again, view the new size by using an Object Snap mode. The target box should now be three times larger than before.

6 Change the target box to any size you like.

7 Type **END** to save your drawing and return to the Main Menu.

Questions

1. Explain the purpose of the Object Snap modes.

_____

_____

_____

2. In order to snap a line to the center of a circle, what part of the circle does the target box need to touch?

_____

3. What command do you use to change the size of the target box? Describe a situation in which you would want to change the target box size.

_____

_____

_____

4. Briefly describe the use of each of the following Object Snap modes.

CEN _____

END _____

INS _____

INT _____

MID _____

NEA _____

NOD _____

PER _____

QUA _____

QUICK, _____

TAN _____

NONE _____

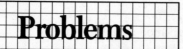

Problems

1. Draw this square.

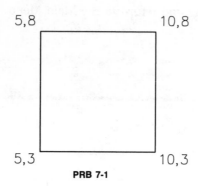

5,8   10,8

5,3   10,3

PRB 7-1

Use Object Snap to make these additions.

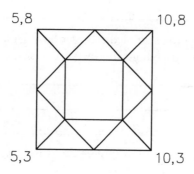

5,8   10,8

5,3   10,3

2. Using Object Snap, construct the following object. Don't worry about exact sizes and locations.

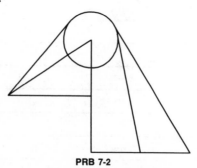

PRB 7-2

Unit 8   Four Special Features

■ **OBJECTIVE:**

To control certain AutoCAD features including Printer Echoing, Coordinate Display, Ortho, and the TIME command

This unit describes several special AutoCAD features. You will have an opportunity to practice these features and learn how they can best be applied in an AutoCAD work environment.

Printer Echoing _____

Simultaneously pressing CTRL (control) and Q on the keyboard will cause AutoCAD to print everything you type. The printing actually occurs after you have typed your text and pressed RETURN. This procedure is called printer echoing.

_____ NOTE: _____

Before you begin, make sure a printer is properly connected to your computer, is turned on, and is loaded with paper.

1 Display the Drawing Editor by entering option 1 or 2 from the Main Menu.

2 Press the **CTRL** and **Q** keys at the same time.

"<Printer echo on>" should appear on your screen.

3 Now enter an AutoCAD command of your choice and complete the entire command.

Did the text echo to the printer?

4 Practice by echoing other information to the printer, such as HELP information.

5 Press **CTRL Q** to turn off the printer echo.

_____ NOTE: _____

As you've just seen, CTRL Q serves to turn the printer echo both on and off. Thus it acts like a toggle switch. Using keys in this manner is referred to as toggling.

Printer echoing is useful when you want to record your steps with AutoCAD. Or, you may want to print Help information. Later, you will discover more applications as you learn to use commands such as LAYER, STATUS, and LIST.

Coordinate Display

Another useful feature is the display of coordinate information. This information, displayed in digital form, is found in the upper portion of your Drawing Editor and is part of what AutoCAD calls the *status line*. The coordinate display, found in the right-hand portion of the status line, reveals the current position (or coordinate position) of your crosshairs as you move your pointing device. It also gives the length and angle of line segments as you use the LINE command.

1 Turn on the coordinate display by pressing **CTRL D**.

2 Move the crosshairs on your screen by moving your pointing device.

Note how the coordinate display changes with the movement of the crosshairs.

3 With the coordinate display on, select the **LINE** command and draw a simple polygon. Note the coordinate display at each step of the polygon development.

As you can see, this information is similar to specifying line endpoints using the polar method of specifying coordinates. How could this information be useful when drawing?

4 While in the LINE command, press **CTRL D** and note the change in the coordinate display as you pick points. How does this coordinate display differ from the one in Step 3?

The Ortho Mode

Now let's focus on an AutoCAD feature called Ortho. Ortho is a very useful feature which allows you to quickly and easily draw lines either horizontally or vertically.

8.4

1 Enter the **ORTHO** command and specify **on**. Or, press **CTRL O**.

Ortho is on if the word "Ortho" is displayed on the status line at the top of the screen.

2 Experiment by drawing lines with Ortho turned on and then with Ortho off. Note the difference.

HINT:

Ortho can be toggled on and off at any time, even while you're in the middle of a command such as LINE. Simply press CRTL O, or, easier yet, press the function key F8.

3 Attempt drawing an angular line with Ortho on. Can it be done?

4 Now, draw the following object, first with Ortho off and then with Ortho on. Don't worry about exact sizes and locations.

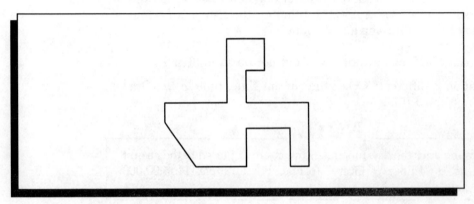

Was it faster with Ortho on?

TIME Command

3.10

While you are in the Drawing Editor, AutoCAD is keeping track of time. With the TIME command, you can review this information.

1 Enter the **TIME** command.

The following should look similar to what you see on your screen. Dates and times will of course be different.

```
Current time:            29  JUN  1989  at  12:25:25.490
Drawing created:         29  JUN  1989  at  10:08:19.470
Drawing last updated:    29  JUN  1989  at  11:32:03.670
Time in drawing editor:  0 days   01:46:38.600
Elapsed timer:           0 days   00:05:42.460
Timer on.
Display/ON/OFF/Reset:                [HOURS] [MINUTES] [SECONDS] [MILLISECONDS]
```

If the current date and time are not displayed on your screen, they were not entered after the computer was turned on. If the date and time are displayed even though you did not enter them, your computer has a built-in clock/calendar, and it enters the date and time automatically.

2 If the date and time are incorrect, exit AutoCAD and enter the **DATE** and **TIME** DOS commands at the DOS prompt (*e.g.*, C>). (To exit AutoCAD, use either the QUIT or END command to return to the Main Menu. Then select option 0.) After entering the DOS commands, load AutoCAD, bring up the Drawing Editor, and enter the **TIME** command again.

3 Enter the **TIME** command, if you did not do so in Step 2.

What information is different? Check the current time, time in the Drawing Editor, and the elapsed time.

NOTE:

The times, found after the day, month, and year, are displayed to the nearest millisecond using 24-hour "military" format. For example, 14:15:00.000 means 2:15 P.M.

4 With the TIME command entered, type **D** for Display, and notice what comes up on your screen.

5 Next, select the **OFF** option, and Display the time information again.

The "Elapsed timer" should now be off.

NOTE:

You would probably specify OFF if you wanted to leave your computer to get a cup of coffee, for instance. When you returned, you would turn the timer ON. This would keep an accurate record of the actual time (elapsed time) you spent working.

6 Reset the timer by entering **R**, and Display the time information once again.

The "Elapsed timer" should show 0 days 00:00:00.000.

7 Last, turn **ON** the timer and Display the time information.

Notice the elapsed timer has kept track of the time since the timer was turned ON.

Why is all of this time information important? In a work/production environment, the TIME command will track specific times spent on each project or job.

8 Enter **END** to save your work and exit, or enter **QUIT** if you choose not to save.

Questions

1. What two keys activate the printer echoing procedure?

   _____

2. Why would you want to echo your text to the printer while entering and responding to AutoCAD commands?

   _____

   _____

3. How do you turn off the printer echo?

   _____

   _____

4. What key, in conjunction with CTRL, allows you to turn on the coordinate display feature?

   _____

5. How do you turn off the coordinate display?

   _____

   _____

6. Of what value is the coordinate display?

   _____

   _____

7. What's the name of the feature that forces all lines to be drawn only vertically or horizontally?

   _____

8. What key, used with CTRL, controls this feature?

   _____

9. Of what value is the TIME command?

   _____

   _____

10. Briefly explain each of the components contained in the TIME command.

    Current time: _____

    Drawing created: _____

    Drawing last updated: _____

    Time in Drawing Editor: _____

    Elapsed timer: _____

1. Practice using Ortho by drawing the following shapes. Utilize Ortho when appropriate. Don't worry about exact sizes and locations. Turn on the coordinate display, and note the display as you construct each of the shapes. Last, when you construct one (just pick one) of the objects, echo everything you enter on the keyboard to the printer.

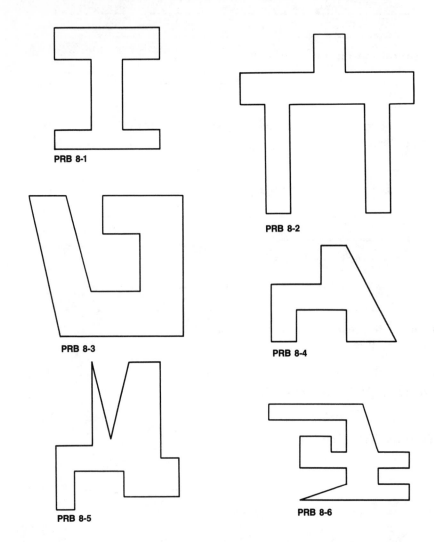

PRB 8-1

PRB 8-2

PRB 8-3

PRB 8-4

PRB 8-5

PRB 8-6

2. With the TIME command, review the time you spent in the Drawing Editor to complete PRB8-1 through PRB8-6. Echo this information to the printer or record it below.

_____   _____

_____   _____

_____   _____

Unit 9 — Helpful Drawing Aids

AutoCAD®
Reference
Manual

■ OBJECTIVE:

To apply the GRID, SNAP, and AXIS commands

This unit focuses on three very helpful construction aids. They are related to one another because each of them assists the AutoCAD user during the layout and placement of objects.

■ GRID Command

The Drawing Editor Grid is a visual aid. The GRID command allows you to set an alignment grid of dots of any desired spacing, making it easier to visualize distances and drawing size.

8.2

Let's work with this feature.

1 Load AutoCAD and Begin a New Drawing. Call it **SNAPPY**.

2 Toggle the Grid feature by pressing **CTRL G**.

There should now be a grid of dots on the screen. (If not, continue anyway.)

3 Enter the **GRID** command and change the grid spacing to .5 unit by simply entering **.5**.

4 Enter the **GRID** command again and change the spacing to **1** unit. (Remember, just press the space bar to reissue the last command.)

5 Next, turn the grid off by pressing **CTRL G** . . .

6 . . . and then turn it back on.

■ Function Keys

There's a quick way to turn on and off some of the AutoCAD features, including Grid, Ortho, and coordinate display. Most personal computer keyboards have function keys called F1, F2, F3, etc. AutoCAD has assigned many of these function keys to AutoCAD features, thereby allowing you to control the features with the touch of one key. Experiment to discover what your function keys are assigned to.

1 Press each of your function keys to find out what each controls.

Use the blanks on the "Quick Reference" at the end of this book to record the function of each key.

NOTE:

All function keys may not be assigned to a specific function or feature.

■ *SNAP Command* _____

The Snap feature is similar to the Grid feature because it is a grid, but it is
an invisible one. You cannot see the Snap feature, but you can realize the
effects of Snap as you move the crosshairs across the screen.

8.1

1 Press **CTRL B** to turn on the Snap feature. The word Snap should
   appear on the status line when Snap is on. If it is not there, press
   CTRL B again.

8.11

2 Slowly move your pointing device and watch closely the movement
   of the crosshairs.

3 Enter the **SNAP** command.

4 Enter .25 to specify the snap resolution.

5 Move your pointing device and note the crosshair movement.

HINT: _____
Turn on the grid to better see the movement of the crosshairs.
Notice the spacing relationship between the snap resolution and the grid.

There will be times when you want the crosshairs to snap one distance
vertically and a different distance horizontally. Here's how to do it:

1 Enter the **SNAP** command.

2 Enter the Aspect option by typing **A** and pressing **RETURN**.

The prompt line will ask for Horizontal spacing.

3 Enter .5.

Next you will be asked for Vertical spacing.

4 For now, enter 1.

5 Use your pointing device to move the crosshairs on the screen. Note
   the difference between the amount of vertical and horizontal
   movement.

Let's experiment with the Rotate option.

1 Enter the **SNAP** command again, and this time select the
   Rotate option.

2 Leave the base point at 0,0 by giving a null response. (Simply press the **space bar** or **RETURN**.)

3 Enter a rotation angle of **30** (degrees).

Did the grid, Snap, and crosshairs rotate 30 degrees?

4 Draw a small object at this rotation angle near the top of your screen.

5 Return to the original rotation of 0.

Now, let's try drawing another object.

1 Draw the following figure with the Snap set at .5 unit each way. Use only your pointing device to specify all points.

HINT:
Turn on Ortho to speed the drawing of the horizontal and vertical lines. Also, use the coordinate display when specifying endpoints.

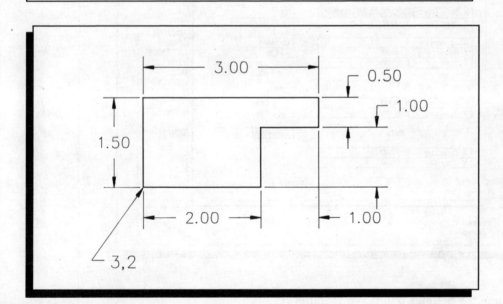

AXIS Command

The Axis feature is similar to the Grid feature because it too provides a visual means of referencing distance. The AutoCAD Grid could be viewed as an electronic alignment grid, whereas the AutoCAD Axis could be viewed as an electronic ruler. Again, both are used for visual reference only; they do not become part of the drawing.

8.3

1 Enter the **AXIS** command. Turn it on by entering **ON**.

② Enter **AXIS** again and change the unit spacing to 1.

③ Enter the **AXIS** command again and select the Snap option.

The axis spacing should have changed to correspond with the Snap spacing.

④ Lastly, experiment with the **A**spect ratio option. Make the
horizontal spacing different from the vertical spacing.

Drawing Aids Dialogue Box ————————————

The Drawing Aids selection found in the Settings pull-down menu assists
you in reviewing and changing the Snap, Grid, and Axis settings. The
Drawing Aids dialogue box is shown here.

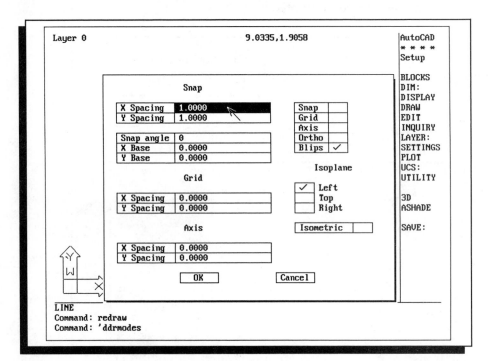

① Choose the **Settings** pull-down menu.

② Select the "**Drawing Aids...**" item found in the Settings menu.

A box should appear on the screen. AutoCAD calls this a dialogue box.

③ Review each of the items in the dialogue box.

④ Experiment with making changes to the current settings using your
pointing device and keyboard.

5 When you are finished making the changes, either save them by picking the **OK** item or discard them by picking **Cancel**.

6 Enter **END** to save your work and exit the Drawing Editor.

Questions

1. What is the purpose of the GRID command? How can it quickly be toggled on and off?

_____

_____

_____

2. Does the axis spacing change when the AXIS Snap option is selected? Explain.

_____

_____

3. How do the Axis ruler lines change as you change the spacing?

_____

_____

4. When would you use the Snap feature? When would you toggle off the Snap feature?

_____

_____

_____

5. How can you set the Snap feature so that the crosshairs move a different distance horizontally than vertically?

_____

_____

6. Explain how to rotate the grid, Snap, and crosshairs 45 degrees.

_____

_____

_____

Problems

Draw the following objects using the Grid, Axis, and Snap settings provided beside each object.

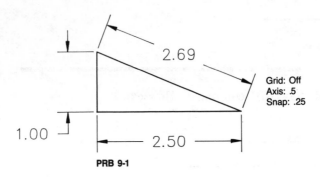

2.69

Grid: Off
Axis: .5
Snap: .25

1.00

2.50

PRB 9-1

2.00

Grid: 1
Axis: Off
Snap: .5

1.00

PRB 9-2

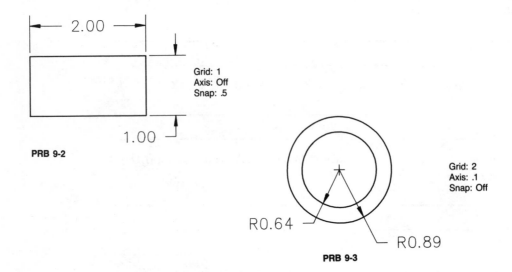

Grid: 2
Axis: .1
Snap: Off

R0.64

R0.89

PRB 9-3

AutoCAD® At Work

*AutoCAD Becomes Fashionable**

With the advent of low-cost CAD packages like AutoCAD, fashion designers are discovering the benefits and possibilities that computer-aided design can offer. Eleanor London, a CAD/CAM/CIM consultant, has helped fashion designers make the transition to CAD.

She points out the similarities between manual tools and CAD tools. Students are given charts that list traditional tools and their CAD equivalents: Tailor's square = Ortho; French curve = Arcs; Transparent rule = Units and snap; Cutting table = Limits; Pattern paper = Grid or layers; Pivot = Rotate; Seam allowance = Offset; Slopers = Blocks; Notches/punch hole = Attributes.

Students then use the computer to explore their new drafting tools with simple exercises like fitting curves between points, drawing various line widths, and drawing continuous line shapes. Next, students draft front and back bodice sloper patterns, which are based on dress form size measurements. The slopers are drafted by connecting a series of points established by the dress form measurements. The completed slopers are saved as a Block for future use in development of construction patterns.

Pattern symbols, such as center front folds, punch holes, grain-lines, and notches, are drawn and stored in a symbol library.

The sloper patterns and the pattern symbols are used in creating the final patterns. The patterns are plotted actual size. The students cut the patterns in muslin and tie them on dress forms. Corrections are made and translated to the patterns on the CAD system. After all corrections are made, the patterns are plotted again and cut in the chosen fabric.

Using AutoCAD for pattern design increases productivity by reducing duplication time and lets the designer work on complicated designs. The final payoff is that AutoCAD provides a competitive edge and a quality product for domestic manufacturers in the world marketplace.

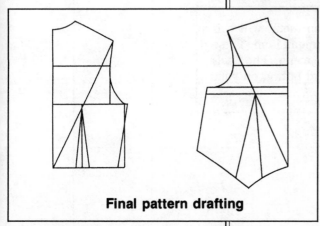

Final pattern drafting

*Based on a story in *CADENCE* magazine, Vol. 2, No. 3.

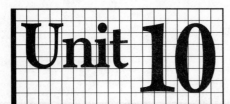

Unit 10 Undoing What You've Done

AutoCAD®
Reference
Manual

■ OBJECTIVE:

To apply the U, REDO, and UNDO commands

AutoCAD allows you to back up to any earlier point in an editing session using the commands U, REDO, and UNDO. Additionally, you can reverse the effect of one Undo if you went one step too far. Let's work with these commands.

■ U Command_____

5.5.1

1 Load AutoCAD and Begin a New Drawing. Name it **UNDO**.

2 Enter the **DONUT** command and place a half dozen donuts on your screen at any size and location.

3 With the **GRID** and **SNAP** commands, reset the grid and snap spacings.

4 At the "Command:" prompt, enter the U command by typing **U** and pressing **RETURN**.

What happened?

5 Enter the **U** command again, and then again.

So you see, the U command simply backs up one step at a time. With it, you can actually back up to the beginning of your editing session.

■ REDO Command _____

5.5.2

1 Enter the **REDO** command and watch what happens.

REDO undoes the last Undo. In other words, it reverses the effect of the last Undo.

HINT:
Both U and REDO are found in the screen menu which is displayed as a result of picking the * * * screen menu item. These two commands are also found in the Tools pull-down menu. The Tools pull-down menu can be displayed by pressing the third button on your pointing device.

AutoCAD®
Reference
Manual

5.5.3

UNDO Command

The UNDO command is similar to the U command, but UNDO provides several powerful options. Let's try a few.

1 Draw the following objects at any size and location using the POLYGON, ELLIPSE, and CIRCLE commands.

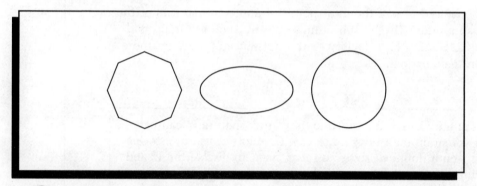

2 Enter the **UNDO** command.

The following subcommands should appear on your screen:

```
Auto/Back/Control/End/Group/Mark/<number>:
```

3 Respond to the "<number>" option by typing the number **2** and pressing **RETURN**.

By entering 2, you told AutoCAD to back up two steps. UNDO 1 is equivalent to the U command.

Now let's try the Mark and Back subcommands.

5.5.3.1

1 Enter the **LINE** command and draw a small rectangle at any size and location.

Let's say, for instance, that you want to proceed with drawing and editing, but you would like the option of returning to this point in your session at a later time. If you choose to do this, you'd like AutoCAD to disregard all operations you are about to make. This is what you must do.

2 Enter the **UNDO** command.

3 Enter the Mark subcommand by typing **M** and pressing **RETURN**.

AutoCAD has (internally) marked this point in your session.

4 Perform several operations, such as drawing and erasing objects and changing mode settings such as Ortho, Snap, and Grid.

Now suppose you decide to back up to the point where you drew the rectangle in Step 1.

5 Enter the **UNDO** command and then the **Back** subcommand.

You have just practiced two of the most powerful and common uses of the UNDO command. Other UNDO subcommands exist, such as Group and End. Refer to AutoCAD's Help facility or the *Reference Manual* for more information on these options.

5.5.3.2

NOTE:

The Undo feature can use a large amount of disk space and can cause a "disk full" situation on a floppy diskette. Therefore if you are storing your drawing on a floppy diskette, you may want to disable the U and UNDO commands, partially or entirely, by using the UNDO Control option.

5.5.3.4

Let's experiment with UNDO Control.

1 Enter the **UNDO** command and then the Control option.

2 Enter the **O**ne option.

3 Draw one item on your screen, such as an arc.

4 Enter the **UNDO** command.

Notice that UNDO now allows you to undo only a single operation.

5 Press **RETURN**.

With UNDO Control set at One, AutoCAD does not have to store nearly as much Undo information. The risk of a "disk full" situation when storing on a floppy diskette is therefore minimized.

6 Enter the UNDO Control option again.

7 This time, enter None.

8 Perform a couple of AutoCAD draw or edit functions.

9 Now enter **UNDO**.

Since you have UNDO Control set at None, AutoCAD does not give you the option of undoing, only the option of changing UNDO Control.

10 Enter **CTRL C** and try the U command by typing **U** and pressing **RETURN**.

The U command is also disabled.

11 With **UNDO**, enter the Control All option.

Now the AutoCAD Undo feature is once again fully enabled.

12 Enter **UNDO** again and note the complete list of subcommands.

13 Further experiment with AutoCAD's Undo feature.

14 Enter **QUIT** to exit the Drawing Editor and return to the Main Menu.

AUTOCAD® AT WORK

Customizing Buses with AutoCAD

Executive Coach Corporation of Fox River Grove, Illinois, specializes in the design and conversion of buses into luxury motor homes and business facilities. And some of the results have been astonishing.

Clients range from Saudi Arabian royalty to country music stars. A typical conversion takes several months and can cost up to $400,000. In addition to standard items such as dining areas, kitchens, and bathrooms, the corporation's craftsmen have installed such exotic features as solid gold fixtures, saunas, steambaths, and even a revolving clothes rack under a bed.

By using AutoCAD, the designers can involve the clients in the design process. Instead of huddling over a bunch of hand drawn sketches, the clients can watch the evolution of their design on a large computer screen. If they want to move the kitchen a few feet or double the size of the bathroom, a designer using AutoCAD can make the changes while the clients watch.

The layering feature of AutoCAD is helpful during both the design stage and the construction stage. With layering, the designer can position all the appliances on one layer, the furniture on a second, and the wiring, plumbing, and heating fixtures on still other layers.

Once the final design is agreed upon, the designer prints out a multicolored copy for the company craftsmen to use as construction "blueprints." Since the company began using AutoCAD, customers and employees are a lot more satisfied. The accurate drawings make customizing easier and faster, and the company can make more conversions in less time and for less money.

Courtesy of Executive Coach Corporation

Questions

1. Explain the differences between the U and UNDO commands.

   _____

   _____

   _____

2. What is the purpose of the REDO command?

   _____

   _____

3. Explain how you would quickly back up or undo your last five operations.

   _____

   _____

4. Explain the use of the UNDO Mark and Back subcommands.

   _____

   _____

   _____

5. Describe the three UNDO Control options.

   All _____

   None _____

   One _____

6. Is the U command enabled or disabled when UNDO Control is set at One? Why?

   _____

   _____

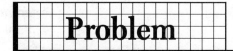

Problem

Draw this simple house elevation at any convenient size. Prior to drawing the roof, use UNDO to mark your current location in the drawing. Then draw the roof.

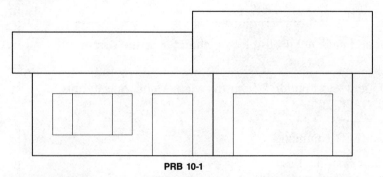

PRB 10-1

With UNDO Back, return to the point prior to drawing the roof. Draw the following roof in place of the old roof. Use the U and UNDO commands as necessary as you complete the drawing.

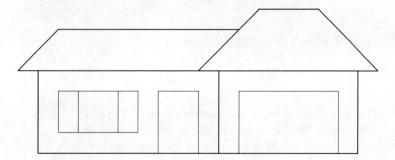

Unit 11   Altering Entities

**AutoCAD®
Reference
Manual**

■ OBJECTIVE:

To practice using the CHAMFER, BREAK, and FILLET commands

These commands allow you to make chamfered or rounded corners and to break a line.

■ *CHAMFER Command* _____

The CHAMFER command enables you to place a chamfer at the corner formed by two lines.

5.3.7

1 Load AutoCAD and select option **2** from the Main Menu. Specify the drawing called **GASKET**.

2 Enter the **CHAMFER** command.

You will receive a prompt line like this:

```
Command: CHAMFER Polyline/Distances/<Select first line>:
```

---

3 Type **D** for Distance or pick it from the submenu.

4 Specify a chamfer distance of **.25** unit for both the first and second distances.

5 Enter the **CHAMFER** command again and place a chamfer at each of the corners of the gasket by picking the two lines which make up each corner. (You will have to enter **CHAMFER** or press the **space bar** before selecting each pair of lines.)

When you're finished, your drawing should look similar to the one below.

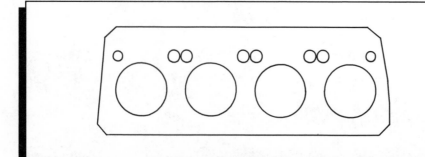

BREAK Command _____

Now let's remove (break out) sections of the gasket so that it looks like the drawing below.

5.3.3

As you know, the bottom edge of the gasket was drawn as a single, continuous line. Therefore, if we were to use the ERASE command to break the line, it would erase the entire line since the line is an entity. The BREAK command, however, allows us to "break" certain entities such as lines, arcs, and circles.

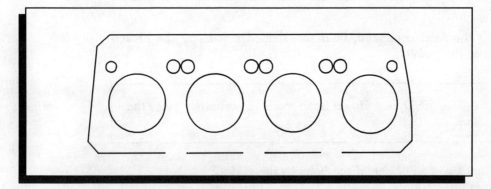

1 Enter the **BREAK** command.

2 Pick a point where you'd like the break to begin. Since the locations of the above breaks are not dimensioned, approximate the location of the start point.

3 Pick the point where you'd like the break to end.

Did a piece disappear?

Let's break out two more sections of approximately equal size as shown in the above gasket drawing.

4 Enter the **BREAK** command and select the line.

5 Enter **F** for first point.

6 Pick a point where you'd like the break to begin.

7 Pick a point where you'd like the break to end.

When you're finished breaking out the small sections, let's place arcs in the broken sections as on the following illustration.

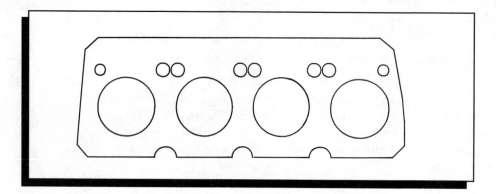

5 Using the **ARC** command, insert arc-shaped ribs along the broken edge of the gasket.

HINT:

Use the ENDpoint Object Snap mode to accurately place the arcs.

Let's break out a section of one of the holes in the gasket.

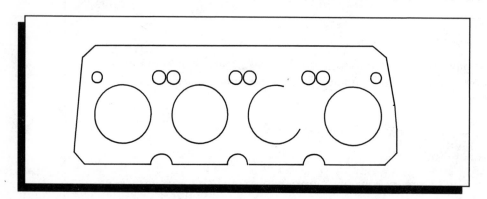

1 Enter the **BREAK** command.

2 Pick the first break point on the circle.

3 Working counterclockwise, pick the second point. Did it work?

4 Enter **OOPS**.

The broken piece of the circle does not return. Why not? OOPS works only in conjunction with the ERASE command and not BREAK.

5 Enter **U**.

The broken piece should have returned. If not, enter U again.

FILLET Command

Now let's change the chamfered corners on the gasket to rounded corners.

1. First, erase each of the chamfered corners.

2. Enter the FILLET command and set the radius at .3 unit. The fastest way to do this is to enter **FILLET**, then **R**, and then **.3**. Be sure to press **RETURN** after each entry.

3. Reenter the **FILLET** command and produce fillets at each of the four corners of the gasket by picking each pair of lines.

Your gasket drawing should now look similar to the following.

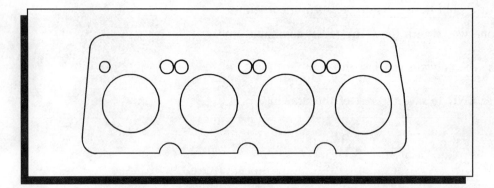

NOTE:

You can also fillet any combination of two lines, arcs, or circles.

Let's move away from the gasket and try something new.

1. Draw lines on your screen similar to the ones on the next page. Omit the numbers.

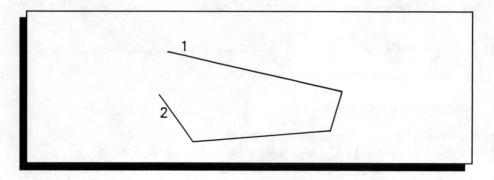

2 Set your fillet radius at **0**.

3 Reenter the **FILLET** command and select lines 1 and 2.

The two lines should have extended to form a corner.

This technique works with the CHAMFER command, too.

4 Erase the polygon you just drew.

5 Enter **END** to save the rest of the drawing.

Questions

1. What is the function of the CHAMFER command?

   _____

   _____

2. How is using the BREAK command different from using the ERASE command?

   _____

   _____

3. If you want to break a circle or arc, in which direction do you move when specifying points: clockwise or counterclockwise?

   _____

4. In what submenu is the FILLET command found?

   _____

5. How do you set the FILLET radius?

   _____

   _____

6. Will the FILLET radius change or stay the same after you END and exit back to the Main Menu?

   _____

7. What can be accomplished by setting either FILLET or CHAMFER to 0?

   _____

   _____

1. Using the pointing device, create the first drawing shown below left. Don't worry about exact sizes and locations, but do utilize SNAP and ORTHO. Then use FILLET to change it to the second drawing. Set the fillet radius at .2 unit.

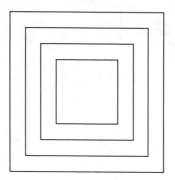 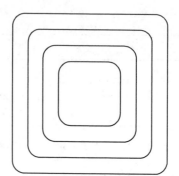

PRB 11-1

2. Create the triangle shown below. Then use CHAMFER to change it into a hexagon. Set the chamfer distance at .66 unit.

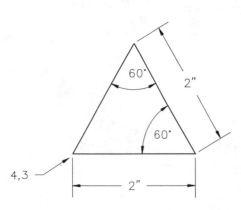

PRB 11-2

3. Draw the following object; don't worry about specific sizes. Use the FILLET command to place fillets in the corners as indicated.

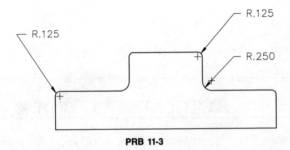

PRB 11-3

4. Draw the following object, but don't worry about specific sizes. Use the CHAMFER command to place a chamfer at each corner.

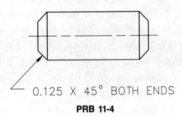

0.125 X 45° BOTH ENDS

PRB 11-4

5. Using the ARC and CHAMFER commands, construct the following object.

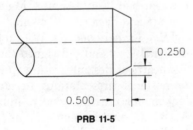

PRB 11-5

AUTOCAD® AT WORK

AutoCAD Is into Rock

The lighting for a typical 1950s rock and roll concert consisted of a few dim stage lights and four or five spotlights aimed at Elvis Presley or Chuck Berry. But as the performers and their music gained sophistication, so did the lighting. Four or five spotlights gave way to thousands of multicolored lights arranged in precise designs.

In 1983 a theatrical lighting company in Atlanta, Georgia, decided that lighting design had become too complicated and time-consuming to do by hand, so they turned to AutoCAD for help. After switching to AutoCAD, the firm won contracts to design two extravagant concert lighting projects— the Jacksons' Victory Tour in 1984 and Madonna's Virgin Tour in 1985. The Atlanta-based firm has also designed the lighting for artists as varied as Hank Williams, Jr., and Kool and the Gang.

One of the biggest advantages of AutoCAD for lighting designers is its speed. Instead of drawing each lamp in a design by hand, for example, the designers can call up an array of lamps from a library of lamp fixtures. Also, by using AutoCAD's zoom feature, designers can magnify areas that need detail work.

AutoCAD also allows the designer to make changes more easily. This easy-revision feature came in especially handy while the firm was working on the Madonna tour. After the lighting for the tour had been designed, Madonna attended a Prince concert and decided she wanted a set to accompany the lighting for her concerts. Within three days the firm had designed a set and redesigned the lighting to fit.

Theatrical designers using AutoCAD can make more professional presentations to musicians and producers looking for creative concert lighting. A designer using AutoCAD can print a multicolored drawing of the proposed lighting system to show clients what the lighted stage will look like during a performance.

The Future. The entertainment industry is just beginning to explore the uses of CAD. Besides lighting design, CAD could be used in live theater (as well as television and moviemaking) for blocking, choreography, special effects, and costume design.

Unit 12 Moving and Duplicating Objects

■ OBJECTIVE:

To apply CHANGE, MOVE, COPY, MIRROR, and OFFSET

When drawing, there are times when you need to move or duplicate an object. With AutoCAD, it's a simple process.

CHANGE Command _____

The CHANGE command is used for a number of purposes, such as fixing the placement of lines. Let's experiment with it.

1   Load AutoCAD and bring up your drawing called **GASKET**.

2   Above the gasket, draw three intersecting lines like the ones below. Omit the letters.

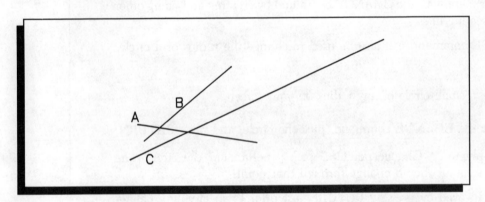

Using the CHANGE command, let's fix these lines to form a perfect arrow as shown in the illustration below.

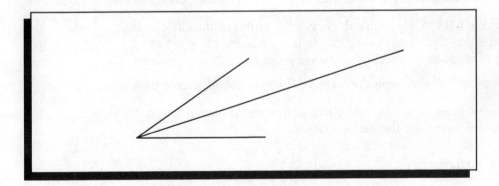

3 Enter the **CHANGE** command.

4 In response to the "Select objects:" prompt, pick lines A and B and press **RETURN**.

5 In reply to " <Change point >," pick the leftmost endpoint of line C. Use the Object Snap ENDpoint mode to accurately select the point.

Did the lines change into the shape of an arrow? If not, try it again.

HINT: ————————————————

AutoCAD provides help on each of its commands, including the CHANGE command. If CHANGE is entered, you can get immediate help on this command by entering 'HELP. (Note the apostrophe.)

6 Experiment with the CHANGE command by creating and fixing other intersecting lines.

The CHANGE command can also be used to change the radius of a circle. Let's do it.

1 Draw a small circle of any radius on your screen.

2 Enter the **CHANGE** command, pick the circle, and press **RETURN**.

3 In reply to " <Change point >," pick a point near the circle. The circle's radius should change through that point.

Drag can be invoked by pressing RETURN just prior to specifying a change point. The new radius can then be dragged into place. Drag mode must be set at "Auto."

4 Enter the **DRAGMODE** command and select the **Auto** option.

5 With the **CHANGE** command, change the radius of the circle again, but this time dynamically drag the circle's radius into place by entering **drag** in reply to "Properties/ <Change point >:".

We'll explore other ways of using the CHANGE command at a later time.

6 For now, erase the arrow and circle so that you'll have room on the computer screen for the next operation.

MOVE Command ————————————————

Let's move the entire gasket to the top of the screen using the MOVE command.

1 Enter the command called **MOVE**.

AutoCAD should now be showing the "Select objects:" prompt.

② Type **W** (or select the **Window** option from the screen menu), place a window around the entire gasket drawing, and press **RETURN**.

③ Respond to the next prompt by placing a base point somewhere on or near the gasket drawing as shown in the following illustration.

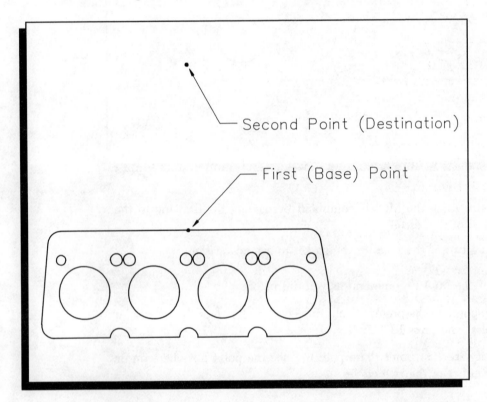

④ Move your pointing device in the direction of the second point (destination). If the gasket does not dynamically drag as you move to the second point, type **drag** and press **RETURN**.

⑤ Pick the second point.

Did the drawing move as illustrated on the next page?

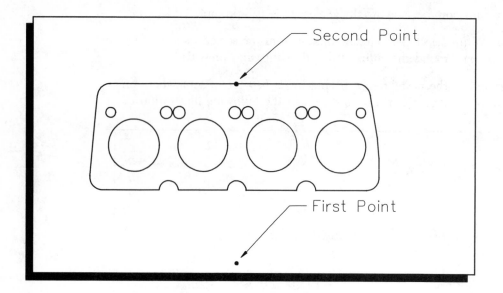

Second Point

First Point

6 Practice using the MOVE command by moving the drawing to the bottom of the screen.

Now let's drag two of the holes in the gasket to a new location.

1 Enter the **MOVE** command as you did before.

2 In response to the prompt "Select objects:" pick two of the four holes (circles) and press **RETURN**.

3 Specify the first point (base point). Place the point anywhere on or near either of the two circles.

4 In reply to "Second point of displacement:" move your pointing device.

5 After you decide on a location for the circles, pick that location with your pointing device.

6 Drag the circles back into the gasket as they were before.

■ *COPY Command* _____

The COPY command works almost identically to the MOVE command. The only difference is that the COPY command does not move the object; it copies it.

5.2.2

1 Erase all of the large holes in the gasket except for one.

2 Enter the **COPY** command, select the remaining circle, and press **RETURN**.

3 Specify the Multiple option by entering **M** and give a base point on or near the circle.

4 Move your crosshairs and place the circle in the appropriate location.

5 Repeat Step 4 until all four large circles are in place; then press **RETURN**.

6 Practice using the COPY command by copying other portions of the gasket.

■ *MIRROR Command* _____

There are times when it is necessary to produce a mirror image of a drawing, detail, or part. However, a simple COPY of the object is not adequate because the object being copied must be reversed, as was done with the butterfly in the following drawing. One side of the butterfly was drawn and then mirrored to produce the other side.

5.2.5

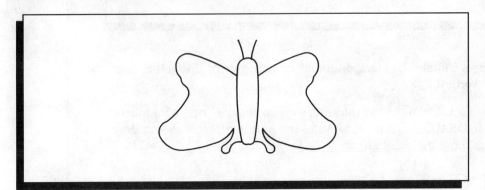

The same is true if the engine head gasket we developed is to be reproduced to represent the opposite side of the engine; that is, if the gasket we are producing is for an eight-cylinder engine.

1 **MOVE** the gasket either to the top or bottom of your screen to allow space for another gasket of the same size.

2 Enter the **MIRROR** command, select the gasket by placing a **Window** around it, and press **RETURN**.

3 Provide a horizontal Mirror Line near the gasket by selecting two points on a horizontal plane as shown below. Ortho should be on.

4 The prompt line will ask if you want to delete old objects. Enter **N** for "no," or press **RETURN** since the default is No.

The gasket should have mirrored as shown below.

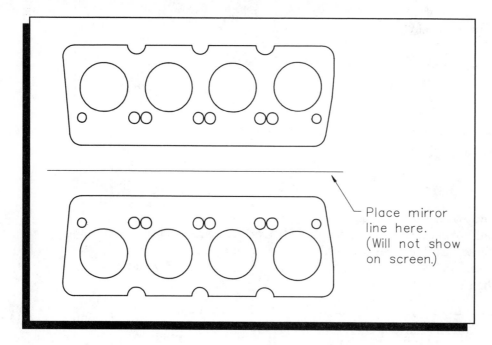

Place mirror line here. (Will not show on screen.)

Mirrored images can also be created around an axis (mirror line) other than horizontal or vertical.

5 Draw a small triangle and mirror it with an angular (*e.g.*, 45°) mirror line. If DRAGMODE is set to Auto, the mirrored object should drag as you move the crosshairs in reply to "Second point:".

OFFSET Command

The OFFSET command provides a means for producing double lines similar to those used in architectural floor plan drawings. Let's practice using the OFFSET command.

1 Enter the **OFFSET** command.

5.3.8

2 For the offset distance, enter **.2**.

3 Select one of the circles in the gasket drawing.

4 Pick a point inside the circle.

Did another circle appear?

5 Select another circle and pick a side to offset.

This time, let's use the Through option of OFFSET.

1 Enter **OFFSET** and select the **Through** option from the screen menu or enter **T**.

2 Pick a line in one of the triangles you previously drew on the screen.

3 Pick a point a short distance from the line and outside the triangle.

4 Do the same with the remaining two lines in the triangle so that you have an object similar to the following.

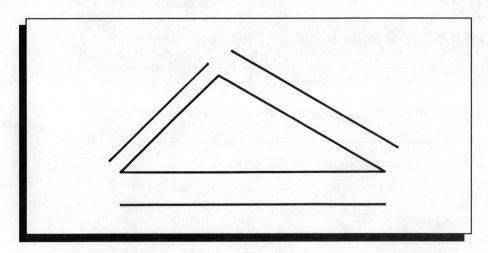

5 Enter **CHAMFER** and set the first and second chamfer distances at **0**. (Note that "dist=0" is an item contained in the CHAMFER submenu.)

6 Enter **CHAMFER** again and pick two of the new offset lines.

7 Do this again at the remaining two corners to complete the second triangle.

8 Clean up your drawing so that only the gasket remains, save it, and return to the Main Menu.

Questions

1. In what submenu is the CHANGE command found?

   _____

2. Describe a situation where CHANGE would be used for changing endpoints of lines.

   _____

   _____

3. In what submenu is MOVE located?

   _____

4. Explain how the MOVE command is different from the COPY command.

   _____

   _____

   _____

5. How does DRAGMODE affect the MOVE and COPY commands?

   _____

   _____

6. Describe a situation in which the MIRROR command would be helpful.

   _____

   _____

7. During a MIRROR operation, can the Mirror Line be specified at any angle? Explain.

   _____

   _____

8. Describe an application for the OFFSET command.

   _____

   _____

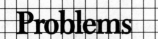

Problems

In problems 1 and 2, follow each step to create the objects. Use the ARC Continue option at Step 2 of problem 1. Use the MIRROR and COPY commands to complete Steps 3 and 4.

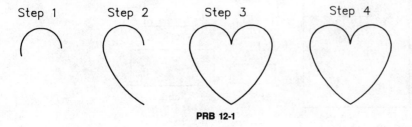

Step 1   Step 2   Step 3   Step 4

PRB 12-1

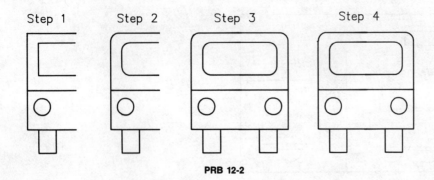

Step 1   Step 2   Step 3   Step 4

PRB 12-2

In problem 3, draw the objects and room as shown. Then use the MOVE and COPY commands to move the office furniture into the room. Omit the lettering on the drawings.

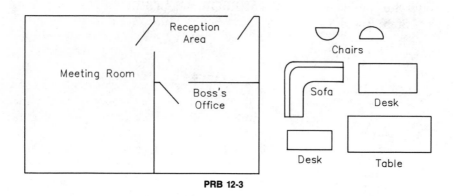

PRB 12-3

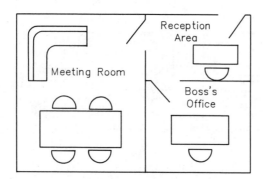

HINT: MOVE and COPY may work better with the Ortho and Snap modes off.

In the drawing made for problem 3, use the OFFSET command to produce double-line walls for the office. Set the Offset distance at .2 and use other AutoCAD commands, such as CHAMFER and BREAK, to complete and clean up the wall constructions. If necessary make the drawing larger for easier editing.

AUTOCAD® AT WORK

Designer/Manufacturer Speeds Up Production 400 Percent

When you're at a basketball game, ballet, movie, or political convention, chances are you're sitting in a seat designed and built by the Hussey Seating Company of North Berwick, Maine. With 25,000 spectator seating installations worldwide, the company is the largest seating supplier in the U.S. Its clients include conference and convention halls, high schools, and theaters.

Late in 1984, Hussey began doing its drafting with AutoCAD. "We wanted the economic benefits of computerization," explains Greg Keene, Contract Coordinator with Hussey for CAD. "The company's growing so fast that we needed that productivity gain."

The company's largest set of contract drawings to date consisted of 80 separate drawings for a 65,000 seat stadium in Saudi Arabia. "You've got to actually show each one of those seats to within one millimeter, in terms of scale and accuracy," explains Keene. "Without AutoCAD, it would have taken our drafters massive amounts of time to both create the drawings and provide needed revisions—probably a good year just to prepare the drawings." With the CAD system, however, eight months were spent on creating the initial designs, and a record four weeks were spent on revisions.

The primary timesaver was AutoCAD's ability to duplicate drawings. Hussey drafters could draw one chair and then have the system duplicate it as many times as needed. Moreover, the duplicate chairs could be positioned wherever the drafter specified.

A second timesaver, Keene reports, has been the use of block libraries. Rather than draw a new chair each time one is needed, drafters create prototype chairs and then store them as blocks in a symbol library.

For a detailed look at drawings, drafters use the CAD system's zoom capabilities. "We just finished up a complex rear view of a twenty-tier telescopic bleacher," notes Keene, "that required at least three zoom modes to get into detail to show drawings in precise scale. We needed to see the actual bleacher, its bracing details, and bolt connections to make sure they were all accurately constructed."

Hussey's drafters also take advantage of CAD's ability to mirror drawings. "We'll draw half of a drafting assignment," Keene explains, "and then mirror the other half to get a whole—which saves us umpteen hours of drawing."

The system's layering capability enables drafters to draw on different layers, much like electronic overlay transparencies. "We've drawn a layer for each different category," reports Keene, "with a yellow layer for dimensioning, a blue layer for the outline of the building, a red layer for a telescopic seating outline, and a green one for hidden lines."

Stadium seating is a highly competitive market. Clear and accurate bid presentations and proposals are essential. With AutoCAD, says Keene, "Our presentations now are much cleaner and more professional."

Courtesy of Peoria Civic Center

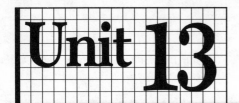
**AutoCAD®
Reference
Manual**

■ OBJECTIVE:

To create rectangular and polar arrays

This unit utilizes the ARRAY command to construct two drawings: (1) a schematic of computer chip sockets and (2) a bicycle wheel with spokes.

5.2.7

Producing Rectangular Arrays

1 Load AutoCAD and Begin a New Drawing. Name it **CHIPS**.

5.2.7.1

2 In the lower left corner of the screen, draw the following and make it small (approximately 1/2 unit wide by 2/3 unit tall).

HINT:

Use the COPY command to duplicate the small circle. Then use the MIRROR command to make the bottom half identical to the top half.

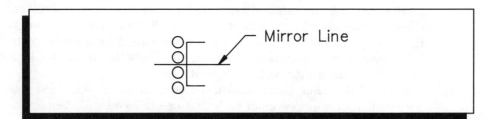

3 Using the **MIRROR** command, mirror the object to complete the opposite side as shown below. If your drawing does not look exactly like the one here, that's okay.

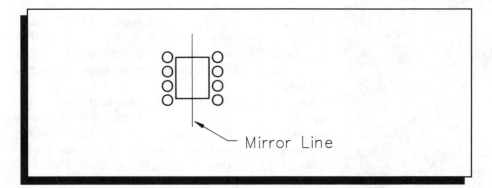

The object you have just drawn represents a computer chip socket. It resembles a schematic of the sockets found inside your computer. The sockets house the RAM chips that are currently holding the information you see on your screen.

4 Enter the **ARRAY** command.

5 In reply to the "Select objects:" prompt, select the chip socket by placing a window around it, and press **RETURN**.

6 Enter the Rectangular array option by typing **R** and pressing **RETURN**, or by selecting it from the screen menu.

7 Specify **3** rows and **5** columns.

8 Specify that you want **1.5** units between the rows and **1.75** units between the columns.

You should now have 15 chip sockets on your screen, arranged in a 3 × 5 array. Does your screen look similar to the illustration below?

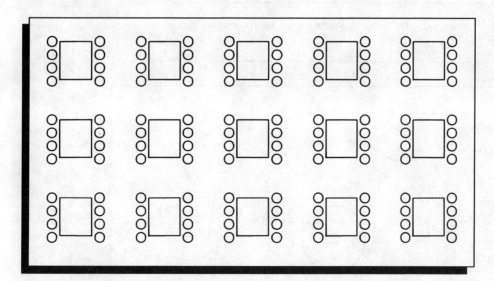

If your array does not look like the above, erase everything except for the chip socket in the lower left corner of your screen and try again.

If it does look like the figure above, good job!

NOTE:

Rectangular arrays can be produced at any angle by changing the Snap rotation angle prior to the ARRAY command.

⑨ Save your array by entering **END**.

Producing Polar (Circular) Arrays

Next, we're going to produce a bicycle wheel using the Polar array option.

5.2.7.2

① Begin a New Drawing and name it **WHEEL**.

② After you arrive at the Drawing Editor, draw a tire/wheel similar to the one in the following drawing. Don't worry about the exact sizes of the circles, but do make the wheel large enough to fill most of your screen.

HINT:

Use the CENter Object Snap mode to make the circles concentric.

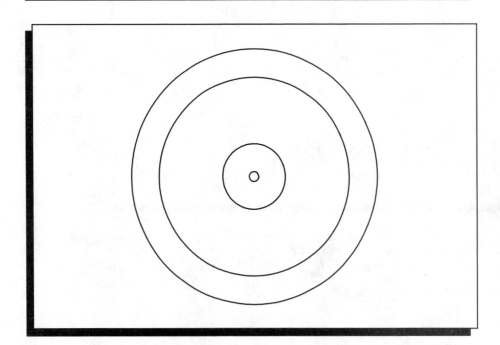

③ Using the **LINE** command, draw two crossing lines similar to the ones on the next page.

HINT:
Use the NEArest Object Snap mode to begin and end the lines on the appropriate circles.

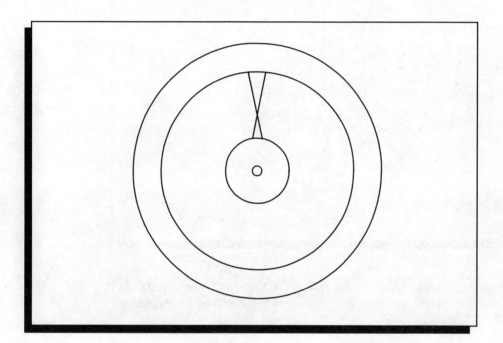

4 Enter the **ARRAY** command and use the following information when responding to each step.

(a) Select each of the two crossing lines for the array.

(b) Choose the Polar array option.

(c) The center point of the array is the center of the wheel. (Use Object Snap to locate the center point precisely.)

(d) Specify **18** for "Number of items."

(e) Enter **360** for "Angle to fill" by pressing **RETURN**.

(f) . . . and yes, you want to rotate the spokes as they are copied.

If you were not successful, try again. The wheel should be similar to the following.

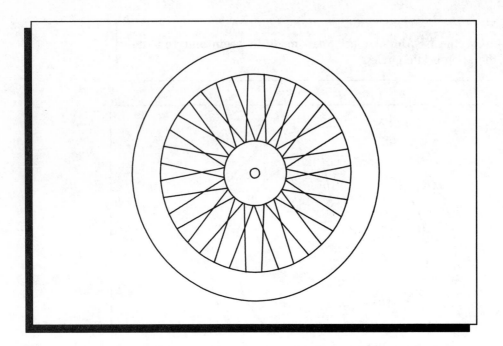

5 Practice using the ARRAY Polar option by arraying other objects. At least once, specify less than 360 degrees when replying to "Angle to fill."

NOTE:

During the ARRAY Polar sequence, the prompt "Angle to fill (+=ccw, −=cw)" appears. AutoCAD is asking for the angle (in degrees) to fill the array. "+=ccw" means that a positive number will produce an array in a counterclockwise direction, and "−=cw" means that a negative number will produce an array in a clockwise direction.

6 Enter **END** to save your work and return to the Main Menu.

Questions

1. In what submenu is the ARRAY command found?

   _____

2. Name the two types of arrays.

   _____

3. State one practical application for each type of array.

   _____

   _____

   _____

4. When creating a polar array, do you have the option of specifying less than 360 degrees of array? Explain.

   _____

   _____

5. Explain how a rectangular array can be created at any angle.

   _____

   _____

1. Using the ARRAY command and the Polar option, draw the following figure.

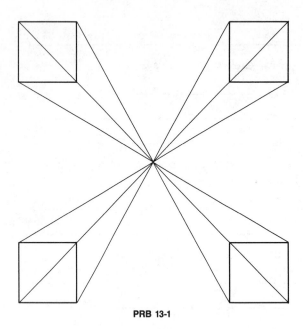

PRB 13-1

2. Use ARRAY again to create the following figure. (Start by drawing an ellipse and then array it.) Experiment to see how changing the shape of the ellipse and the number of ellipses changes the figure.

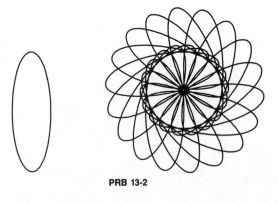

PRB 13-2

3. Develop an auditorium with rows and columns of seats using the ARRAY command. Design the room any way you'd like.

4. Identify another practical application for using an array. Draw the first object and then array it.

5. Load your drawing called GASKET. Erase each of the circles. Replace the large ones according to the locations shown below, this time using the ARRAY command. Also reproduce the small circles using the ARRAY command, but don't worry about their exact locations. The radius of the large circles is .6; the small circles have a radius of .12.

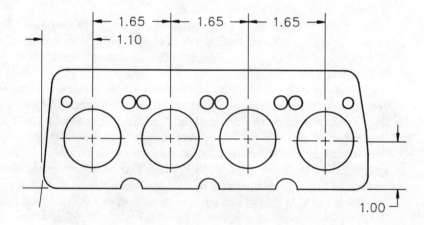

6. Using the ARRAY command (you decide how), draw the following figure.

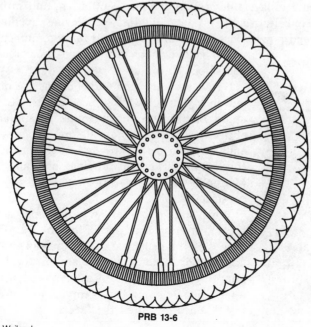

PRB 13-6

Courtesy of Bob Weiland

AUTOCAD® AT WORK

CAD Goes Underground for Seattle Tunnel Design

By any measure, the Seattle Underground Transit Tunnel is an ambitious project. Slated for completion in 1991, the $415 million tunnel will allow commuter buses to pass beneath the streets of the city, relieving surface traffic in Seattle's congested central district.

The tunnel's designers, in order to manage the project's complexity, turned to AutoCAD. "We couldn't do this without CAD," says Rick Deranleau, CAD operations supervisor for the Seattle office of Parsons Brinkerhoff Quade & Douglas, Inc. (PBQ&D).

PBQ&D, one of the nation's largest architectural and engineering firms, uses CAD to design electrical, mechanical, and telecommunications plans for the tunnel and its five bus stations. The firm began using CAD just in time for the tunnel project. Base maps of the tunnel and its stations were drawn manually by architectural subconsultants and digitized into the CAD system, using an E-size (36″ × 48″) tablet and 16-button puck. To speed up the digitizing, CAD operators devised their own tracking machine, called Digitrack, to guide the puck as it traces over the drawing. An operator moves the puck while speaking commands such as "erase," "copy," and "array" into a headset. A speech recognition program called Pronounce translates the command into AutoCAD. "The system is incredibly fast," says Deranleau. "We can enter five D-size drawings on a single shift."

CAD operators create additional layers directly on-screen. Seven mechanical layers describe plumbing, ventilation, and sprinkler systems, while ten electrical layers detail lighting, power runs, ancillary power, and overhead power lines for electric buses and telecommunications systems, which include phone lines, closed-circuit security cameras, and smoke alarms.

Layers are separated and combined as desired, plotted out on Mylar polyester film, and then distributed to the appropriate engineering disciplines for appraisal. A number of electrical layers are merged, for instance, so that electrical engineers can design the overall power distribution and conduit plan. The final drawings, once approved by Seattle Metropolitan Transit District engineers, will be released for construction bids.

What started out as an experiment at PBQ&D has become an established part of the firm. "CAD has definitely proved itself here in Seattle," Deranleau says. "We've saved an enormous amount of time and money. PBQ&D is now adopting AutoCAD in many of its national and international offices. Our company's made a commitment to CAD as the way of the future."

Courtesy of Seattle-King County
Convention and Visitors Bureau

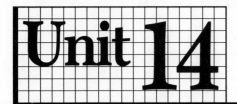

Unit 14 — Modifying and Maneuvering

**AutoCAD®
Reference
Manual**

■ **OBJECTIVE:**

To apply the STRETCH, SCALE, ROTATE, TRIM, and EXTEND commands

AutoCAD offers numerous editing commands for changing the appearance of drawings. For instance, you can stretch the end of a house to make it longer, scale it down if it is too large, rotate it to better position it on a lot, trim sidewalk lines that extend too far, and extend driveway lines which are too short. We will do all of this, and more, in the following steps.

1   Begin a New Drawing and name it **SITE**.

2   Draw the following site plan according to the dimensions shown. With Snap on, place the lower left corner of the property line at absolute point 1,1. Omit dimensions. All points in the drawing should fall on the Snap grid.

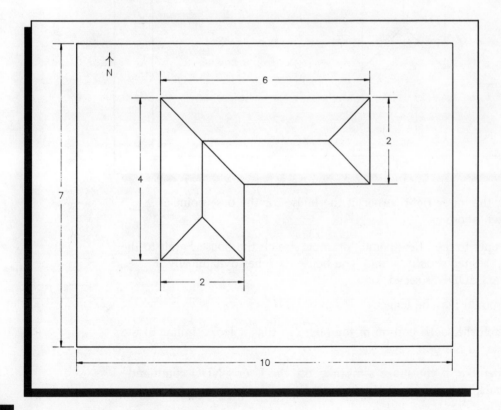

STRETCH Command _____

5.2.6

1   Enter the **STRETCH** command and specify a window using the Crossing option. Make it around the east end of the house as shown in the next drawing, and press **RETURN**.

If you select STRETCH from the screen or pull-down menu, the Crossing option is embedded in the command sequence and therefore is entered for you automatically.

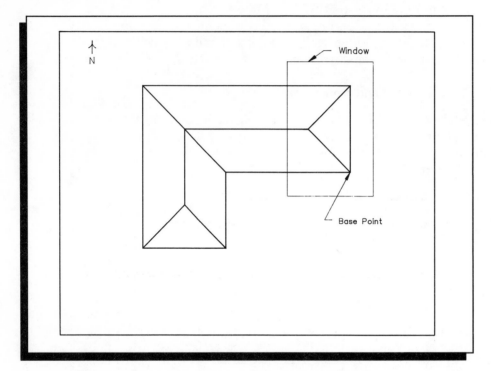

2 Pick the lower right corner of the house for the base point as shown above.

3 In reply to the "New point:" prompt, stretch the house 1 unit to the right. (Snap should be on.) The house stretches dynamically if DRAGMODE is set to Auto.

The house should now be longer.

4 Stretch the south portion of the house so that it looks similar to the house on the next page.

Remember, if you make a mistake, use the U or UNDO command to back up.

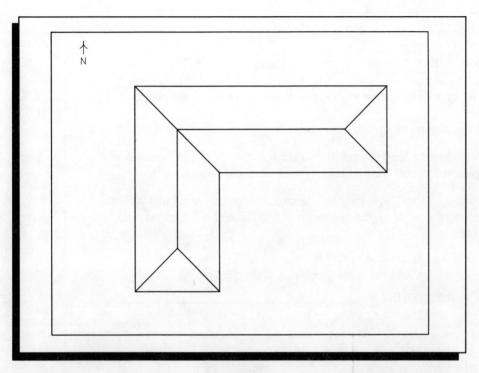

NOTE:

STRETCH is also applied to alter dimensions. This is part of the associative dimensioning feature and is covered in the section titled "Associative Dimensioning" in Unit 23.

SCALE Command

5.2.4

Since the house is now a bit too large, let's scale it down to fit the lot.

1   Enter the **SCALE** command, select the object by placing a window around the entire house, and press **RETURN**.

2   Pick the lower left corner of the house as the base point.

At this point, the house can be dynamically dragged into place or a scale factor can be entered.

3   Move the crosshairs and notice the dynamic scaling. (DRAGMODE must be set to Auto.)

4   Enter **.5** in reply to "<Scale factor>."

Now the house is a bit too small. Let's scale it up using the SCALE Reference option.

1 Enter **SCALE** and select the house as before.

2 Pick the lower left corner of the house again for the base point.

3 Enter the Reference option.

4 For the reference length, pick the lower left corner of the house, and then pick the corner just to the right of it as the second point.

5 In response to the "New length:" prompt, move the crosshairs about 1/2 unit to the right of the second point. (Ortho should be on and Snap off.)

Did the house enlarge according to the specified length?

ROTATE Command

5.2.3

Let's rotate the house.

1 Enter the **ROTATE** command, select the entire house, and press **RETURN**.

2 Pick the lower left corner of the house for the base point.

3 Move your crosshairs and notice that the object rotates dynamically. (Ortho should be off.)

NOTE:

Drag is embedded in the command sequence and therefore is entered for you automatically.

4 For the Rotation angle, enter **25** (degrees).

Did the house rotate 25 degrees counterclockwise?

Let's rotate the house again, but this time with the Drag option.

1 Enter **ROTATE**, select the house, and press **RETURN** after you have made the selection.

2 Pick the lower left corner of the house for the base point.

3 At the "<Rotation angle>/Reference:" prompt, drag the house in a clockwise direction a few degrees so that it is positioned similarly to the one on the next page.

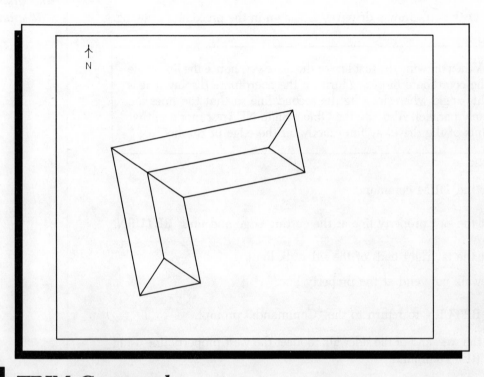

TRIM Command

5.3.4

1 With Ortho on and Snap off, draw two lines near the bottom of the site plan to represent a sidewalk. Extend the sidewalk beyond the east and west property lines as shown here.

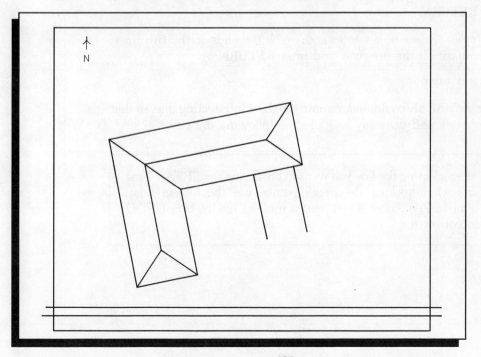

2 With Ortho off, draw a driveway as shown in the preceding drawing.

HINT:
When drawing the first line of the driveway, notice the line angle found in the coordinate display. (Turn on the coordinate display if it is off.) Use this angle when drawing the second line so that the lines are approximately parallel. Also, use the Object Snap NEArest mode so that the endpoints of the driveway fall exactly on the edge of the house.

3 Enter the **TRIM** command.

4 Select the east property line as the cutting edge and press **RETURN**.

5 Select the far right ends of the sidewalk lines.

Does the sidewalk now end at the property line?

6 Press **RETURN** to return to the "Command:" prompt.

7 Trim the west end of the sidewalk to meet the west property line using the TRIM command.

EXTEND Command

5.3.5

1 Enter the **EXTEND** command.

2 Select the south property line as the boundary edge and press **RETURN**.

3 In reply to "Select object to extend:" pick the ends of the two lines which make up the driveway and press **RETURN**.

Did the driveway extend?

4 Using the BREAK command, remove the short intersecting lines so that the sidewalk and driveway look like the following drawing.

HINT:
After selecting the line you want to break, use the BREAK First option. Then, when picking the Break points, use the Object Snap INTersection mode. Remember, if you make a mistake, use the U or UNDO command to correct it.

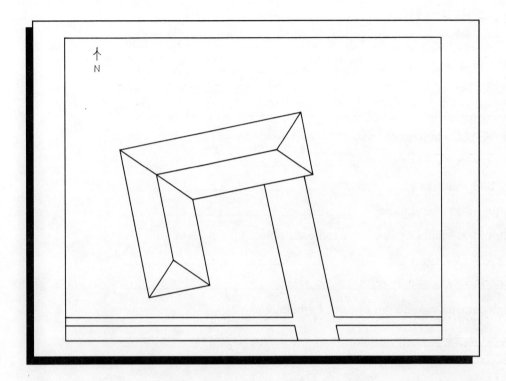

Questions

1. Explain the purpose of the STRETCH command.

   _____

   _____

2. Using the SCALE command, what number would you enter to

   enlarge an object by 50 percent? _____

   enlarge it to 3 times its present size?_____

   reduce it to 1/2 its present size? _____

3. Explain how you would dynamically scale an object up or down.

   _____

   _____

4. Can you dynamically rotate an object? Explain.

   _____

   _____

5. How would you accurately specify a 90-degree clockwise rotation of an object?

   _____

   _____

6. Explain the purpose of the TRIM command.

   _____

   _____

7. Describe a situation in which the EXTEND command would be useful.

   _____

   _____

Problem

Bring up the SITE drawing you created in this unit. Perform each of the following operations on the drawing.

- Stretch the driveway by placing a (Crossing) window around the house and across the driveway. Stretch the driveway to the north so that the house is sitting farther to the rear of the lot.

- Add a sidewalk parallel to the east property line. Use the TRIM and BREAK commands to clean up the sidewalk corner and the north end of the new sidewalk.

- Reduce the entire site plan by 20 percent using the SCALE command.

- Stretch the right side of the site plan to the east 1 unit.

- Rotate the entire site plan 10 degrees in a counterclockwise direction.

- If you'd like, place trees and shrubs to complete the site plan drawing. Use the ARRAY command to create one tree and one shrub. Use the COPY command to duplicate them.

The site plan should now look similar to the one below.

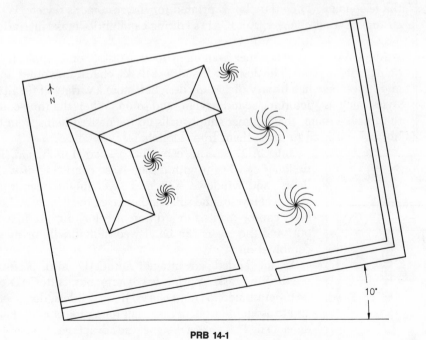

PRB 14-1

AUTOCAD® AT WORK

Designing Interiors Using AutoCAD

The job of an interior designer is to transform empty space into homes and offices. AutoCAD helps designers put together attractive, functional rooms. By reducing the labor involved in making and changing drawings, AutoCAD gives designers more time to be creative.

The interior designer using AutoCAD begins by viewing the architect's drawings on the computer screen. The next step is to fill the empty space, starting with interior walls and ending with details, such as the color of the telephones. Then the plan is printed for the customer's review. When customers want changes, AutoCAD's editing capabilities make alterations easy.

AutoCAD frees the designer from many routine tasks. For example, it can help furnish a room. The designer first draws desks, chairs, and other items and stores them in a library file. Many designers store a variety of furniture styles, such as Victorian, Scandinavian, and so on. When the time comes to furnish a room, the designer simply calls up the desired items from the library—no need to draw them from scratch.

AutoCAD's layering capability is another useful aid. The designer can begin with a base layer consisting of walls, doors, and windows. The next layer might include the electrical layout, and still another layer, the furniture. Each layer can be printed in a different color to make it stand out, and the layers can be viewed individually or in any combination.

As an added advantage, AutoCAD also performs nondrafting tasks. With a few commands, AutoCAD can be programmed to count chairs, lights, outlets, doors, etc., and to assemble a bill of materials for a project as it's being developed. This gives a designer the advantage of accurately estimating the cost of building and furnishing an entire office.

Finally, AutoCAD saves calculating time. It can compute the area of any shape, an indispensable feature for a profession that charges by the square foot!

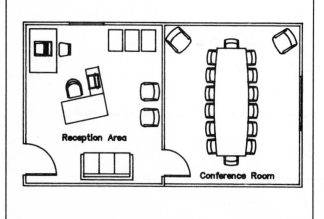

Reception Area

Conference Room

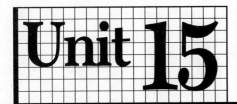
Unit 15 — AutoCAD's Magnifying Glass

■ OBJECTIVE:

To practice the ZOOM, REGEN, and VIEWRES commands

The ZOOM command allows you to increase and decrease the apparent size of drawings on the screen. ZOOM can magnify objects as much as ten trillion times! This unit utilizes the ZOOM command to practice this process, and it covers the effects of screen regenerations caused by ZOOM.

■ *ZOOM Command* _____

Let's apply the ZOOM command.

6.2

1 Load AutoCAD and Begin a New Drawing. Name it **ZOOM**.

2 Draw the following room, including the table and chair.
Don't worry about exact sizes and locations of the objects, but do fill most of your screen.

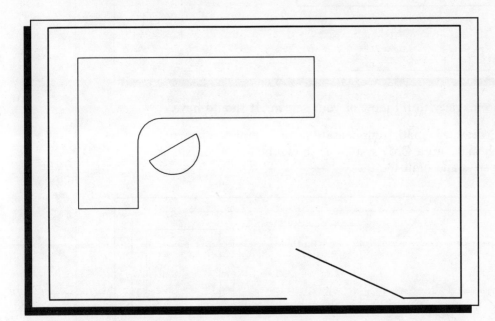

3 Enter the **ZOOM** command. Note each of the ZOOM options, as shown below.

```
Command: ZOOM
All/Center/Dynamic/Extents/Left/Previous/Window/<Scale(X)>:
```

4 Select the **W** (Window) option and place a window around the table as shown below.

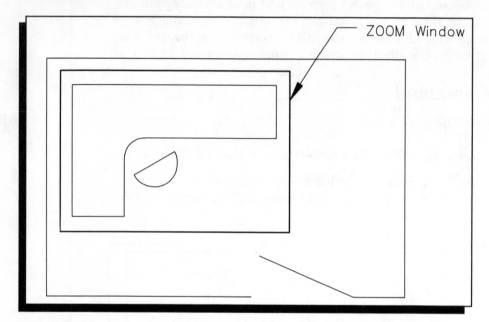

ZOOM Window

Did the table magnify to fill most of your screen? It should have.

5 Next, draw schematic representations of several components which make up a CAD system as shown below. Approximate their sizes and omit the text.

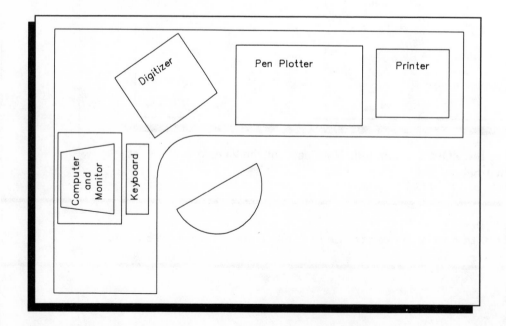

Digitizer

Pen Plotter

Printer

Computer and Monitor

Keyboard

**AutoCAD®
Reference
Manual**

Now let's zoom in on the keyboard. This can be done using ZOOM L.

6 Enter **ZOOM** and then enter the **L** (Left) option.

6.2.6

The prompt line will ask for a lower left corner point.

7 With your pointing device, pick a point near the lower left corner of the keyboard. (If you pick a point *within* the keyboard, you may lose the borders of the keyboard.)

The prompt line will now ask for magnification or height.

8 Use the pointing device to pick a point just above the keyboard.

You may have to zoom again so that the keyboard fills most of your screen.

9 In the lower left corner of the keyboard, draw a small square to represent a key, as shown below.

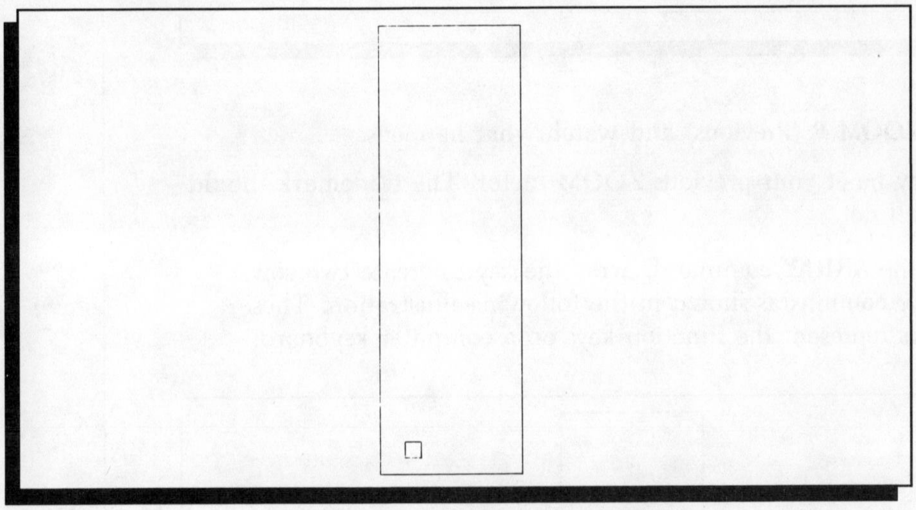

10 Zoom in on the key, this time using **ZOOM C** (Center). Pick a center point of your ZOOM by picking the center of the key and then specify the height by picking points below and above the key.

6.2.5

11 Using the POLYGON command, draw a small trademark on the key as shown in the following drawing.

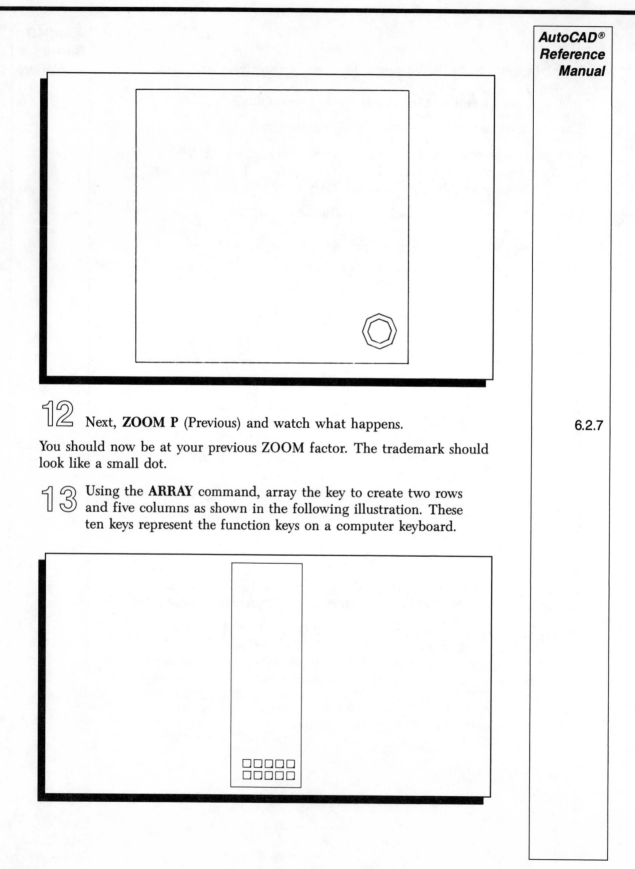

12 Next, **ZOOM P** (Previous) and watch what happens.

6.2.7

You should now be at your previous ZOOM factor. The trademark should look like a small dot.

13 Using the **ARRAY** command, array the key to create two rows and five columns as shown in the following illustration. These ten keys represent the function keys on a computer keyboard.

HINT:

You can use your pointing device to indicate the row/column distances. The format is:

Unit cell or distance between rows (---): *Pick point 1.*
Other corner: *Pick point 2.*

The following illustrates this operation.

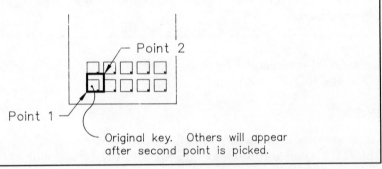

14 Next, **ZOOM A** (All).

6.2.2

Is your original drawing now on the screen?

15 **ZOOM E** (Extents) and watch what happens.

6.2.3

How is ZOOM E different from ZOOM A?

16 Continue to practice using the ZOOM command by zooming in on the different CAD components of the drawing and including detail on each.

NOTE:

The ZOOM Dynamic option is discussed fully in the following unit.

Screen Regenerations

Screen regenerations are often caused when ZOOM is entered. A screen regeneration, unlike REDRAW, calculates each vector (line) contained in the drawing. This can take some time, especially with large, complex drawings.

Let's force another screen regeneration with the ZOOM command.

1 Enter **ZOOM A.**

Since your current drawing is not large and complex, it does not take long to regenerate.

HINT:

To save time when drawing with AutoCAD, you should avoid screen regenerations as much as possible. The ZOOM command will cause a regeneration when the ZOOM area is outside the normal drawing area defined by the drawing limits (see Unit 20 for a discussion on the drawing limits), or if ZOOM All is issued, or if the ZOOM magnification is beyond the virtual screen (32,000 pixels × 32,000 pixels). See the discussion on virtual screens near the beginning of Chapter 6 in the *AutoCAD Reference Manual.*

Screen regenerations can also be caused by using other AutoCAD commands, including the REGEN command.

6.9

2 Enter **REGEN**.

Did your screen regenerate as it did when you entered ZOOM All? As you work with AutoCAD commands such as QTEXT and FILL, you will identify applications for REGEN.

VIEWRES Command

6.15

The VIEWRES command controls "fast zoom" mode and sets the resolution for arcs and circles.

1 Enter the **VIEWRES** command.

2 Enter No.

All ZOOMs, PANs, and VIEW Restores will now perform regenerations.

The "circle zoom percent" enables you to control the appearance of circles and arcs. A high number will make circles and arcs appear smooth but at the expense of regeneration speed.

3 Enter **20**.

4 Construct an arc or circle and notice its "coarse" appearance.

As you can see, arc and circle entities now contain fewer vectors and therefore will generate more quickly on the screen.

5 Enter **VIEWRES** again and enter Yes.

AutoCAD will now maintain a large (32,000 pixel × 32,000 pixel) virtual screen and will perform ZOOMs, PANs, and VIEW Restores at REDRAW speed whenever possible.

6 Enter **150** and notice the appearance of arcs and circles on the screen.

Transparent ZOOM

With AutoCAD, you have the capability to perform transparent zooms. This means you can use ZOOM while another command is in progress. To do this, enter 'ZOOM (notice the apostrophe) at any prompt that is not asking for a text string. Let's try it.

1 Enter the **LINE** command and pick a point on the screen.

2 At the "From point:" prompt, enter **'ZOOM**.

3 Choose the Window option and zoom in on any portion of your screen.

4 Pick an endpoint for the line.

Transparent zooms give you great zoom magnification flexibility while using other commands. For instance, if your line endpoints require greater accuracy than your present display will allow, the transparent zoom provides you with a solution.

___ NOTE: ___

Some restrictions and operational hints are noted here.

- Fast ZOOM mode (set by the VIEWRES command) must be ON in order for ZOOM to operate transparently.
- Transparent operations can be done only if a screen regeneration is not required.
- ZOOM All and ZOOM Extents cannot be used transparently since they always require a screen regeneration.

These items also apply to the PAN and VIEW commands, which are covered in the next unit.

5 When you are finished working with REGEN and ZOOM, enter **END** to save your work and to exit the Drawing Editor.

Questions

1. Explain why the ZOOM command is useful.

   _____

2. Cite one example of when it would be necessary to use the ZOOM command for completing a technical drawing and explain why.

   _____

   _____

3. In what submenu is the ZOOM command found?

   _____

4. Describe each of the following ZOOM options.

   All _____

   Center _____

   Dynamic _____

   Extents _____

   Left _____

   Previous _____

   Window _____

   Scale _____

5. Explain a screen regeneration.

   _____

   _____

6. How is REGEN different from REDRAW?

   _____

   _____

Problem

Create a drawing such as an elevation plan of a building, a site plan of a land development, or a view of a mechanical part. Using the ZOOM command, zoom in on your drawing and include detail. Zoom in and out on your drawing as necessary using the different ZOOM options.

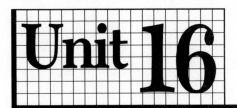
■ OBJECTIVE:

To apply the PAN and VIEW commands and perform dynamic zooms and pans

Like most CAD systems, AutoCAD provides a means for moving around on large drawings so that you can add details. This unit illustrates and applies this method and offers suggestions for doing it the most efficient way possible.

Note the degree of detail in the following architectural floor plan.

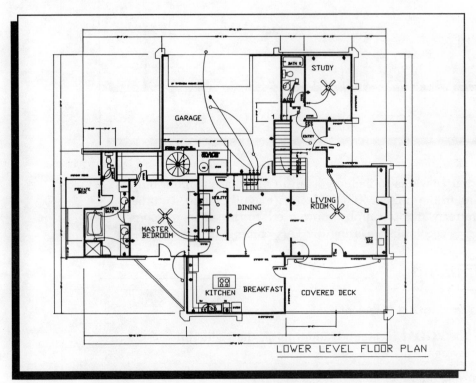

AutoCAD Drawing Courtesy of Lansing Pugh, Architect

The drafter who completed this CAD drawing zoomed in on portions of the floor plan in order to include detail. For example, the drafter zoomed in on the kitchen to place the kitchen cabinets and appliances.

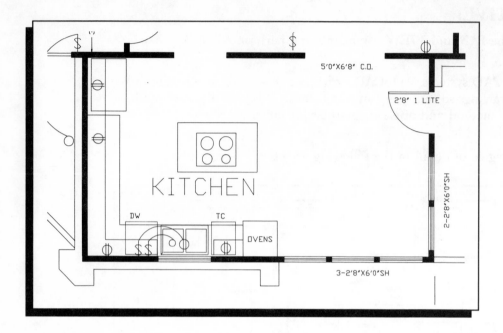

Suppose the drafter wants to include detail in an adjacent room but
wants to maintain the present ZOOM factor (magnification). In other
words, the drafter wants to simply "move over" to the adjacent room.
This operation is accomplished using the PAN command.

PAN Command

6.3

1 Load the drawing called **ZOOM**.

2 Using the **ZOOM** command, zoom in on the right third of
the drawing.

Let's pan (move) to the left side of the drawing.

3 Enter the **PAN** command.

4 For Displacement, specify two points: the first point in the left
portion of your screen, the second point in the right portion of
your screen.

The drawing should have moved to the right the distance you specified. If
it did not, try it again.

5 Experiment further with the PAN command until you feel
comfortable with it.

Wouldn't it be nice if you could somehow save ZOOM windows for later retrieval? Imagine you are working on an architectural floor plan like the one shown previously. You've zoomed in on the kitchen to include details such as the appliances, and now you're ready to pan over to the utility room. Before leaving the kitchen, you foresee a need to return to the kitchen for final touches or revision. But, by the time you're ready to do this final work on the kitchen, you may be at a different ZOOM magnification and/or at the other end of your drawing. The VIEW command solves the problem.

VIEW Command

Let's apply the VIEW command with the ZOOM drawing.

6.4

1 ZOOM in on a portion of your ZOOM drawing, if you have not done so already.

2 Using the **VIEW** command, save your present ZOOM window by entering **S** (or **save**) and giving it a one-word name.

3 Now **PAN** to a new location.

4 Enter the **VIEW** command, and this time restore your previously named view by entering **R** (or **restore**) and the name of the view.

If it did not work, try again.

5 Enter the **VIEW** command once again and this time issue the Window option.

6 Type another view name and press **RETURN**.

7 Define the VIEW Window by specifying two corner points.

8 Practice using the VIEW command by zooming and panning to different locations on your drawing and saving views. Also define new views using the VIEW Window option. Then restore those named views.

After storing several views, it is possible to forget their names. Therefore there is a way of listing all named views.

1 Enter the **VIEW** command and then enter a question mark (?) or select **listing** from the screen menu.

You should receive a listing of all views. What other information was produced?

117

2 Return to the drawing by pressing the flip screen function key (usually **F1**).

3 Use the **VIEW D**elete option to delete one of your saved views.

4 **ZOOM A**ll to restore your original zoom magnification.

Transparent PAN and VIEW _____

The PAN and VIEW commands can be used transparently. Transparent PAN and VIEW are particularly useful for reaching line endpoints that are located off your current display. However, certain transparent pans and "view restore" operations cause a screen regeneration. As a consequence, the transparent pan or view is not allowed. To help avoid this potential problem, use transparent pans and views only within the virtual screen boundary. For more information on the virtual screen and on screen regenerations, see the section titled "Screen Regenerations" in Unit 15.

Here is an example of the transparent use of PAN.

> Command: LINE
> From point: (*Pick an endpoint*)
> To point: 'PAN (*Notice the leading apostrophe.*)
> >>Displacement: (*Pick a point*)
> >>Second point: (*Pick a point*)
> Resuming LINE command.
> To point: (*Pick an endpoint*)

See Unit 15 for some restrictions and operational hints on transparent use of commands.

_____

Dynamic Zooms and Pans_____

6.2.8

The ZOOM Dynamic option can help to minimize screen regenerations. It displays the area you should stay within during zooms and pans to avoid time-consuming screen regenerations.

Let's take a closer look.

 Enter **ZOOM** and issue the Dynamic option.

You should see something similar to the following on your screen. You should also see a large flashing (refreshing) box on your screen with an "X" in the center. This is called the "view box."

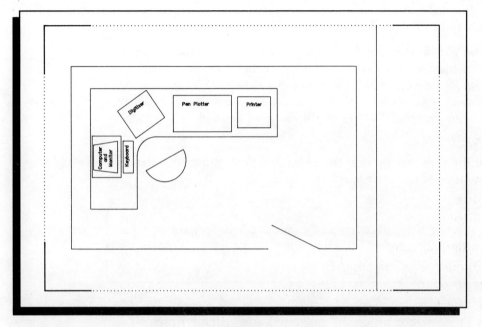

If you have a color monitor, the outside four corners will be in red. On a monochrome monitor, the corners should stand out such as in the above drawing. The current zoom magnification is depicted by a dotted/green box.

The four corners are very important because they represent the portion of the drawing AutoCAD has previously generated and stored in memory. Sections in this area can be viewed at high speed using the ZOOM and PAN commands unless the ZOOM window is made unusually small.

2 Press the pick button on your pointing device, and move it to the left to decrease the size of the box to about 1/2 its original size. (Do not press RETURN.)

An arrow at the right side of the view box should have appeared. This indicates "zoom" mode.

NOTE:

If you were to press the RETURN key at this time, AutoCAD would perform a zoom on the area defined by the view box. If the view box extends outside the four corners (generated area), AutoCAD will force a regeneration of the screen. A small hourglass will appear in the lower left corner of your display screen to remind you that a lengthy regeneration will be required if that view is chosen.

3 Press the pick button again and move the view box around the screen.

119

You should again have an "X" in the center of the view box. This means you are presently in the "pan" mode.

So you see, the pick button toggles the way the view box appears. When you are able to increase and decrease the size of the view box, the "zoom" mode is active. When you are able to move the entire box at a fixed size about your screen, you are in the "pan" mode. By pressing RETURN in either mode, your drawing changes to fill the area defined by the view box.

4 Move the view box outside the generated area and notice the appearance of the hourglass.

HINT:
It is best to avoid zooms and pans outside the generated area depicted by the four corners. Therefore when the hourglass appears on your screen, avoid pressing RETURN.

5 With the view box inside the generated area, (finally) press **RETURN.**

Note how quickly the drawing appeared on your screen—at REDRAW speed.

6 Enter **ZOOM D**ynamic again.

Notice the box on your screen defined by dotted lines (and green, if you have color). This represents the current ZOOM magnification.

7 Change the size of your view box with your pick button, reposition the view box, and press **RETURN.**

So you see, this can be a very useful and time-effective way of moving about your drawing.

8 Practice using the dynamic zoom and pan, and avoid time-consuming screen regenerations.

9 Enter **END** to save your work and exit the Drawing Editor.

Questions

1. Explain why the PAN command is useful.

_____

_____

_____

2. Explain why the VIEW command is useful.

_____

_____

_____

3. How do you list all named views?

_____

_____

4. What other information does the listing provide?

_____

_____

5. Within the ZOOM Dynamic screen, what do the four outside corners represent?

_____

_____

6. Explain the difference between the dynamic zoom and pan modes while in the ZOOM Dynamic screen.

_____

_____

7. What does the small hourglass represent? What happens if a view box is chosen when the hourglass is present?

_____

_____

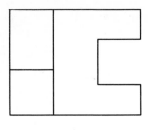

Problems

1. Draw each of the following shapes on your screen. Don't worry about their exact sizes and locations. Zoom in on one of the shapes and store it as a View. Then pan to each of the other shapes and store each as a View. Restore each named View and alter each shape by adding and erasing lines. Be as creative as you wish.

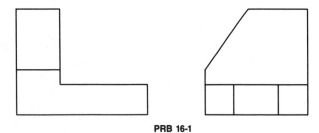

PRB 16-1

2. Perform dynamic pans and zooms in the above drawing. Avoid time-consuming screen regenerations caused by panning and zooming outside the generated area.

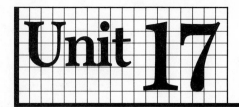

Unit 17 Multiple Viewports

■ OBJECTIVE:

To learn how to use AutoCAD's multiple viewport facility

AutoCAD contains a facility called viewports that allows you to see two, three, or four views of a drawing at once. The drawing information in each of the viewports can be viewed at any magnification, and you are able to draw and edit from one viewport to the next. For instance, you can begin a line in one view and complete it in another.

6.1.1

The following illustration gives an example of applying multiple viewports. Notice that each viewport is different both in content and magnification.

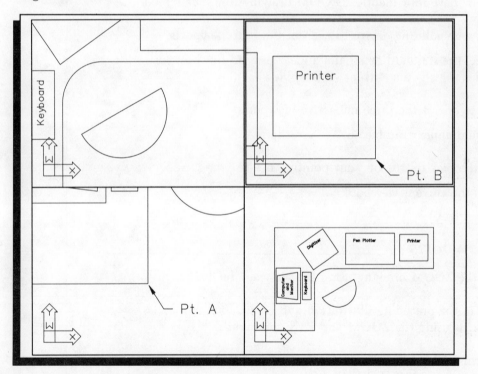

Creating Multiple Viewports

6.7

Viewports are controlled with the VPORTS (also called VIEWPORTS) command. In addition, your computer system may support AutoCAD's pull-down menus, which give access to the viewport facility.

However, the pull-down menu option only reveals a portion of the VPORTS command. Therefore, use either the keyboard or the standard screen menu to enter the VPORTS command in the following steps.

1 Load the drawing file named **ZOOM**.

2 Using the **ZOOM** command, make the drawing fill most of the screen.

123

③ Enter the **VPORTS** command.

The following options should appear after the "Command:" prompt.

```
Save/Restore/Delete/Join/Off/?/2/<3>/4:
```

④ Enter 4.

You should now have four identical ZOOM drawings on your screen.

⑤ Move your pointing device to each of the four viewports.

As you can see, the standard crosshairs appear only in the viewport with the bold border. This is the current (active) viewport.

⑥ Move to one of the three nonactive viewports.

An arrow should appear in place of the crosshairs.

⑦ Press the pick button on your pointing device.

Now which is the current viewport?

Using Viewports

Let's modify the ZOOM drawing using the viewport facilities.

1 Refer to the preceding illustration and create four similar viewports using the **ZOOM** and **PAN** commands.

2 Save this viewport configuration by entering **VPORTS** Save option and name it **WORKPLACE**.

3 Make the lower left viewport current.

4 Enter the **LINE** command and pick point A. Refer to the preceding illustration for Point A.

HINT:
Use the Object Snap feature to accurately locate the point.

5 Move to the upper right viewport and make it current.

6.7

6.1.1

Notice that the LINE command is now active in this viewport.

6 Pick point B.

The line represents the hard surface on which the chair can roll.

So you see, you can easily begin an operation in one viewport and continue it in another. And, the change is reflected in all viewports. This is especially useful when working on large drawings with lots of detail.

Let's move the printer from one viewport to another.

NOTE:

You may need to shrink the printer a small amount, using the SCALE command, so that it will fit its new location.

7 With the upper right viewport current, enter the **MOVE** command and select the printer.

8 Pick a base point at any convenient location on or near the printer.

9 Move to the lower left viewport and make it current.

10 Place the printer in the open area on the table by picking a second point at the appropriate location.

Did the printer location change in the other viewports?

VPORTS Command Options

6.7

First, let's combine two viewports into one.

1 Enter the **VPORTS** command and select the Join option.

2 Choose the upper left viewport in reply to "Select dominant viewport <current>:".

3 Now choose the upper right viewport in reply to "Select viewport to join:".

As you can see, the Join option enables you to expand—in this case, double—the size of the viewport.

4 Enter the **VPORTS O**ff option.

As you can see, the screen changed to single viewport viewing. This single viewport is inherited from the current viewport at the time VPORTS Off is issued.

5 Enter the **VPORTS ?** option.

Notice that AutoCAD stores information about the active viewports as well as the stored viewport configurations, such as WORKPLACE.

6 Enter the **VPORTS** Restore option and enter **WORKPLACE**.

As you can see, the viewports returned as they were when you stored them under the name WORKPLACE. But the drawing does not return to its earlier form. The printer remains next to the monitor, for example. In short, saving viewport configurations stores only the viewports themselves, not the drawing information.

7 Enter **VPORTS** and then enter **3**.

The message "The specified division would create too many viewports" should appear. Therefore ...

8 ... enter **VPORTS O**ff option.

9 Enter **VPORTS** and 3 once again.

The following should appear.

```
Horizontal/Vertical/Above/Below/Left/<Right>:
```

10 Enter the Horizontal option.

11 Step through each of the remaining options on your own.

HINT: Enter **VPORTS O**ff prior to entering each of the options.

12 If your computer system supports AutoCAD's pull-down menus, experiment with the **Set Viewports** option found in the **Display** menu.

A.3.2.4

The following shows the viewport settings dialogue box.

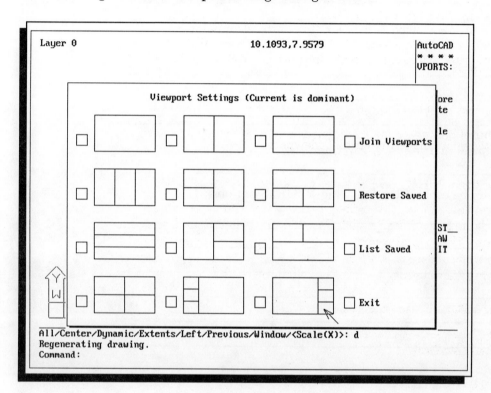

NOTE:

The REDRAW and REGEN commands affect only the current viewport. If multiple viewports are active and you want to redraw or regenerate all of them, you can use the REDRAWALL or REGENALL command. REDRAWALL can be used transparently.

13 Enter **END** to save your work and exit the Drawing Editor.

Questions

1. How can multiple viewports help you to construct drawings?

   _____

   _____

   _____

2. How is a viewport made the current viewport?

   _____

3. Briefly describe each of the following VPORTS options.

   Save_____

   Restore _____

   Delete_____

   Join _____

   Off _____

   ? _____

   2 _____

   3 _____

   4 _____

4. What do you enter to obtain two viewports in the top half of the screen and one viewport in the bottom half of the screen?

   _____

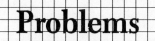

Problems

1. Create each of the following viewport configurations and save each under a name of your choice.

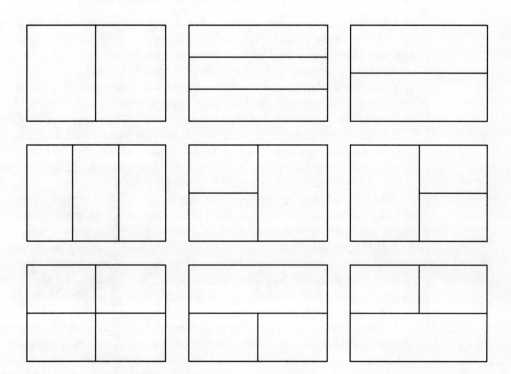

2. Select one of the viewport configurations from Problem 1. Complete a moderately complex drawing entirely within the viewport facility.

AUTOCAD® AT WORK

Who's Manufacturing with AutoCAD?*

CADENCE magazine conducted a survey to learn the answer to that question. The staff found that many manufacturers are using AutoCAD, in ways that are almost as varied as the products produced.

At BIMBA Manufacturing in Monee, Illinois, AutoCAD is used for tooling and fixture design and, in some cases, for the design of NC machines used to manufacture pneumatic cylinder components. Additionally, the company uses the system for facilities planning and project management.

At McDonnell Douglas in St. Louis, AutoCAD plays a part in design of systems for nondestructive testing. It provides a cost effective 2-D capacity and complements the company's current Unigraphics system, which is used for analysis and 3-D design.

Ford Motor Company in Dearborn uses AutoCAD for conceptual design of manufacturing systems, specifically for systems which produce engine parts. Basically, the Advanced Manufacturing Development group uses AutoCAD for generating concept sheets. A typical drawing incorporates notes describing specific manufacturing phases—how a part should be produced, how it should be folded and fixtured, how much metal should be removed, etc. These drawings are transferred to a Computervision mainframe system for further analysis and for the actual design work.

Custom Tool & Manufacturing in Lexington, Kentucky, makes automated assembly equipment, including robotic tool changers. AutoCAD is used to design equipment, add marketing touches to the drawings, and incorporate these drawings in the company's product literature. Additionally, mechanical and electrical drawings, as well as printed circuit board layouts, are produced.

Another interesting application is the use of AutoCAD for design of walk-in coolers for such fast food giants as McDonalds and Burger King. Vollrath in Sheboygan, Wisconsin, generates a design and sends a disk with the drawings to the client for incorporation into the restaurant drawings. The disk is then returned to Vollrath with the appropriate dimensions for manufacturing.

The list goes on, including such well-known companies as General Foods, General Electric, and AT&T Bell Laboratories. The question "Who's manufacturing with AutoCAD?" can be answered in many ways since manufacturing integrates so many different functions in a production environment. AutoCAD is used in many aspects of manufacturing—from plant design to packaging design. As a productivity tool in a production environment, AutoCAD is clearly a leader.

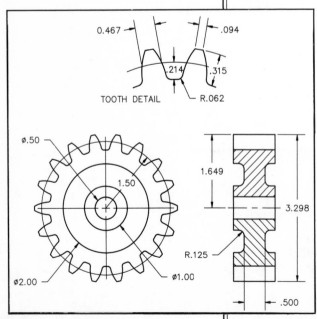

*Based on a story in *CADENCE* magazine, Vol 1, No. 5.

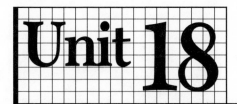

Unit 18 — A Look at DOS Functions Within AutoCAD

AutoCAD®
Reference
Manual

■ OBJECTIVE:

To use the File Utility Menu and the FILES, SHELL, and SH commands

When working with AutoCAD, there are times when you'd like to use certain DOS (Disk Operating System) functions such as DIRectory, REName, or COPY. This unit gives you practice in using these functions.

The File Utility Menu

Unit 1 showed you how to start a file for a new drawing. By now, you probably have several AutoCAD drawing files on disk. Suppose you want to delete files, rename them, or simply see a list of what you've got. AutoCAD has a File Utility Menu which allows you to do these operations and others too.

1 Load AutoCAD and bring up the Main Menu.

2 Select option 6, "File Utilities."

You should now have a new menu on your screen.

```
File Utility Menu

    Ø.   Exit File Utility Menu
    1.   List Drawing files
    2.   List user specified files
    3.   Delete files
    4.   Rename files
    5.   Copy file

    Enter selection  (Ø to 5) <Ø>:
```

3 Select option 1, "List Drawing files," and press **RETURN**.

3.8.1

You will get a message like the following:

```
              Enter drive or directory:
```

4 Press **RETURN** again.

You should get a listing of all the drawings stored on the default drive or directory.

5 If your drawings reside on a drive or directory other than the default, select option 1 again, but this time specify the correct drive or directory. An example of a directory specification is shown below.

Enter drive or directory: **USER**

In this example, "USER" is the name of the directory containing user drawing files.

Now let's produce a list of *all* files located on one drive or directory.

1 Press **RETURN** to bring back the File Utility Menu.

2 Select option 2, "List user specified files."

3 Type *.* (the wild-card or global specification) and press **RETURN**.

NOTE:

See Appendix F for more uses of wild cards.

You should have received a list of all files located on the default drive. If not, try again.

Note that different types of files are listed. The type of file is indicated by the three-letter file extension following the period. For example, for a file named GASKET.DWG, "DWG" is the file type. Appendix F provides additional information on file extensions.

4 Select option 2 again, and this time type *.LSP and press **RETURN**.

All files with the extension LSP should have appeared.

5 Select option 2 again; type **ACAD.** * and press **RETURN**.

Only AutoCAD system files, such as ACAD.EXE, should have appeared.

6 Experiment with each of the menu options, except for #3, "Delete files." Also, save option 0, "Exit File Utility Menu," until last. Option 0 will take you back to the Main Menu. (Be sure to read the note on the next page before you begin.)

NOTE:

If you'd like to select each of the options, but don't want to actually perform each of them, simply cancel the operation by pressing CTRL C.

■ *FILES Command*

Next, we're going to gain access to the File Utility Menu while in the Drawing Editor.

3.8

1 Bring up the Drawing Editor by choosing option 1 or 2 from the Main Menu.

2 Enter the **FILES** command.

Did you receive the same File Utility Menu as before?

3 Experiment with the File Utility Menu again.

4 Select **0**, "Exit File Utility Menu."

The "Command:" prompt and Drawing Editor should now be present.

■ *SHELL Command*

There is another way of performing DOS functions while using AutoCAD. The SHELL command allows you to access DOS commands directly and also lets you execute utility programs while remaining in AutoCAD. With SHELL you can load, for example, a word processor and create or edit a text file. Later, you may find this very useful when creating and editing screen and tablet menus and script files.

3.12

Let's apply the SHELL command.

1 First, obtain help on the SHELL command.

HINT:

See Unit 5 if you are unsure how to obtain help.

2 Then, enter the **SHELL** command.

NOTE:

If you received an error message, then your computer does not contain sufficient free memory to run SHELL.

3   If you were successful in entering SHELL, try the DOS DIRectory command by typing **DIR** and pressing **RETURN**.

4   If you have access to another program such as a word processor like VOLKSWRITER® or a spreadsheet like LOTUS 1-2-3™ on your hard disk drive, try loading one of them.

NOTE:

If you have changed your current directory to another directory using the DOS CD command, be sure to change back to your original AutoCAD directory before returning to AutoCAD's "Command:" prompt. If you do not, you may obtain unpredictable results while in AutoCAD.

5   Return to the AutoCAD "Command:" prompt and enter **SHELL** once more.

At this point, you are able to execute one DOS-related function. AutoCAD then returns you automatically to the AutoCAD "Command:" prompt. It is possible to remain in DOS if you need to execute a series of DOS functions; just ...

6   ... press **RETURN**.

You should now have a DOS prompt such as "C>>". Note the second ">". This is present to remind you that you are operating DOS within AutoCAD.

Also notice the note "Type EXIT to return to AutoCAD."

7   Enter the DOS **DIR** command, and notice that at the end you return to the DOS "C>> " prompt rather than the AutoCAD "Command:" prompt.

8   Type **EXIT** and press **RETURN**.

The "Command:" prompt should now be on your screen.

SH Command

The SH command is almost identical to SHELL. The only difference is that SH allows you to execute internal DOS commands only, such as DIR, COPY, and DEL.

1   Enter **SH**.

At this point, you are able to press RETURN to obtain the "C>> " prompt, or enter a single DOS command as before.

Obtain your AutoCAD "Command:" prompt once more.

 Return to the Drawing Editor by using **Fl** (the flip screen function key).

4 Enter **QUIT** to exit the Drawing Editor.

AUTOCAD® AT WORK

CAD Helps Steam Engines Keep Chugging

At one time, all locomotives were powered by steam. Today, however, most locomotives are diesel-electric. What, then, would CAD have to do with old-fashioned steam engines? In Lomita, California, there's a shop that sells kits for miniature working steam trains, and the design drawings for those kits are being produced with AutoCAD.

When Moodie Braun, a former Lieutenant Colonel in the U.S. Air Force Space and Missile System Division, bought the Little Engines shop eight years ago, he found an archive of about 3,000 drawings. The drawings—for sixteen different models of trains in three scales—dated back to the 1930s. Each kit typically included drawings with details for machining, drilling, filing, soldering, and painting.

As materials ceased to be available or if errors were discovered, the drawings had to be revised. It was a tedious job. Braun and his staff were making erasable photocopies, revising the copies, and having new sepias (brown prints) made.

Recently, the shop began using AutoCAD. Drawing time has been cut in half, and it's much easier to update drawings. Instead of altering photocopies, Braun and his staff simply revise on the computer and plot out new drawings. Considering the complexity of some kits (the largest train can carry 75 people), the improvements in the accuracy and quality of the drawings are a benefit to the customers as well as the shop.

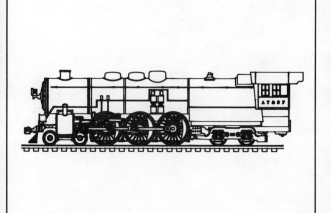

Courtesy of Little Engines and Autodesk, Inc.

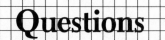

Questions

1. What is the purpose of the File Utility Menu?

   _____

   _____

2. What is the purpose of the FILES command?

   _____

   _____

3. Explain the purpose of the SHELL command.

   _____

   _____

4. Identify a practical application for using the SHELL command.

   _____

   _____

5. Can a sequence of DOS functions be executed without reentering the SHELL command for each function? Explain.

   _____

   _____

6. Explain the difference between the SHELL and SH commands.

   _____

   _____

Problems

Using the commands described in this unit, complete the following.

1. Generate a list of all drawing files from each of your drives or directories and print the list.

2. Generate a list of all menu files found on each of your drives or directories and print the list.

HINT:
AutoCAD menu files have an extension of .MNU. Therefore enter *.MNU.

3. Generate a list of all AutoCAD drawing BAK files.

4. Rename one of your drawing files. Then change it back to its original name.

5. Delete the .BAK file from one of your drawing files.

6. While in AutoCAD, load another program such as a word processor, create a text file, and then return to AutoCAD.

AUTOCAD® AT WORK

*Going First Class with AutoCAD**

Reese Design of Austin, Texas, specializes in the design of aircraft interiors—but not for ordinary aircraft. This design firm creates state-of-the-art showcase aircraft that provide unparalleled luxury, comfort, and entertainment for their clients. It's all done with skill, imagination, and AutoCAD.

When planning a project, Reese Design creates conceptual drawings that can be modified to suit a client's choice of options. Final selections evolve into working specifications and technical drawings for product fabrication.

To begin with, a prototype drawing is selected and loaded into the Drawing Editor. Next, a block drawing is created or inserted from a symbol library. The designers then modify the item—whether it's furniture or a coffee maker—to create the look and feel preferred by the client. The design is saved as a Block so that options can be reviewed using the slide show commands. This is an ideal method for reviewing a number of alternatives that cannot be fully described with their alphanumeric file names alone.

Just as slide show commands review different product options, the dynamic ZOOM command is manipulated so floor plans can be checked closely for tolerances and overall balance and continuity.

Once the floor plan is finalized, the designer prepares cross section views of each aircraft bulkhead and compartment. These cross sections detail the overhead space. When these views are generated, the designer references them with the floor plans to develop elevations.

Once the space planning is complete, interior design embellishments are added. For instance, a sculpture or accessory item can be designed using the SKETCH command and later actually produced by an artist.

When asked if AutoCAD suits his corporate needs, Michael Reese, president of Reese Design, said, "Since our international clientele require design services for a wide range of projects, the scope of our corporate abilities and innovative processes is continually expanding. With quality and professionalism being our foremost objectives, we are creatively participating in the development of our clients' futures. The capabilities of AutoCAD have been very useful."

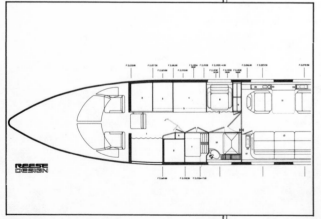

*Based on a story in *CADENCE* magazine, Vol. 2, No. 1.

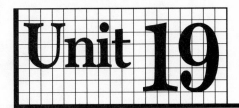

Unit 19 Placing Notes and Specifications

■ OBJECTIVE:

To practice the use of TEXT, DTEXT, STYLE, and QTEXT

This unit focuses on the placement of text using the TEXT and DTEXT commands and on the creation of new text styles using the STYLE command. The QTEXT command is practiced as a time-saving device during screen regenerations.

The following drawing shows the number of notes and specifications typical in many drawings. Some drawings, of course, contain more.

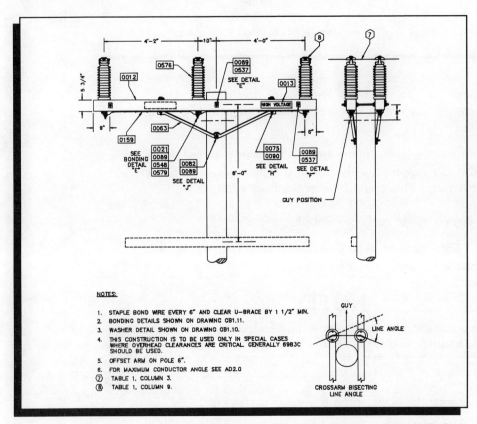

AutoCAD Drawing Courtesy of Russ Burns, Sacramento Municipal Utility District

As you can see, the text information is an important component in describing the drawing. With traditional drafting, the text would be placed by hand, consuming numerous hours of tedious work. With CAD, the words are placed on the screen almost as fast as you can type them.

TEXT Command _____

1 Load AutoCAD and Begin a New Drawing. Name it **TEXT**.

2 Enter the **TEXT** command.

You should now have the following information on your screen.

```
Command: TEXT
Start point or Align/Center/Fit/Middle/Right/Style:
```

---

3 In response to "Start point" place a point near the left portion of your screen. Your text will be left justified (aligned) beginning at this point.

4 Reply to the "Height" prompt by moving your pointing device up a short distance (approximately .25 unit) from your starting point. Pick that point. (You could type in the height instead.)

5 Enter **0** (degrees) in reply to "Rotation angle."

6 At the "Text:" prompt, type your name using both upper- and lowercase letters and press **RETURN**.

_____ NOTE: _____

If you make a mistake when typing, use the backspace key to correct it. If that doesn't work, press CTRL C to cancel and start over.

7 After entering the above, press the **space bar** twice.

You should again have the "Text:" prompt.

8 Type your P.O. Box, rural route, or street address and press **RETURN**.

Where was it placed?

9 Press the **space bar** twice again and type your city, state, and zip code.

Now let's enter the same information you entered above, but this time in a different format.

1 Repeat each of the above steps, but this time select the **C** (Center) option from the list of TEXT options. Place the center point near the center of your screen and set your text height at .2 unit. Do not insert the text at an angle.

When you're finished, your text should have a format like the one below. If it doesn't, try again.

Mr. John Doe
601 West 29th Street
Caddsville, CA 09876

AutoCAD has another TEXT option very similar to Center called Middle.

1 Enter **TEXT** again and this time select the Middle option.

4.10.1.3

2 Place another string of text such as "Vance and Shirley."

How is the Middle option different from Center? If you're not sure, try the Center option again.

AutoCAD also allows for placement of text between two specified points. The options Align and Fit have similarities, but there is a difference. Let's experiment.

1 Enter **TEXT** and select the Align option.

4.10.1.5

2 Pick a point at the left of your screen and press **RETURN**.

3 Pick a second point near the right of your screen.

HINT: If you want the text to appear perfectly horizontal, turn on Ortho.

4 Type the following: **This sentence will be aligned between two points.**

Let's use the Fit option and try to determine the difference between Fit and Align.

1 Enter **TEXT** and the Fit option.

4.10.1.6

2 Pick two points approximately 4 units apart.

3 Specify a height of .25 unit.

Was "height" part of the Align option?

4 Enter the following text: **Check this out!**

Do you recognize the difference between Fit and Align? Fit adjusts the width of the text only, at a specified height. Align adjusts both the width and the height.

5 Continue to experiment with both options.

STYLE Command _____

AutoCAD provides 24 individual text fonts. For samples of these fonts, see Appendix O. (Additional fonts can be created as described in Appendix B of the *AutoCAD Reference Manual*.)

_____ NOTE: _____

Samples of the text fonts are also contained in the Fonts dialogue box. To view them, pick the "Options" pull-down menu and then pick the "Fonts" menu item. The first screen of the dialogue box is shown here.

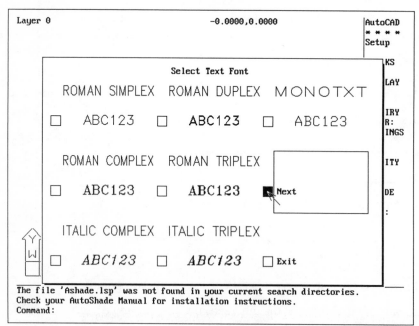

Picking one of the fonts from the dialogue box will issue the STYLE command and will perform a function similar to Step 1 on the next page, but it will not allow you to vary the text style.

New text styles are created using the STYLE command. During their creation, you are able to expand, condense, slant, and even draw them upside down and backwards.

1. Enter the **STYLE** command and reply to each of the prompts using the following information.

Text style name:	**COMP1**
Font file:	**COMPLEX**
Height:	**0** (This means the height is not fixed; it can be varied.)
Width factor:	**1**
Obliquing angle:	**0**
Backwards:	**N**
Upside-down:	**N**
Vertical:	**N**

When you're finished, you are ready to use the new COMP1 text style with the TEXT command. Notice the statement on your screen: "COMP1 is now the current text style."

NOTE:

COMP1 is now the current text style for dimensions too.

1. Enter the **TEXT** command.

2. Right-justify the text by selecting **R** (Right) from the list of options. Place the endpoint near the right side of your screen.

3. Set the height at .3 unit.

4. Set the rotation angle at **0**.

5. For the text, type the following three lines. Be sure to press the space bar twice after each.

4.10.1.4

```
          Computer-aided
    Design and Drafting
              Saves Time
```

Your text style should look like the one above.

HINT:

If you've made a spelling error, erase the entity (line of text) which contains the error and enter the correct text. You can also change the text by using the CHANGE command. The CHANGE command is dicussed on the following page.

With the STYLE command, you can develop an infinite number of text styles. Therefore try creating other styles of your own design. You can give them any name, up to thirty-one characters. The ROMANS text font is recommended for most applications.

NOTE:

The text styles you create remain within your current drawing file. They cannot be transported into other drawings unless the *entire* drawing containing the styles is inserted into the other drawings.

As you create more and more text styles within your current drawing file, you may occasionally want to check their names.

1 Enter the **STYLE** command.

2 In response to "Text style name (or ?):" enter ?.

You should have received a listing of all the text styles available for your current drawing. What information is included about each style? Notice that the STANDARD style was developed using the TXT font.

NOTE:

The MONOTXT font is identical to the TXT font, but it is mono-spaced, whereas TXT is proportionally spaced.

Changing Your Current Text Style

Next, let's set a new current text style from our above list of defined styles.

1 Enter the **TEXT** command and select the Style option.

At this point, you can generate a list of styles as before or select a new current style. Let's bring back the STANDARD text style.

2 Type **STANDARD** and press **RETURN**.

3 Place some new text on the screen or cancel.

4.10.1.7

Correcting Text with CHANGE _____

5.3.1.2

You can make changes to text you've placed on the screen using the CHANGE command. CHANGE was introduced in Unit 12, where it was used for changing endpoints of lines.

1 Enter the **CHANGE** command, select the text "Check this out!" (which was done using the STANDARD text style), and press **RETURN**.

2 In reply to " <Change point>:" pick a point at any convenient location.

The start point of the text should move to this point.

3 Enter **COMP1** for the new style and **.25** for the new height. Leave the rotation angle at 0.

4 Enter **Check out this text!** in reply to "New text:" and press **RETURN**.

So you see, text can be modified using the CHANGE command.

Special Characters and Control Codes _____

4.10.1.9

AutoCAD also allows you to underscore (underline) words, place degree or circle diameter symbols within your text, and more.

Let's underscore a word.

1 Enter the **TEXT** command and pick a start point at the left of your screen.

2 Set the text height at **.25** and leave the insertion angle at 0.

3 Type the following exactly as it appears and press **RETURN**.

> **AutoCAD is a %%upowerful%%u tool.**

Was the word "powerful" underlined?

The AutoCAD control codes are:

%%o	— Toggle overscore mode on/off
%%u	— Toggle underscore mode on/off
%%d	— Draw "degree" symbol
%%p	— Draw "plus/minus" tolerance symbol
%%c	— Draw "circle diameter" dimensioning symbol
%%%	— Force a single percent sign
%%nnn	— Draw special character number "nnn"

4 Experiment with each of them.

DTEXT Command

DTEXT, short for Dynamic Text, lets you see the text develop on your screen as you type it. With this command, you can see whether or not the new text you are entering will fit as you would like it to. This is especially important in tight areas of your drawing.

1 Enter the **DTEXT** command.

Your options are the same as with the TEXT command.

2 Pick a start point near the left of your screen, give a height of .3, and do not specify an insertion angle.

Notice the small box at your start point.

3 Type the following and watch the text appear on your screen.

Dynamic Text!

4 Experiment further with DTEXT. When you're finished, press **RETURN** in reply to the "Text:" prompt.

QTEXT Command

The QTEXT command saves time when the screen regenerates or redraws, especially when drawings contain large amounts of text.

1 Enter **QTEXT** and specify **On**.

2 Enter **ZOOM All** or **REGEN**.

Rectangles, containing only four vectors each, should have replaced each string of text.

3 Place more text on the screen.

Does it appear on the screen?

4 Force another regeneration of your screen by entering **ZOOM ALL** or **REGEN**.

QTEXT (short for Quick Text) replaces text with lines which form rectangles where your text once was. The purpose of this is to speed up screen regenerations and redraws. As you may know, each text character is made up of many short lines. The greater the number of lines on your screen, the longer it takes to regenerate the screen. QTEXT temporarily reduces the total number of lines and consequently saves time, especially with heavy use of text.

5 Enter **QTEXT** again and specify **Off**.

6 Force another regeneration of your screen.

Your text should reappear.

7 Last, enter **END** to save your work and exit the Drawing Editor.

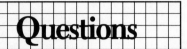

Questions

1. In connection with the TEXT command, describe the following:

   Align _____

   Center_____

   Fit _____

   Middle _____

   Right _____

   Style _____

2. Name at least six text fonts provided by AutoCAD.

   _____

3. What command is used to create a new text style?

   _____

4. How does turning on QTEXT speed screen regenerations?

   _____

   _____

5. Briefly describe how you would create a tall and thin text style.

   _____

   _____

6. If you entered the text 72%%d, what would the result be?

   _____

7. Explain the changes that can be made to text using the CHANGE command.

   _____

   _____

8. How is DTEXT different from the TEXT command?

   _____

   _____

Problems

In problems 1 and 2, create new Text styles using the information provided.

1. Style name: **SIMP**
    Font file: **SIMPLEX**
    Height: **.25** (fixed)
    Width factor: **1**
    Obliquing angle: **15**
    Backwards: **N**
    Upside-down: **N**
    Vertical: **N**

2. Style name: **ITAL**
    Font file: **ITALIC**
    Height: **0** (not fixed)
    Width factor: **.75**
    Obliquing angle: **0**
    Backwards: **N**
    Upside-down: **N**
    Vertical: **N**

In problems 3 and 4, place text on your screen using the information provided. Use the DTEXT command.

3. Use the SIMP Text style.
   Right-justify the text.
   Do not rotate the text.
   The text should read:

> *Someday,*
> *perhaps in the near future,*
> *drafting boards*
> *will be obsolete.*
>
> **PRB 19-1**

4. Use the ITAL Text style.
   Center the text.
   Set the text height at .3 unit.
   Rotate the text 90 degrees.
   The text should read:

This Text Configuration Would Work Well For A Title Page

PRB 19-2

Notice that the word "Well" is underscored.

5. Use the CHANGE command to change the style to SIMP and the height to .2 unit.

Unit 20   Preparing for a New Drawing

■ OBJECTIVE:

To apply and practice the use of UNITS, LIMITS, STATUS, and prototype drawings

The purpose of this unit is to focus on the process of creating the foundation for new drawings. Considerations include: identifying the type of drawing you are about to create, the scale, and the paper size; determining the drawing units and limits; setting the grid and snap resolution; and checking settings and parameters with the STATUS command.

The first several steps necessary for setting up a new drawing are important and deserve special attention. Once a setup has been stored in a prototype drawing, subsequent drawing setups are fast.

■ *Creating a Prototype Drawing* _____

Simply stated, a prototype drawing is any AutoCAD drawing file that contains drawing settings and parameters, such as the snap and grid spacings. Prototype drawings do not typically contain graphics. Some users do, however, choose to include a border and title block in the prototype drawing.

1.3
2.5.1
A.1

The purpose of a prototype drawing is to minimize the need to establish new drawing settings each time you begin a new drawing. When you use a prototype drawing, its contents are automatically loaded into the new drawing at the beginning. The prototype's settings thus become the new drawing's settings.

Prototype drawing development includes the following steps. Note that the first three steps are common to traditional means of planning drawings using drafting boards.

1) Determine what you are going to draw (*e.g.*, mechanical detail, house elevation, etc.)
2) Determine the drawing scale.
3) Determine the paper size. (Steps 2 and 3 normally are done simultaneously.)
4) Set the drawing units.
5) Set the drawing limits.
6) ZOOM All. (This will zoom your entire limits.)
7) Set the grid.
8) Set the snap resolution.
9) Enter STATUS to review your settings.
10) Establish several new layers with colors, linetypes, etc.
11) Set linetype scale (LTSCALE).
12) Create new text styles.
13) Set DIMSCALE, dimension text size, arrowhead size, etc.
14) Store as a prototype drawing.

This unit and the next three will provide an opportunity to practice these steps in detail as well as introduce you to new commands and features.

Let's begin.

1 Load AutoCAD and Begin a New Drawing. Name it **PROTO1**.

NOTE:

PROTO1 will be our first prototype drawing. Prototype drawings are stored with a .DWG file extension, like any other AutoCAD drawing file. Prototype drawings can also be edited and updated like any other AutoCAD drawing file.

A standard prototype drawing comes with AutoCAD and contains all the default settings you have been using up to this point. Details on this prototype drawing, named ACAD.DWG, can be found in Appendix K.

Let's identify a specific drawing, such as a stair detail for a house or commercial building, on which to base our new prototype drawing.

Next, we should determine the drawing scale for the stair detail. This information will give us a basis for setting our limits, linetype scale, and DIMSCALE later. Let's use a scale of 1/2″ = 1′.

We also need to decide on the paper size for our drawing. Let's use 11″ × 17″ paper.

It's time now to enter information into the computer.

2 Enter the **UNITS** command (contained in the SETTINGS submenu) and select choice **4**, "Architectural."

3 Specify the following for each of the architectural unit options.

Denominator of smallest fraction to display: **16**
Systems of angle measure: **1**
Number of fractional places for display of angles: **1**
Direction for angle 0.0: **0.0**
Do you want angles measured clockwise? **N**

NOTE:

To see how the new units affect the coordinate display, press the flip screen function key and then turn on the coordinate display. Move the pointing device and note how the coordinate display changes.

Scaling Your Drawing

The next step is to set the drawing limits. The limits are a sized boundary for constructing your drawing, and they should correspond to both your drawing scale and paper size. (See Appendix L for a chart showing the relationships among paper size, drawing scale, and drawing limits.)

NOTE:

Actual scaling does not occur until you plot your drawing, but you should set your limits to correspond with your scale and paper size. The limits and paper size can be increased or decreased up to the time you plot the drawing. The plot scale can also be adjusted prior to plotting. For example, if a drawing will not fit on your sheet at 1/4″ = 1′, enter new drawing limits to reflect a scale of 1/8″ = 1′. Likewise, enter 1/8″ = 1′ instead of 1/4″ = 1′ when you plot.

1 Enter the **LIMITS** command.

3.5

2 Leave the lower left limit at 0,0.

As mentioned above, your limits—specifically, your upper right limit—should reflect the drawing scale and paper size. Let's look at an example.

If the paper size is 17″ × 11″, your active plotting (and drawing) area is approximately 15″ × 10″. This is the area on 17″ × 11″ paper in which most plotters are able to plot. If your drawing scale is 1″ = 1′, then the upper right limit would be set at 15′,10′. Why? Because 15 inches horizontally on your paper will occupy 15 scaled feet, and 10 inches vertically on your paper will occupy 10 scaled feet.

Let's consider another one. If your drawing scale is 1/4″ = 1′, what should be your upper right limit, given that the lower left remains at 0,0? Since each plotted inch on your paper will occupy 4 scaled feet, it's a simple multiplication problem: 15 × 4 = 60 and 10 × 4 = 40. Your upper right limit should be set at 60′,40′ because each plotted inch will represent 4′.

Since *our* scale is 1/2″ = 1′, what would be the upper right limit?

HINT:

How many 1/2″ units will 15″ include? How many 1/2″ units will 10″ include?

3 Enter **30′,20′** for the upper right limit.

NOTE:

When entering 30′,20′ type it exactly as you see it here; use an apostrophe for the foot mark. If you do not use a foot mark, the numbers will be assumed to represent inches. Inches can be specified using ″ or no mark at all.

4 ZOOM All.

This zooms your entire limits to fill most of your display. The screen will then reflect your paper size, which corresponds to your limits. To realize this . . .

5 . . . move your crosshairs to the upper right portion of your screen and review the coordinate display. (If the coordinate display is not on, turn it on.)

6 Enter **GRID**, and set it at **1′**.

The purpose of setting your grid is to give you a visual sense of the size of your units and limits. The grid fills your entire limits, with a distance of 1′ between the grid dots.

7 Enter **SNAP**, and set it at **6″**.

Use the quote key for the inch mark if you wish. As stated earlier, if no mark is used, the entry defaults to inches.

NOTE:

SNAP will provide for a 6″ modular layout of your drawing components.

8 Move your crosshairs to the upper right corner of the grid.

The coordinate display should read exactly 30′,20′.

Status of Prototype Drawing

1 To review your settings up to this point, enter the **STATUS** command.

You should receive a screen similar to the following. Note each of the components found in STATUS.

3.4

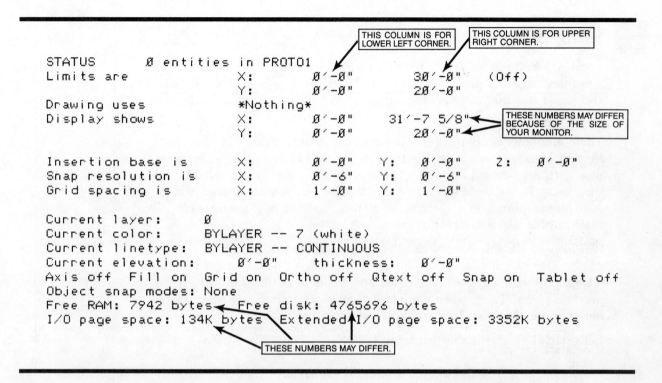

```
                                    ┌──────────────────┐  ┌──────────────────────┐
                                    │THIS COLUMN IS FOR│  │THIS COLUMN IS FOR UPPER│
                                    │LOWER LEFT CORNER.│  │RIGHT CORNER.          │
                                    └──────────────────┘  └──────────────────────┘

STATUS        Ø entities in PROTO1
Limits are              X:        Ø'-Ø"          30'-Ø"     (Off)
                        Y:        Ø'-Ø"          20'-Ø"
Drawing uses            *Nothing*                        ┌─────────────────────────┐
Display shows           X:        Ø'-Ø"      31'-7 5/8"◄──│THESE NUMBERS MAY DIFFER │
                        Y:        Ø'-Ø"          20'-Ø"◄──│BECAUSE OF THE SIZE OF   │
                                                         │YOUR MONITOR.            │
                                                         └─────────────────────────┘
Insertion base is       X:        Ø'-Ø"   Y:   Ø'-Ø"   Z:     Ø'-Ø"
Snap resolution is      X:        Ø'-6"   Y:   Ø'-6"
Grid spacing is         X:        1'-Ø"   Y:   1'-Ø"

Current layer:       Ø
Current color:       BYLAYER -- 7 (white)
Current linetype:    BYLAYER -- CONTINUOUS
Current elevation:      Ø'-Ø"      thickness:    Ø'-Ø"
Axis off  Fill on  Grid on  Ortho off  Qtext off  Snap on  Tablet off
Object snap modes: None
Free RAM: 7942 bytes◄─ Free disk: 4765696 bytes
I/O page space: 134K bytes  Extended I/O page space: 3352K bytes
                        └──────┐         │
                          ┌─────────────────────────┐
                          │THESE NUMBERS MAY DIFFER. │
                          └─────────────────────────┘
```

Our prototype drawing, PROTO1, now contains several settings and
parameters specific to creating architectural drawings at a scale of 1/2" =
1'. It would also work well for beginning the stairway detail mentioned
earlier.

The next steps in creating a prototype drawing deal with establishing
layers. Use of the LAYER command will be practiced in the next unit,
and the remaining steps for creating a prototype drawing will be covered
in Unit 23.

② For now, enter **END** to save all you have entered to this point
and exit the Drawing Editor.

③ Produce a backup copy of your prototype drawing named
PROTO1.DWG.

For details on producing copies of files, see Appendix F, "Commonly Used
DOS Commands."

Backup copies are important because if you accidentally lose your original
(and you may, sooner or later), you will have a backup. A backup can be
produced in just a few seconds, and it can save you hours of lost work.
An entire day's work can be lost in a few seconds, so be prepared!

Setup Shortcut

AutoCAD contains a "shortcut" setup facility which expedites and simplifies Steps 2-6 (from page 151). It allows you to easily pick the scale and paper size for your drawing, and it automatically draws a border on the screen. The border outlines the size of your paper.

There are, however, two noteworthy drawbacks to this shortcut facility. First, it bypasses the optional settings in the UNITS command. Therefore these settings may not be set to your expectations. Second, the facility sets your limits to the overall paper size and not to the smaller area in which your plotter plots. Thus, there is the chance that you will mistakenly draw outside the active plotting area.

It is okay to use this shortcut facility if you understand exactly how it works. Also very important is your understanding of how to identify and set up, on your own, the scale, units, and limits as outlined on the previous pages. Then, when you need to make adjustments to your scale, units, limits, etc., you don't come to a standstill.

Let's step through the shortcut setup facility.

1 Begin a New Drawing and name it **PROTO2**.

2 Select **SETUP** from the root page of the AutoCAD screen menu.

It may take a couple of seconds for the facility to load.

3 Select **enginrng** from the screen submenu.

4 Select the engineering scale **1″=10′**.

5 Select the **24×36** inch sheet size.

The border should appear and the appearance of the units in your coordinate display change.

6 Move your crosshairs to check your new upper right limit.

It should read 360′,240′.

7 Proceed with Steps 7, 8, and 9 (from page 151) to further this prototype drawing setup.

8 Enter **END** to save PROTO2 and exit the Drawing Editor.

Questions

1. Explain the purpose and value of prototype drawings.

   _____

   _____

   _____

2. What is the purpose of the UNITS command?

   _____

   _____

3. What function does the LIMITS command serve?

   _____

   _____

4. Describe the information displayed as a result of entering the STATUS command.

   _____

   _____

   _____

   _____

5. Describe the shortcut method of establishing the drawing scale, units, limits, etc.

   _____

   _____

   _____

   _____

Problems

In problems PRB20-1 and PRB20-2, establish the settings for a new drawing based on the information provided. Set each of the commands as indicated.

PRB20-1. Drawing type: Mechanical drawing of a machine part

Scale: 1″ = 2″

Paper size: 17″ × 11″

UNITS: Engineering (You choose the appropriate options)

LIMITS: Lower left corner 0,0
        Upper right corner 30″,20″

(Reminder: Be sure to ZOOM All)

GRID value: .5″

SNAP resolution: .25″

(Review settings with STATUS command.)

PRB20-2. Drawing type: Architectural drawing of a house and plot plan

Scale: 1/8″ = 1′

Paper size: 24″ × 18″

UNITS: Architectural (You choose the appropriate options)

LIMITS: Lower left corner 0,0
        Upper right corner 184′,136′

(Reminder: Be sure to ZOOM All)

GRID value: 4′

SNAP resolution: 2′

(Review settings with STATUS command.)

In PRB20-3 and PRB20-4, fill in the missing data, based on the information provided.

PRB20-3. Drawing type: Architectural drawing of a detached garage

Approximate dimensions of garage: 32′ × 20′

Other considerations: Space around the garage for dimensions, notes, specs., border, and title block

Scale?_____

Paper size? _____

UNITS?_____

LIMITS? _____

GRID value? _____

SNAP resolution? _____

PRB20-4. Drawing type: Mechanical drawing of a bicycle pedal

Approximate dimensions of pedal: 4″ × 2.75″

Other considerations: Space around pedal for dimensions, notes, specs., border, and title block

Scale?_____

Paper size? _____

UNITS?_____

LIMITS? _____

GRID value? _____

SNAP resolution? _____

AUTOCAD® AT WORK

*Profile of an Architect**

Reed Settle, Architect, and Associates is a small architectural design firm in Prescott, Arizona. It specializes in custom residential and commercial design. The firm uses AutoCAD and AutoCAD AEC Architectural to produce most of its working drawings, as well as some presentation and design development drawings.

Plan drawings are created adhering to the layering system used by AutoCAD AEC, with the exception that all of the plan drawings (foundation, floor plans, framing plans, electrical plans, and mechanical plans) are overlaid in one drawing file. The firm uses a three-character prefix (such as fdn, flr, ffr, rfr) at the beginning of each of the layer names associated with a particular plan. This allows them to selectively turn on or off all of the layers of a certain plan using the prefix for that plan followed by wildcard characters or a full layer name.

For elevations they create their own layers, most of them descriptive of the elevation features they are used for, such as trim, siding, deck, and so on. For major plane intersections such as wall lines, eaves, gables, and roof lines, they try to use a layer with a unique color that can be assigned a heavier line weight when plotting to give those lines more definition. They also give a different layer and color assignment to entities created by hatching, such as shingles, siding, and stucco, so that these entities can be plotted with a green pen and therefore appear screened on the final blueprints.

John McCutcheon, a CAD designer with the firm, notes that the company began with AutoCAD Version 2.17 and has updated its system with each new AutoCAD release. "Each update has provided more useful capabilities to an already powerful drafting/design tool, and we are confident that future releases will continue to do the same. Through our use of AutoCAD we plan on realizing even more gains in productivity and quality in the future."

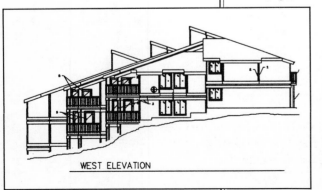

WEST ELEVATION

*Based on a story in *CADENCE* magazine, Vol 3, No. 7.

 **Unit 21** Layering Your Drawings

**AutoCAD®
Reference
Manual**

7.1

■ OBJECTIVE:

To apply the LAYER command options, practice setting linetype scale, and further the prototype drawing development

This unit focuses on AutoCAD's layering capability. It covers creating layers; setting the current layer; assigning colors and linetypes to layers; turning layers on and off; freezing and thawing layers; and setting the linetype scale.

This unit will enable you to create the following layers:

Layer name	State	Color	Linetype
Ø	On	7 (white)	CONTINUOUS
OBJ	On	1 (red)	CONTINUOUS
HID	On	2 (yellow)	HIDDEN
DIM	On	3 (green)	CONTINUOUS
CEN	On	2 (yellow)	CENTER
PHANT	On	5 (blue)	PHANTOM
BORD	On	4 (cyan)	CONTINUOUS

Creating New Layers

It may be helpful to think of layers as transparent overlays. Certain components can be drawn on these layers, the layers can be visible or invisible, and specific colors and linetypes can be assigned to each layer.

For example, a house floor plan could be drawn on a layer called FLOOR and displayed in red. The dimensions of the floor plan could be drawn on a layer called DIM and displayed in yellow. Furthermore, a layer called CEN could contain blue center lines.

Layers and their colors are also very important when plotting since pens are assigned to colors. You'll gain a much better feel for all of this after you have stepped through the following.

1 Load AutoCAD and bring up the drawing called **PROTO1**.

NOTE:

Be sure to make a backup copy of PROTO1.DWG if you have not already done so. Instructions for making backup copies are in Appendix F.

2 Enter the **LAYER** command.

You should now have the following information after the "Command:" prompt.

```
?/Make/Set/New/ON/OFF/Color/Ltype/Freeze/Thaw:
```

First, let's create layer OBJ (short for "objects").

3 After the list of layer options, type **N** and press **RETURN** (or select New from the screen menu).

7.7.4

AutoCAD will ask you for the new layer name(s).

4 Type the name **OBJ** and press **RETURN**.

The layer options should again appear.

5 Request a layer listing by entering **?** and pressing **RETURN**.

7.7.1

6 Enter * (the global or wildcard specification) for a list of all layers. Since * is the default setting, you can simply press RETURN.

Your listing should look similar to the following.

Layer name	State	Color	Linetype
Ø	On	7 (white)	CONTINUOUS
OBJ	On	7 (white)	CONTINUOUS

Current layer:Ø

A fast way to create the remaining five layers is to do it in one step. Let's try it.

7 Enter the New option again.

8 This time, type each of the layer names separated by a comma as shown on the next page. Do not put spaces between the layer names.

```
New layer name(s): HID,DIM,CEN,PHANT,BORD
```

⑨ Do another layer listing to see if the layers were created.

If they were not, try again.

Changing the Current Layer

Let's change your current layer from layer O to layer OBJ.

① Enter the **LAYER** Set option and type the layer name **OBJ**. Press **RETURN** twice.   7.7.3

Did the change occur? Look at the beginning of the status line in the Drawing Editor. It should read: "Layer OBJ." If it doesn't, try making the change again.

Creating and Setting a Layer in One Step

The LAYER Make option provides a one-step method for creating a single layer and setting that layer.   7.7.2

① Enter **LAYER** and the Make option.

② In reply to "New current layer:" type the word **NOTES** and press **RETURN** twice.

The layer NOTES should now be your current layer.

③ Do another layer listing to see if NOTES is contained there too.

So you see, if you need to quickly create and set a new layer, the Make option is available.

Assigning Colors

Now, let's assign colors to our new layers. We'll begin by assigning color 1 (red) to layer OBJ.   7.1.2

① Enter the **LAYER** Color option. Specify color 1 (and **RETURN**) and layer **OBJ** (and **RETURN**).   7.7.7

② Do a listing of layers to check whether color 1 is now assigned to layer OBJ.

NOTE:

Even though you may be using a computer with a monochrome (single-color) monitor, it is important to practice assigning colors to layers. Colors are directly associated with plotter pens. The colors, therefore, define the relationship between the layer and its pen color and thickness.

3 Assign colors to the other layers as indicated in the layer listing at the beginning of this unit.

NOTE:

AutoCAD also contains a command called COLOR. The COLOR command allows you to set the color for subsequently drawn entities. Therefore you can control the color of each entity individually.

The ability to set the color of objects either individually, using the COLOR command, or by layer gives you a great deal of flexibility, but it can become confusing. It is recommended that you avoid use of the COLOR command and that its setting remain at BYLAYER. The BYLAYER setting means that the color is specified by layer.

Drawing on Layers

1 Set layer **OBJ** and draw a circle (at any size) on this layer.

2 Set layer **HID** and draw a large triangle on it.

NOTE:

At times, you may draw an object on the wrong layer. If this happens, use the CHANGE command, selecting the Properties and LAyer options. This lets you move entities from one layer to another. The same thing can be accomplished using the CHPROP command.

Turning Layers On and Off

1 Now turn off layer OBJ by entering **LAYER (RETURN)**, then **Off** **(RETURN)**, and typing **OBJ (RETURN** twice after OBJ).

The circle should disappear.

2 Do a layer listing. The current state of OBJ should be "Off".

3 Turn on layer OBJ by entering **LAYER**, then **On**, and typing **OBJ**. (Be sure to press **RETURN** twice after OBJ).

The circle should reappear.

Assigning Linetypes ────────────────

Next, let's take a look at the different linetypes AutoCAD makes available to us.

1 To obtain a listing of linetypes, enter the **LINETYPE** command and then enter the **?** option. (Press **RETURN** in reply to "File to list < acad > :".)

7.9

This lists the linetypes contained in the ACAD.LIN library file.

Your screen should look similar to the following.

```
Linetypes defined in file C:\A10\ACAD.lin:

    Name              Description
    ----------------  --------------------------------------------------

DASHED            ____  ____  ____  ____  ____  ____  ____  ____  ____
HIDDEN            __ __ __ __ __ __ __ __ __ __ __ __ __ __ __ __ __
CENTER            ____ _ ____ _ ____ _ ____ _ ____ _ ____ _ ____ _
PHANTOM           ____ _ _ ____ _ _ ____ _ _ ____ _ _ ____ _ _ ____
DOT               . . . . . . . . . . . . . . . . . . . . . . . . . . .

DASHDOT           ____ . ____ . ____ . ____ . ____ . ____ . ____ .
BORDER            __ __ . __ __ . __ __ . __ __ . __ __ . __ __ .
DIVIDE            ____ . . ____ . . ____ . . ____ . . ____ . . ____
```

2 Enter the Load option.

3 Enter **∗** in reply to "Linetype(s) to load:".

4 Enter **ACAD** in reply to "File to search:". (ACAD should be the default setting, so you could press **RETURN** instead.)

5 Press **RETURN** to finish the command.

6 Press the flip screen function key to return to the graphics screen.

7 Enter the **LAYER** command.

8 Enter the Ltype option.

7.7.8

9 Enter the linetype called **hidden**, assign it to layer **HID**, and press **RETURN** twice. (The linetype name must be typed out fully and spelled correctly.)

Did the triangle on layer HID change from a continuous line to a hidden line? It probably did, but don't be surprised if you don't see it.

10 Do a layer listing to see if the linetype change did in fact occur.

If the linetype change did occur, but the triangle appears as though it did not change, the linetype scale (LTSCALE) needs to be set. Regardless, LTSCALE should be set according to the following steps.

■ LTSCALE Command

1 Enter the **LTSCALE** command.

7.10

Now let's scale your linetypes to correspond to your drawing scale. This is done by setting the linetype scale at 1/2 the reciprocal of the plot scale. By doing this, your broken lines, such as hidden and center lines, will be plotted similar to ANSI standards.

HINT:
Our scale is 1/2" = 1'. Another way to express this is 1" = 2' or 1" = 24". This can be written as 1/24. The reciprocal of 1/24 is 24, and half of 24 is 12. Therefore, in this particular case, you would set the LTSCALE at 12.

2 In reply to "New scale factor:" enter **12**.

3 Now view the triangle. Is it made up of hidden lines?

4 If you're not sure, zoom in on it.

5 Next, assign the center linetype to layer CEN and the phantom linetype to layer PHANT. Remember, use the LAYER Ltype option.

6 Do a layer listing to view the changes.

NOTE:
The LINETYPE command contains a Set option, which allows you to set the linetype for subsequently drawn entities. All new entities you create will be drawn with this linetype, regardless of which layer is current. This gives you a great deal of flexibility, but it can become confusing. Therefore it is recommended that you avoid using the LINETYPE Set option and that its setting remain at BYLAYER. The BYLAYER setting means that the linetype is specified by layer.

7.9.1

■ Freezing and Thawing Layers

1 Select the **LAYER** command once again.

**AutoCAD®
Reference
Manual**
7.7.9

2 Enter the Freeze option.

3 Freeze layer **OBJ** and press **RETURN** twice.

4 Do a layer listing and note the change.

5 Thaw layer OBJ by entering **Thaw** and typing **OBJ**. Press **RETURN** twice.

7.7.10

Did the circle return? As you can see, freezing and thawing layers is similar to turning them off and on. The difference is that AutoCAD will regenerate a drawing faster if the unneeded layers are frozen rather than turned off. Therefore in most cases Freeze is recommended over the Off option. Note that you cannot freeze the current layer.

6 Erase both the circle and the triangle. Set layer OBJ as the current layer.

Layer Control Dialogue Box _____

7.13

Layer information can be created and modified using the layer control dialogue box. The dialogue box is displayed by picking the "Settings" pull-down menu and the "Modify Layer ..." menu item. Or, enter the DDLMODES command.

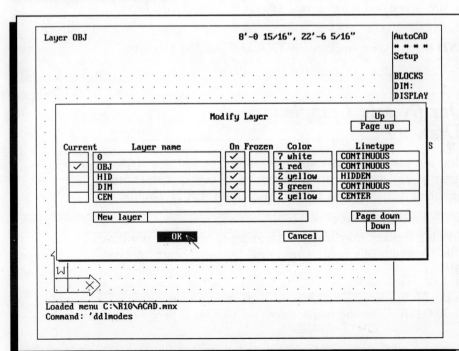

If you pick any one of the colors contained in the previous dialogue box the following will appear.

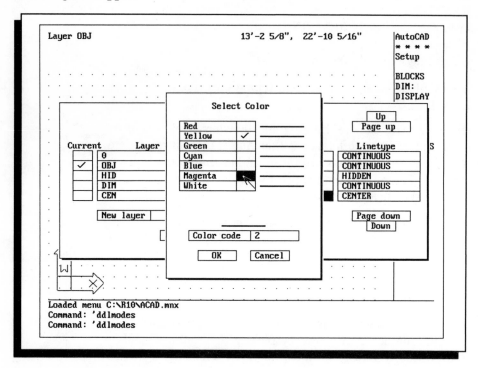

This box enables you to see and select a new color for the specified layer.

⌐┐ Enter **END** to save your work in PROTO1 and exit the Drawing
└┘ Editor.

Applying Our (Nearly Complete) Prototype Drawing

The prototype drawing preparation is nearly complete. The last few steps (12, 13, and 14 from p. 151) typically involve creation of new text styles and setting the dimensioning variables and DIMSCALE. Both will be covered in the next unit.

The prototype drawing concept may lack full meaning to you until you have actually applied it. Therefore let's begin a new drawing using our prototype drawing PROTO1.

⌐┐ While in the Main Menu, Begin a New Drawing and name it
└┘ **STAIRD=PROTO1**. Type the name exactly as you see it here.

2 After you arrive at the Drawing Editor, notice the status line at the top of your screen. Enter **STATUS** and note each of the drawing settings, parameters, etc.

They should look familiar.

3 Do a layer listing.

They too should look familiar. Do you now see why prototype drawings are valuable?

4 Enter **END** to save and exit the new drawing called STAIRD.

NOTE:

The contents of PROTO1 were loaded into STAIRD at the beginning, so there is no need to specify PROTO1 when editing STAIRD. In other words, prototype drawings are used only when you begin a new drawing. Furthermore, you are not locked into the prototype drawing environment. When STAIRD is brought up for editing, more layers can be created and different settings made to tailor it to the drawing application.

PROTO1 is also available for the creation of other new drawings, saving you time when starting new drawings.

Questions

1. Explain at least two purposes of layers.

_____

_____

2. Briefly describe the meaning of each of the following layer options.

? _____

Make _____

Set _____

New _____

On _____

Off _____

Color _____

Ltype _____

Freeze _____

Thaw _____

3. How do you change the current layer?

_____

_____

4. Describe the purpose of the LTSCALE command and explain how it is set.

_____

_____

_____

5. Why/when would you want to freeze a layer?

_____

_____

6. Name each of the linetype options available.

_____

_____

7. What is the purpose of the COLOR command?

_____

_____

8. If you accidentally draw on the wrong layer, how can you correct your mistake without erasing and redrawing?

_____

_____

9. What LAYER option creates a new layer and sets it as the current layer in one step?

_____

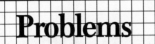

Problems

Create the following layers with corresponding settings.

PRB 21-1

Layer name	State	Color	Linetype
Ø	Off	7 (white)	CONTINUOUS
OBJ	On	1 (red)	CONTINUOUS
HID	On	2 (yellow)	HIDDEN
DIM	On	3 (green)	CONTINUOUS
CEN	On	2 (yellow)	CENTER
PHANT	On	5 (blue)	PHANTOM
BORD	On	4 (cyan)	CONTINUOUS
TEXT	Frozen	8	CONTINUOUS

Current layer: OBJ

PRB 21-2

Layer name	State	Color	Linetype
Ø	On	7 (white)	CONTINUOUS
FOUND	On	6 (magenta)	DASHED
WALLS	On	1 (red)	CONTINUOUS
ELECT	On	4 (cyan)	CONTINUOUS
PLUMB	Frozen	7 (white)	CONTINUOUS
DIM	On	2 (yellow)	CONTINUOUS
TITLE	Frozen	3 (green)	CONTINUOUS
HID	On	5 (blue)	HIDDEN
CEN	Off	5 (blue)	CENTER
NOTES	On	2 (yellow)	CONTINUOUS

Current layer: ELECT

AUTOCAD® AT WORK

Pillsbury Turns to CAD for High-Tech Designing

Few of us give much thought to cardboard cartons. They're just the containers that other things come in—wrappings to be torn apart so we can get at the goodies inside. But every carton, whether we notice or not, has to be carefully designed with precisely symmetrical folds so that corners fit together, end flaps lock, and contents are kept safe and secure. Every new carton design, however simple, requires at least several drawings: a template (a drawing that can be used as a full-size model by the keyliner, plate maker, and carton manufacturer) and specification drawings (scale drawings that give precise dimensions and other important information).

Paul Mueller is the computer technologist in the packaging group of the Research and Development Laboratories at The Pillsbury Company in Minneapolis, Minnesota. The group designs hundreds of cartons to hold the food products available under the Pillsbury banner, including such brands as Green Giant, Jeno's, French's Potatoes, and Azteca, among others.

Traditionally, all of Pillsbury's design work has been done by hand, with the final specification drawings and templates carefully drawn in pencil on a drafting board. But it takes skill and concentration to create a final drawing accurate to 1/32″ or better by hand. It also takes time, especially when alterations must be made to a complicated drawing. Creating drawings with a consistent look to them, even in minor matters, is no easy task either.

With a CAD program such as AutoCAD, drawings can be done more quickly, and with greater precision and consistency, than is possible with hand drafting. Furthermore, the drawings can be edited electronically and the modified drawings reproduced quickly.

To build a carton on the computer screen, Mueller and his coworkers use layering. By putting the basic outline of the carton in one layer, the score lines (along which the carton will be folded) in another layer, the dimen-

Courtesy of The Pillsbury Company

sions in yet another, and any text in still another, designers can easily view a drawing in different ways—just the outline and the score lines, for example, or just the outline and the dimensions. In addition, they can now make both template and specification drawings from one electronic original, printing the outline and score layers full-size for the template and then including the text and dimensions in a scale drawing for the specifications.

Another benefit of using the CAD system has been increased precision in the drawings. Because the templates that are sent to the carton manufacturers are used as full-size models, it's important that all their measurements be absolutely accurate and consistent. Says Mueller, "After our drawings are done, we sit down with a ruler—and we still do this with AutoCAD, by the way—and measure it all up. We've found we get far fewer errors using AutoCAD than we did before when our work was done by hand."

172

 **Unit 22** Basic Dimensioning

■ OBJECTIVE:

To apply AutoCAD's basic dimensioning capabilities

One of AutoCAD's powerful features is its semiautomatic dimensioning. This unit covers the different types of dimensioning, including linear, angular, diameter, and radial dimensioning. Attention is also given to the dimensioning variables and dimensioning utilities.

AutoCAD's dimensioning capability uses numerous dimensioning commands, utility commands, dimensioning variables, and dimensioning terms. Though all of this may seem quite complex, it isn't.

10.1.

■ *Checking the Status of the Dimensioning Variables*

1 Load AutoCAD and Begin a New Drawing. Name it **DIMEN**.

NOTE:

We will continue (and complete) PROTO1 near the end of the following unit.

Before we begin dimensioning, let's preview the *dimensioning variables*.

2 Select **DIM:** from the root page of the screen menu.

10.1.1

You should now have the dimensioning submenu on the screen and the "Dim:" prompt at the bottom rather than the usual "Command:" prompt.

NOTE:

You must always have the "Dim:" prompt at the bottom of your screen instead of the "Command:" prompt when dimensioning.

3 Select **status** from the dimensioning submenu to obtain the current status of the dimensioning variables.

10.1.7.5

You should receive a list similar to the one on the next page.

```
DIMALT    Off                    Alternate units selected
DIMALTD   2                      Alternate unit decimal places
DIMALTF   25.4000                Alternate unit scale factor
DIMAPOST                         Default suffix for alternate text
DIMASO    On                     Create associative dimensions
DIMASZ    0.1800                 Arrow size
DIMBLK                           Arrow block name
DIMBLK1                          First arrow block name
DIMBLK2                          Second arrow block name
DIMCEN    0.0900                 Center mark size
DIMDLE    0.0000                 Dimension line extension
DIMDLI    0.3800                 Dimension line increment for continuation
DIMEXE    0.1800                 Extension above dimension line
DIMEXO    0.0625                 Extension line origin offset
DIMLFAC   1.0000                 Linear unit scale factor
DIMLIM    Off                    Generate dimension limits
DIMPOST                          Default suffix for dimension text
DIMRND    0.0000                 Rounding value
DIMSAH    Off                    Separate arrow blocks
DIMSCALE  1.0000                 Overall scale factor
-- Press RETURN for more --
DIMSE1    Off                    Suppress the first extension line
DIMSE2    Off                    Suppress the second extension line
DIMSHO    Off                    Update dimensions while dragging
DIMSOXD   Off                    Suppress outside extension dimension
DIMTAD    Off                    Place text above the dimension line
DIMTIH    On                     Text inside extensions is horizontal
DIMTIX·   Off                    Place text inside extensions
DIMTM     0.0000                 Minus tolerance
DIMTOFL   Off                    Force line inside extension lines
DIMTOH    On                     Text outside extensions is horizontal
DIMTOL    Off                    Generate dimension tolerances
DIMTP     0.0000                 Plus tolerance
DIMTSZ    0.0000                 Tick size
DIMTVP    0.0000                 Text vertical position
DIMTXT    0.1800                 Text height
DIMZIN    0                      Zero suppression

Dim:
```

Note each of the dimensioning variables, their current settings, and their brief definitions. We will work with a few of these variables shortly. But first, let's dimension the object on the next page.

10.1.11

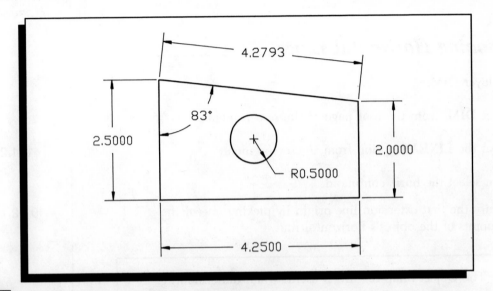

Preparing to Dimension _____

Before we can dimension this object, we need to prepare a few drawing settings and parameters and then draw the object.

1 If you still have the "Dim:" prompt, restore the "Command:" prompt by entering **EXIT**.

2 Create two new layers using the LAYER command. Call one of them **OBJ** and the other **DIM**.

3 Set layer OBJ.

NOTE: _____

When you draw the object, place the object lines on layer OBJ and the dimensions on layer DIM.

4 Set your Snap at .25 unit.

5 Draw the object, omitting dimensions at this point. Don't worry about the exact location of the circle.

After you have drawn the object, let's dimension it.

*Dimensioning Horizontal Lines*_____

1 Set layer DIM.

2 Select **DIM:** from the root page of the screen menu.

3 Select the **LINEAR** option from the screen menu. 10.1.2

4 Then select the **horiz** command.

5 Specify the first extension line origin by picking one of the 10.1.2.1
endpoints of the object's horizontal line.

HINT:
The Object Snap feature is useful when dimensioning.

6 Then pick the second extension line origin (the other end of the
horizontal line).

7 Use your pointing device to locate the dimension line 10.1.2.3
approximately 1 unit away from the object.

8 Accept the default dimension text; simply press **RETURN**. 10.1.2.4

Did the dimension appear correctly? If not, use the "undo" 10.1.7.7
dimensioning command found in the dimensioning submenu to erase your
last dimension, and try it again.

9 **ZOOM** in on the dimension to examine its detail, and then
ZOOM Previous.

HINT:
Use the transparent ZOOM capability.

Dimensioning Vertical Lines _____

Now, let's dimension the vertical lines in the object. Start with either line.

1 Enter **DIM:** to receive the "Dim:" prompt.

2 Select the VERTICAL command (**vertical**) from the LINEAR
submenu.

3 Select the first and second extension line origins as you did before.

4 Specify the placement of your dimension line as you did before, and press **RETURN** at the "Dimension text:" prompt.

Let's dimension the other vertical line, but this time let's do it a faster and easier way.

1 Select **vertical** again.

2 This time when the prompt line asks for the first extension line origin, press **RETURN**.

10.1.2.2

The crosshairs should change.

3 Now pick any point on the vertical line.

4 Proceed with the next two steps as you did before until the dimension appears on the screen.

5 Enter **redraw** from the dimensioning submenu or enter 'REDRAW.

Dimensioning Inclined Lines ⎯⎯⎯⎯⎯

Let's dimension the inclined line by "aligning" the dimension to the line.

1 Again select the **LINEAR** item, but this time choose **aligned** from the submenu.

2 Proceed exactly as you did with the last dimension until the aligned dimension appears on the screen.

If it appears to be correct on your screen, then you did it right.

Dimensioning Circles and Arcs ⎯⎯⎯⎯⎯

Now let's dimension the circle.

1 Select **radius** from the dimensioning submenu.

10.1.5

2 Pick the circle at the point where the arrow touches it in the drawing on page 175.

3 Press **RETURN** in response to "Dimension text."

4 Specify a short leader length, and locate it down and to the right as shown in the drawing. Ortho should be off.

The radial dimension should appear.

Dimensioning Angles

Last, let's dimension the angle as shown in the drawing.

1 Select **angular** from the screen menu.

10.1.3

2 Pick both lines which make up the angle. Be sure to pick the two lines in a counterclockwise direction.

3 Pick a convenient location for the dimension arc.

4 Press **RETURN** in response to "Dimension text."

5 Specify where you'd like the text to appear.

The angular dimension should appear similar to the one on page 175.

NOTE:

At the top of the dimensioning submenu, notice the two menu items "DIM:" and "DIM1:". The only difference between them is that the use of DIM1 allows you to execute only one dimensioning command and then returns to the normal "Command:" prompt. Use DIM: if you plan to execute a series of dimensioning commands.

6 Enter **END** to save your drawing and exit the Drawing Editor.

Questions

1. Describe the alternative to specifying both endpoints of a line when dimensioning a line.

   _____

   _____

2. Explain the difference between the DIM and DIM1 commands.

   _____

   _____

3. What prompt must be present in order to enter dimensioning commands?

   _____

4. Describe the purpose of the undo utility command found in the dimensioning submenu.

   _____

   _____

5. What dimensioning command is used to dimension inclined lines? Angles?

   _____

6. With what dimensioning command is the status of dimensioning variables listed?

   _____

Begin a New Drawing for each of the following problems. Place object lines on a layer named OBJ and place dimensions on a layer named DIM. Approximate the locations of the circles.

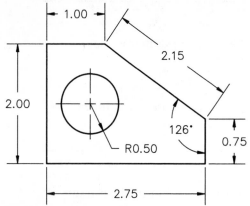

PRB 22-1

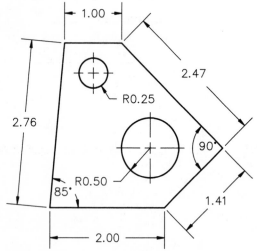

PRB 22-2

AutoCAD®
Reference
Manual

■ OBJECTIVE:

To apply AutoCAD's advanced dimensioning capabilities, including associative dimensioning

This unit introduces additional semiautomatic dimensioning techniques and allows you to practice them. With this knowledge, you will step through the completion of the PROTO1 prototype drawing. First, let's prepare to dimension the following drawing.

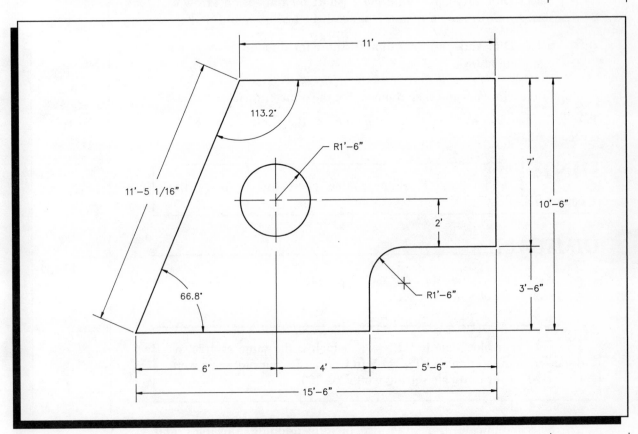

1 Begin a New Drawing and name it **DIMEN2=PROTO1**.

The prototype drawing PROTO1 is not entirely complete, but it will work for this exercise.

■ *Dimensioning Variables* _____

10.1.11

Before dimensioning the above object, it is necessary to scale the dimensions, using dimscale, to properly fit the dimensions to the drawing scale. Otherwise, the dimensions will be much too small. In addition, changes to other dimensioning variables, such as the text height, are important prior to dimensioning.

Let's review all dimensioning variables by obtaining a DIM status listing.

1 Select **status** from the dimensioning submenu to get the listing.

It should look similar to the listing you obtained in the previous unit but should now contain fractional inches because of the use of PROTO1.

Let's change both the dimension text and arrowhead size to 1/8″.

2 Select **Dim Vars** and then **dimasz** (short for dimension arrow size) from the screen menu. Change it to **1/8″**.

3 Select **Dim Vars** and then **dimtxt** (short for dimension text), and again enter **1/8″**.

4 Enter **Dim Vars** and then **dimcen**. Set the dimcen variable to −1/8″.

This will allow you to place full center lines on the circle with 1/8″ center marks.

HINT:
Use the "center" dimensioning command to place the center lines.

DIMSCALE

1 Next, determine the DIMSCALE setting by calculating the reciprocal of your plot scale.

HINT:
Your plot scale is 1/2″ = 1′, which is the same as 1/24, as discussed in the section on LTSCALE in Unit 21. If your plot scale were 1″ = 120″, your dimscale setting would be 120.

2 Select **dimscale** from the list of dimensioning variables and enter **24**.

Now let's focus on the text style to be used in the dimensions.

The text style used most recently in your drawing will be the one used for the dimensioning text. Therefore the text style last set in PROTO1 would be the default text style. However, let's create and use a new text style for the dimensioning text.

1 Create a text style using the ROMANS text font. Name it ROM, and do not make the style height fixed; leave it at 0.

2 Default through each of the text STYLE options.

10.1.11

ROM is now the current text style and will be the default style when dimensioning the drawing.

**AutoCAD®
Reference
Manual**

NOTE:

A style dimensioning command is contained in the dimensioning submenu. It allows you to quickly set a new current text style for use in your dimensions while remaining in the "DIM:" prompt.

10.1.7.6

③ Create and dimension the drawing shown on page 181. Be sure to place the object lines on layer OBJ and the dimensions on layer DIM.

HINT:

For best results, begin at the lower left corner of the object and draw the object in a counterclockwise direction.

When creating the horizontal string of dimensions in the drawing, use the DIM continue option found in the dimensioning submenu. First, do either the left- or rightmost dimension by selecting the first and second extension line origins and completing the dimension. Then select the continue option. At this point, select the next extension line origin to produce an adjacent dimension. Select the continue option again to finish the continuous string of dimensions.

④ If you know how to operate your plotter, plot the drawing using a thick pen (*e.g.*, .7 mm) for color 1 and a thin pen (*e.g.*, .3 mm) for color 3.

⑤ Experiment with the other dimensioning commands, such as LEADER. Also experiment with the dimensioning variables to see how they affect the appearance of the dimensions.

10.1.7.3

⑥ Enter **SAVE** to save your work but do not exit the Drawing Editor.

Associative Dimensioning

10.1

Associative dimensions are created by using dimensioning commands while the variable DIMASO is on. (The default setting for DIMASO is "on.") Associative dimensioning provides for automatic updating of dimensions when the dimensioned object is altered using the commands SCALE, STRETCH, ROTATE, EXTEND, TRIM, MIRROR, and ARRAY.

10.1.6

① Enter the **SCALE** command and select the entire object.

② Specify a base at any convenient location.

3 In reply to "Scale factor," enter **1.25**.

Notice the changes in the dimensions.

4 Enter the **STRETCH** command and stretch the rightmost portion of the object approximately 2' to the right. (When selecting the portion to be stretched, be sure to use the Crossing option.)

The dimensions should change to reflect the new size.

NOTE:

You can use the EXPLODE command to split an associative dimension into its component parts.

Also available are the dimensioning subcommands UPDATE, NEWTEXT, and HOMETEXT. Particularly useful are UPDATE and NEWTEXT.

1 Enter **DIM** to obtain the "Dim:" prompt.

2 Enter the **NEWTEXT** Command.

3 Enter an arbitrary number, such as **10**.

4 Select one of the dimension numbers in the drawing.

Did the dimension change to 10?

5 Restore the "Command:" prompt by entering **EXIT**.

6 Next, enter the **UNITS** command, change the units to architectural, and choose the default options.

7 Enter **DIM** and then the **UPDATE** subcommand.

8 Place a window around the entire object, including the dimensions, and press **RETURN**.

The dimensions should change to architectural units. The UPDATE command will also update dimensions according to current settings of the dimensioning variables and the current text style.

9 Restore the "Command:" prompt by entering **EXIT**.

10 Enter **END** to save your changes and exit the Drawing Editor.

Completing the Prototype Drawing _____

Now that we know how to perform the remaining steps (12-14, page 151) in creating a prototype drawing, let's finish PROTO1.DWG.

1   Load PROTO1 into the Drawing Editor.

2   Using the **STYLE** command, create a new text style using the **ROMANS** text font, and name it **ROM1**.

_____ NOTE: _____

> If you'd like your prototype drawing to contain more text styles, create them at this time. The last style you create will be the current style in your prototype drawing. Use of a style created with the ROMANS font is recommended for most applications.

Now let's set a few dimensioning variables.

1   Select **DIM:** from the root page of the screen menu.

2   Enter **status**.

3   Change **dimasz** to 1/8″.

4   Set **dimtxt** at 1/8″.

5   Change **dimcen** to −1/8″.

6   Using **dimscale**, scale all of the dimensioning variables to correspond with your prototype drawing scale: enter **24** as discussed on page 182.

Other changes in the dimensioning variables could be made at this time, but let's stop here.

7   Enter **END** to save your changes in PROTO1 and exit the Drawing Editor.

Your prototype drawing is now complete and ready for use with a host of new drawings.

As you continue to use this prototype drawing, as well as others you may create, feel free to modify them further to tailor them to your specific needs.

Documenting Your Prototype Drawings

It is important that you are able to access your prototype drawings in the future. To know what is contained in each prototype drawing, you must document the contents of each by printing certain information, such as your DIM status. Then you and others will be able to review the settings of each prototype drawing prior to choosing the one you need.

A sample of the information you should print is found in Appendix K. At the top of your printout, write the name of the prototype drawing, the directory on which it resides, and the drawing scale and paper size.

AUTOCAD® AT WORK

AutoCAD Artistry

When we think of an artist at work, we usually think of someone dabbing paint onto a canvas. But for some innovative artists who are experimenting with AutoCAD's creative potential, the easel is being replaced by the computer screen.

Ed Dadey, an artist in Nebraska, is using AutoCAD to design ceramics, commercial art, typography, graphics, and fine art. In addition, he collaborates with his wife to design handmade quilts and wall hangings.

Dadey became interested in setting up a CAD workstation in the fall of 1983, but he had trouble finding software that offered the accuracy and detail that his drawings required—until he tested AutoCAD: "The minute I saw the system's zoom feature, I was convinced this was the drafting program for me," Dadey says. "With AutoCAD's floating point format, I knew that I would get accuracy to the five or more decimal places I needed."

At present Dadey uses his drafting package most often for designing commercial art, such as logos for businesses and products. When designing logos, Dadey can zoom in to make sure that intersecting lines meet precisely, and he can try different colors, shapes, and scales by entering a few commands.

When Dadey isn't using AutoCAD for commercial work, he and his wife experiment with different quilt designs. Dadey matches airbrush paints to the fabrics his wife has selected, and he prepares a full-color design on paper. With AutoCAD, Dadey can experiment with an infinite number of shape, pattern, and color combinations until he and his wife find the quilt design they are looking for.

Questions

1. Why is it important to place dimensions on one layer and object lines on another layer?

   _____

   _____

2. Explain how to specify a text style to be used when dimensioning.

   _____

   _____

3. What is the purpose of the DIM VARS (dimensioning variables)?

   _____

   _____

4. How do you determine the DIMSCALE setting?

   _____

5. Explain the difference between AutoCAD's center marks and center lines, and describe how to generate each. Hint: Refer to the *Reference Manual*, Section 10.1.1.

   _____

   _____

   _____

6. Explain the use of the continu option found in the dimensioning submenu.

   _____

   _____

7. Describe the purpose of the UPDATE command.

   _____

   _____

Problems

Begin a New Drawing and establish the following drawing settings and parameters. Store as a prototype drawing. (You could name it PROTO3.) Then complete the following dimensioning problems using this prototype drawing.

UNITS: Engineering

Scale: 1″ = 10′ (or 1″ = 120″)

Paper Size: 17″ × 11″

LIMITS: Lower left corner 0,0

        Upper right corner 150′,100′

GRID: 10′

(Reminder: Be sure to ZOOM All)

SNAP resolution: 2′

LAYERs:

Name	Color
Thick	1
Thin	2

Text: Create a new text style using the ROMAND font. Do not make the style height fixed; leave it at 0.

DIMASZ: .125

DIMTXT: .125

DIMSCALE: 120

DIMALT: On

Create a new arrow block and enter it using the DIMBLK dimensioning variable. (Refer to Section 10.1.10 of the *AutoCAD Reference Manual* for directions on how to create and use an arrow block.)

After creating PRB 23-2, change the units to architectural. Using the DIM UPDATE command, update the dimensions to architectural units.

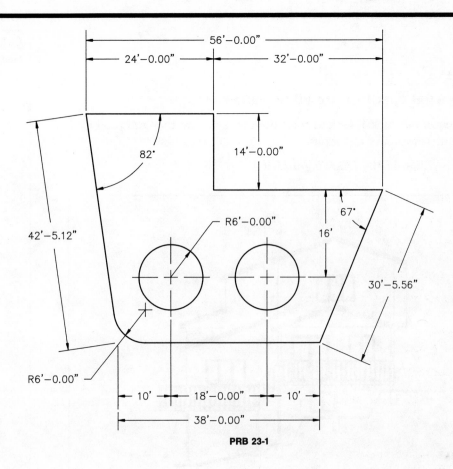

PRB 23-1

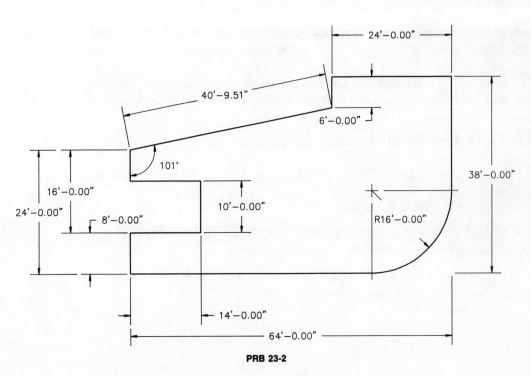

PRB 23-2

Unit 24 — Heavy Lines and Solid Objects

■ OBJECTIVE:

To apply the TRACE, SOLID, and FILL commands

This unit focuses on thick lines and solid objects and how they are produced in drawings such as house elevations.

Note the heavy lines in the following drawing.

AutoCAD Drawing Courtesy of Tim Smith, Hyland Design

The AutoCAD SOLID and TRACE commands were used to create the thick lines and solid filled areas. Let's draw similar lines and solid objects.

■ *TRACE Command*

1 Load AutoCAD and Begin a New Drawing. Name it **TRACE=PROTO1**.

2 Enter the **TRACE** command.

The TRACE command is used very much like the LINE command, except TRACE requires you to enter a trace width in units.

3 Specify a TRACE width of **4** inches and draw the figures on the next page. Don't worry about exact sizes.

4.5

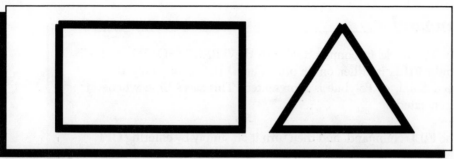

HINT:

To get the last line of the object to appear, just press RETURN.

You'll notice that it is difficult to produce a perfect corner at the first and last points of a polygon. This is simply the nature of the TRACE command.

4 Practice using TRACE by creating several more objects.

SOLID Command

Now let's work with the SOLID command to produce solid-filled objects.

1 Enter the **SOLID** command.

4.7

2 Produce a solid filled object similar to the one below. Pick the points in the exact order shown, and press **RETURN** when you are finished.

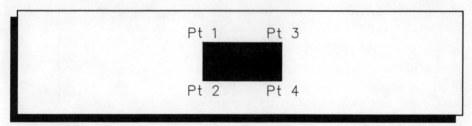

3 Pick a fifth and sixth point.

4 Experiment with the SOLID command. What happens if you pick the points in a different order?

Leave your objects on the screen so that you can practice the FILL command.

FILL Command _____

The FILL command works in conjunction with the TRACE, SOLID, and PLINE commands. FILL is either on or off. When FILL is off, only the outline of a Trace, Solid, or Polyline is represented. This saves time whenever the screen is regenerated.

1 Enter the **FILL** command, and then turn it off simply by entering **OFF**.

_____ NOTE: _____

After turning FILL on or off, a regeneration of the screen must occur before the change will take place...

2 ... therefore enter the **REGEN** command.

Your objects should no longer be solid-filled.

3 Reenter the **FILL** command and turn it on.

4 Enter **REGEN** to force a screen regeneration.

5 Enter **END** to save your drawing and exit to the Main Menu.

Questions

1. In what screen submenu is the SOLID command found?

   _____

2. The FILL command is used in conjunction with both TRACE and SOLID. What is its purpose and how is it used?

   _____

   _____

3. What might be a limitation of using the TRACE command?

   _____

   _____

4. How would you draw a triangle using the SOLID command?

   _____

   _____

5. Can you draw curved objects using the SOLID command?

   _____

Problems

1. Construct PRB24-1 using the TRACE and SOLID commands. Specify a TRACE width of .05 unit. Don't worry about the exact size and shape of the roof.

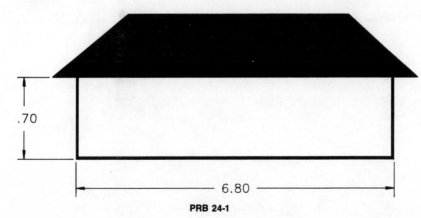

PRB 24-1

2. After you have completed PRB24-1, place the solid shapes as indicated below. Don't worry about their exact sizes and locations.

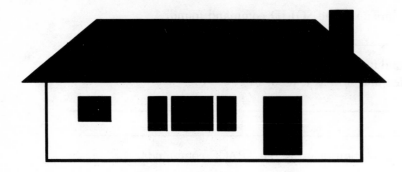

3. Are the TRACE and SOLID commands entities like the LINE, CIRCLE, and ARC commands? To find out, try removing a small piece of the roof in PRB24-1. What is your conclusion?

_____

_____

4. Construct the elevation drawing shown on the first page of this unit. You may choose to use one of your prototype drawings when you begin this drawing.

AUTOCAD® AT WORK

Cracking Down on Crime with AutoCAD

The police in Concord, California, are winning the fight against crime by using CAD to help them stop burglaries before they begin.

In order to prevent burglaries, police look for "crime patterns": What areas of the city are hit most often? What kinds of places are being burglarized? And what property is being stolen? Before AutoCAD, keeping track of all this information was nearly impossible. Recording burglary information on city maps didn't work because they soon became too crowded with information to read. And using "pin maps" didn't work because they couldn't indicate the number or kinds of burglaries that were committed at the same location.

By using AutoCAD, the Concord Police Department can not only record the number and types of burglaries, but it can also display that information on a map of the city. In addition, the department uses AutoCAD's "zoom" feature to make detailed maps of the officers' assigned areas so that they can do a better job of patrolling.

According to Concord's chief of police, AutoCAD is having a big impact on the city's crime rate. "We've found that the presence of police officers in areas where crime is predicted discourages people from committing crimes. Our AutoCAD program shows us graphically where our patrol cars should be and when they should be there." AutoCAD also allows the police department to track the movement of burglaries from one area of the city to another and to chart what effect the arrest of especially active burglars might have on the crime rate in certain areas of the city. **Other Uses.** In addition to the police department, several other city departments in Concord are planning projects involving AutoCAD. Various departments are funding a joint project that would take advantage of AutoCAD's layering feature to make above-ground maps of city streets and addresses and underground maps of water, sewer, and gas lines. The city's traffic department is using AutoCAD to map traffic density and to record traffic accidents.

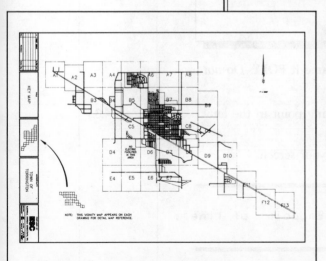

Courtesy of Electrical Systems Consultants, Inc.

Unit 25

Joining Straight, Curved, and Solid Objects

■ OBJECTIVE:

To apply Polylines using the PLINE, PEDIT, BREAK, and EXPLODE commands

This unit deals mostly with Polylines. A Polyline is a connected sequence of line and arc segments. It is treated by AutoCAD as a single entity. Polylines are often used in lieu of conventional lines and arcs because they are more versatile during creation and editing. The examples below illustrate some uses of Polylines.

4.6

■ *PLINE Command* ─────────────────

Let's try creating a simple Polyline, such as the one below, using the PLINE command.

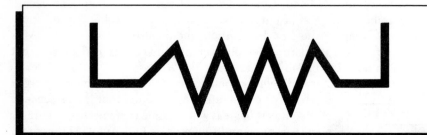

1 Load AutoCAD, Begin a New Drawing, and name it **POLY**. Do *not* use a custom prototype drawing.

2 Enter the **PLINE** command and specify a starting point in the left portion of your screen.

4.6.1

You should now have the following PLINE options on your screen.

```
Arc/Close/Halfwidth/Length/Undo/Width/<Endpoint of line>:
```

3 Enter Width and give a starting and ending width of .15 unit. Notice that the ending width value defaults to the starting width value.

4 Now draw the object by specifying endpoints. Don't worry about exact sizes and placement of the endpoints. Press **RETURN** when you're finished.

HINT:

If you make a mistake, use PLINE'S Undo option.

5 When you are finished, enter the **ERASE** command and pick any point on the Polyline or enter **Last**.

Notice that the entire object is treated as a single entity.

6 Enter **OOPS** to restore the Polyline if you completed the erasure.

PEDIT Command

Now let's edit the Polyline using PEDIT.

1 Enter the **PEDIT** command and select the Polyline you just drew. The Polyline will not highlight as it does during a normal object selection.

5.4.1

You should now have the following PEDIT command options on your screen.

```
Close/Join/Width/Edit vertex/Fit curve/Spline curve/Decurve/
Undo/eXit <X>:
```

Let's change the Polyline width.

2 Enter Width and specify a new width of .1 unit.

As you can see, PEDIT could be useful in changing the width of a series of thick lines.

Now let's close the Polyline as shown on the next page.

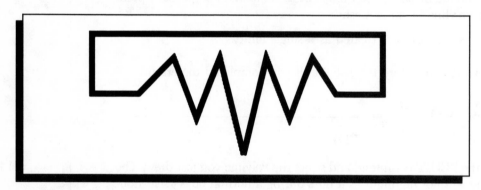

3 Enter **Close**.

Your object should now be closed.

Let's do a simple curve fitting operation.

4 Enter the **Fit** curve option.

How did the drawing change?

5 Enter **Decurve** to bring it back to its previous form.

Next, let's move one of the object's vertices as shown below.

6 Enter the **Edit** vertex option.

7 Move the "X" to the vertex you want to change by pressing **RETURN** several times.

8 Select **Move** from the new list of options and specify a new vertex location.

Try it again if it did not work.

9 To exit the PEDIT command, enter **X** (short for exit) twice.

Note that there are many more editing features contained within PEDIT. Experiment with each of these on your own.

Spline Curves

With AutoCAD, you have the capability of creating spline curves, also referred to as B-splines.

The PEDIT "Spline Curve" option uses the vertices of the selected Polyline as the control points of the curve. The curve passes through the first and last control points and is "pulled" toward the other points but does not necessarily pass through them. The more control points you specify, the more "pull" they exert on the curve.

1 Enter the **PEDIT** command and select the Polyline you previously drew.

2 Choose the Spline curve option.

Do you see the difference between the "Spline" curve and the "Fit" curve?

3 Enter Undo to restore the original drawing.

4 Enter **X** to exit the PEDIT command

NOTE:

AutoCAD offers two spline options: quadratic B-splines and cubic B-splines. An example of each is shown below.

Original   Fit Curve   Quadratic B—spline   Cubic B—spline

The system variable SPLINETYPE controls the type of spline curve to be generated. Set the value of SPLINETYPE at 5 to generate quadratic B-splines. Set its value at 6 to generate cubic B-splines.

The PEDIT Decurve option enables you to turn a spline back into its frame. Or, if you wish to see both the spline curve and its frame, set the system variable SPLFRAME to 1.

Breaking Polylines

5.3.3

Small pieces can be removed from Polylines using the BREAK command. Let's try it.

1 Enter the **BREAK** command.

2 Pick a point on the Polyline where you'd like the break to begin.

3 Pick a second point a short distance from your first point.

Did a piece of the Polyline disappear?

Exploding Polylines

The EXPLODE command gives you the ability to break up a Polyline into individual line/arc segments.

5.4.2

1 Enter the **EXPLODE** command.

2 Pick the Polyline.

Notice the message "Exploding this polyline has lost width information. The UNDO command will restore it."

This is the nature of applying EXPLODE to a Polyline that contains a width greater than 0. On the one hand, you now have an object that contains numerous entities for easier editing. On the other hand, you have lost your line thickness. As stated, if you need the thickness, you can restore your Polyline using the UNDO command.

3 To illustrate that the object is now made up of numerous entities, edit one of them.

PLINE's Arc Option

4.6.1.2

In some drafting applications, there is a need to draw a series of continuous arcs to represent, for example, a river on a map. If the line requires thickness, the ARC Continue option will not work. But the PLINE Arc option can handle this task.

1 Enter the **PLINE** command and pick a point in any convenient location on your screen.

2 Enter the Arc option.

The following list of options should now be on your screen.

```
Angle/CEnter/CLose/Direction/Halfwidth/Line/Radius/Second pt/
Undo/Width/<Endpoint of arc>:
```

3 Enter the Width option and enter a starting and ending width of .1 unit.

4 Move your crosshairs and watch the arc begin to develop.

5 Pick a point a short distance from your first point...

6 ... then pick a second point, and a third...

7 Press **RETURN** when you're finished.

8 Enter **END** to save your work and exit the Drawing Editor.

3DPOLY Command

4.6.2

The 3DPOLY command enables you to create Polylines consisting of x, y, and z vertices. 3D Polylines are made up of straight line segments only and they cannot take on a specified thickness.

3D Polylines can be edited with the PEDIT command, and you can fit a 3D B-spline curve to the vertices of a 3D Polyline.

Refer to Units 34-39 to learn about AutoCAD's 3D environment and how the 3DPOLY command may be applied within it.

Questions

1. Briefly define a Polyline.

   _____

2. Briefly describe each of the following PLINE options.

   Arc _____

   Close _____

   Halfwidth _____

   Length _____

   Undo _____

   Width _____

3. Briefly describe each of the PEDIT command options.

   Close _____

   Join _____

   Width _____

   Edit vertex _____

   Fit curve _____

   Spline curve _____

   Decurve _____

   Undo _____

   eXit _____

4. Describe one application for the PLINE Arc option.

   _____

5. Of what importance is the EXPLODE command to Polylines?

   _____

6. What effect does EXPLODE have on Polylines that contain a width?

   _____

7. Is it possible to remove a small piece (smaller than an entity) of a Polyline? Explain.

   _____

   _____

8. Describe the system variable SPLINETYPE.

   _____

   _____

Problems

1. Create the approximate shape of the following racetrack using PLINE. Specify .4 unit for both the starting and ending widths. Select the Arc option for drawing the figure.

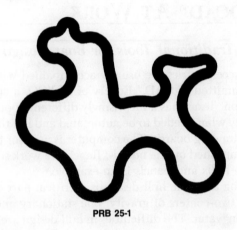

PRB 25-1

2-6. Draw each of the following objects using the PLINE and PEDIT commands.

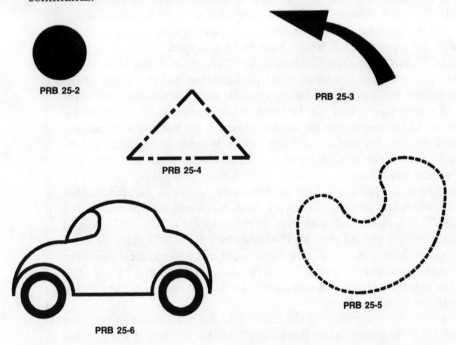

PRB 25-2

PRB 25-3

PRB 25-4

PRB 25-5

PRB 25-6

AUTOCAD® AT WORK

*Mixing CAD and Traditional Tools for Boat Design**

In the CAD industry, success stories are usually accompanied with the claim, "We are totally committed to CAD." Ed Fry of FRYCO, a custom yacht design firm in Houston, Texas, has a surprisingly different approach; FRYCO has automated only what needed to be automated and left the rest of the work to be done on drawing boards. The computer is used for things that cannot be easily accomplished on the boards. Repetitive work such as fairing and framing of the hulls and panels is an example.

Boat design is a balancing act. The hull design is a critical part of the balance because there are two centers of gravity: one stationary and one in flux, and the balance is in water. The difficulties in hull design are compounded when the skin is put on the frames of the boat. If the boat has not been properly faired, the skin will come out wrinkled and the boat will not only lose aesthetic appeal but will also require more horsepower to meet the speed specifications.

Before computers, a boat's hull was laid out on the drawing board and fairing was hand calculated. "That used to take us at least two days," Fry says. If a customer changed his mind about the length, girth, or overall design of a hull designed on the boards, the whole process would start over and most of the previous work would have to be scrapped.

Today FRYCO uses a combination of AutoYacht (from Coast Design) and AutoCAD. AutoYacht is a stand-alone package that includes many of the sophisticated features a boat designer needs, most importantly, the creation of master curves that can be imported into other CAD packages for finishing. The master curves are used to construct the hull to specifications. Some of the other features of AutoYacht include hydrostatic and intact stability analysis, sail plan analysis, spar design, a velocity prediction program, and weight estimating.

Fry transfers the work done in AutoYacht to AutoCAD for further manipulation and plotting. The work from AutoYacht is imported with a simple DXFIN command, and most of the drawing is done full size and scaled when it's plotted out. FRYCO also uses AutoCAD alone to draw mechanical details, electrical schematics, and other mechanical drawings to insure accuracy during construction. The majority of the AutoYacht/AutoCAD output is sent directly to the boat builder as just another page in the set of plans.

While Fry is conservative in the CAD field, he is a pioneer in the boat design field. No matter what the future holds for the rest of the boating industry, FRYCO has a promising future with its carefully blended mix of modern technology and old fashioned design skill.

*Based on a story in *CADENCE* magazine, Vol 3, No. 10.

Unit 26 A Calculating Strategy

■ OBJECTIVE:

To apply the ID, DIST, AREA, LIST, DBLIST, DIVIDE, SETVAR, and MEASURE commands

This unit focuses on the commands that allow you to perform a variety of calculations on your drawings. In addition, it covers the AutoCAD commands that reveal hidden (but important) data about specific components within your drawing.

The drawing below shows an apartment complex with parking lots, streets, and trees. When constructing a drawing such as this, you may need to perform certain calculations on the drawing, such as determining the square footage of the parking lot or the distance between the parking stalls.

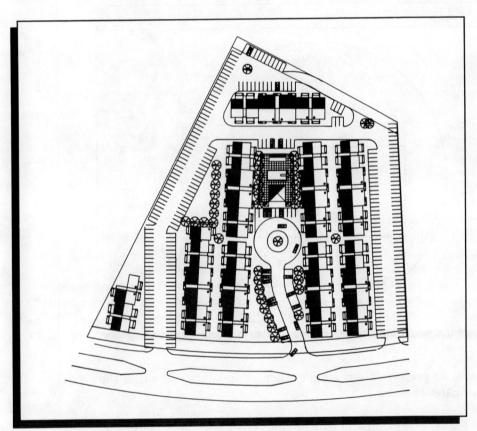

AutoCAD Drawing Courtesy of Buday-Wells, Architects

Let's bring up AutoCAD and practice these functions.

ID and DIST Commands _____

1 Load AutoCAD and Begin a New Drawing called **CALC**.

2 Draw a rectangle with a circle around it at the sizes shown below. Omit the numbers and dimensions; don't worry about the exact placement of the circle in relation to the rectangle.

HINT: Set your snap resolution at .25 before drawing the object, and use your coordinate display as you construct it.

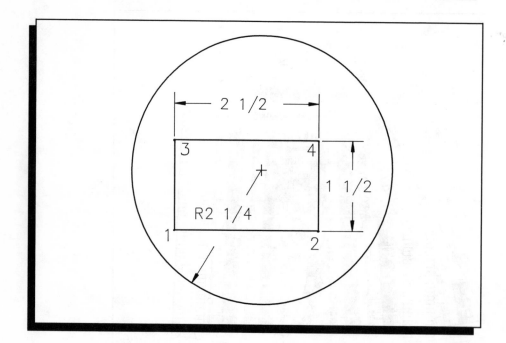

Now we're ready to perform a few simple calculations. First, let's find the absolute coordinates of point 1.

3 Enter the **ID** command and pick point 1. (ID stands for "identify.")

5.6.3

HINT: Use the Object Snap feature to obtain accurate locations (unless your points are located on your snap resolution and Snap is on).

The absolute coordinates of point 1 should appear.

AutoCAD®
Reference
Manual

4 Try it again with point 2.

5 Enter the **DIST** command and obtain the distance between points 1 and 2. (Simply pick point 1 and point 2.) Again, you may need to use Object Snap to obtain accurate locations.

5.6.4

What is the distance between points 1 and 2? What other information is produced?

AREA Command

1 Enter the **AREA** command and calculate the area of the rectangle by picking each of its corners. Press **RETURN** or the **space bar** when you've picked all the points.

5.6.5

What is the area of the rectangle? What is its perimeter?

The AREA command will calculate the area of a circle or a Polyline if you select the Entity option and point to the object. Also, a running total of measured areas can be kept and you can ask AutoCAD to add or subtract areas from the total. For example, if a closed Polyline contains a hole, the area of the hole can be subtracted.

2 Create a closed Polyline and include a circle within it.

3 Step through the following.

Command: **AREA**
<First point >/Entity/Add/Subtract: **A**

<First point >/Entity/Subtract: **E**
(ADD mode) Select circle or polyline: (*Point to Polyline*)

(Area of Polyline will be displayed.)

(ADD mode) Select circle or polyline: (*Press RETURN*)
<First point >/Entity/Subtract: **S**

<First point >/Entity/Add: **E**
(SUBTRACT mode) Select circle or polyline: (*Point to hole*)

(Total area—Polygon minus hole—will be displayed.)

(SUBTRACT mode) Select circle or polyline: (*Press RETURN*)
<First point >/Entity/Add: (*Press RETURN*)

("Command:" prompt will be restored.)

LIST and DBLIST Commands_____

These commands restore database information on selected entities.

1 Enter the **LIST** command and pick any point on the circle. Press **RETURN**.

The circle's layer, center point, radius, circumference, and area should appear.

2 Enter **LIST** again, but this time pick the line between points 1 and 2.

What information did you receive?

3 Last, enter **DBLIST** and watch what you get.

You should receive information on all entities in your drawing data base.

_____ NOTE: _____

Use CTRL S to stop the scrolling; hit any key to resume scrolling.

DIVIDE Command _____

The DIVIDE command is used to divide an entity into a specified number of equal parts. Let's try it.

1 Enter the **DIVIDE** command.

2 Select any point on the circle.

3 In reply to "<Number of segments>," enter **20**.

Does it appear as though nothing happened? Something did happen: the DIVIDE command divided the circle into 20 equal parts using 20 point entities; you just can't see them. Here's how to use them.

4 Enter the **LINE** command.

5 Enter the **NODe** Object Snap mode. (Node is used to snap to the nearest point entity.)

6 Pick any place on the circle.

AutoCAD should snap to the nearest of the 20 point entities. If it doesn't, move your pointing device slightly and try again. Make sure Ortho is off.

7 Snap to the center of the circle using the Object Snap mode **CEN**ter. (Remember, you have to pick a point on the circle.)

8 Enter the **NOD**e mode again and snap to another point entity on the circle.

You should now have an object that looks similar to the following.

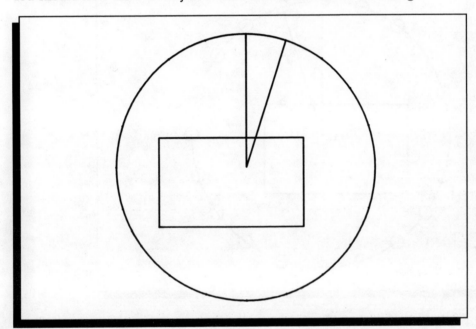

Making the Points Visible with SETVAR

3.11

SETVAR, short for Set System Variables, allows you to change a number of pre-established modes, sizes, and limits. (See Appendix K for a complete list of System Variables.)

One of the variables, called PDMODE, is used to control the appearance of point entities. Let's use the SETVAR command and PDMODE to make the points on our circle visible.

1 Enter the **SETVAR** command.

2 Enter ? to obtain a listing of the System Variables and to look for the PDMODE.

Did you find PDMODE? What was its value?

③ Enter **SETVAR** again, and then enter **PDMODE**.

④ Enter **32** for the new value, and enter the **REGEN** command.

Did 20 equally spaced circles appear on your circle as shown on the next illustration?

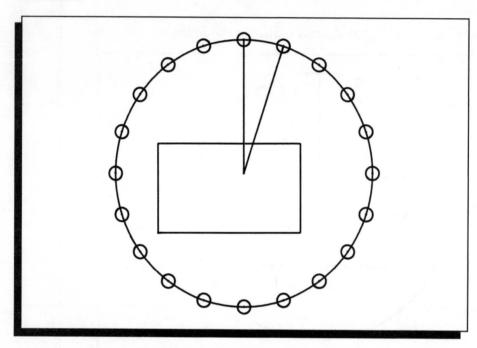

The following list and the illustration show how other values control the appearance of point entities.

Value	Draws
0	a dot at the point (default setting)
1	nothing
2	a cross through the point (like a "blip")
3	an X through the point
4	a vertical line upward from the point

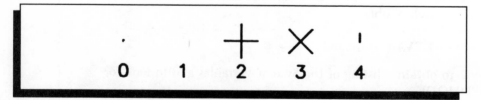

To each of the above values, you can add 32, 64, or 96 to select a figure to be drawn around the point in addition to the figure drawn through it, as shown on the next illustration. For example, 2 + 32 = 34, and 34 represents a cross with a circle on it.

Value   Draws
  32   a circle around the point
  64   a square around the point
  96   both a circle and a square

⊙	○	⊕	⊗	◔
32	**33**	**34**	**35**	**36**
⊡	□	⊞	⊠	⊓
64	**65**	**66**	**67**	**68**
⊡	◰	⊞	⊠	◕
96	**97**	**98**	**99**	**100**

5 Experiment with several of these values, and remember to regenerate your screen each time.

MEASURE Command

5.3.10

The MEASURE command is similar to DIVIDE except that MEASURE does not divide the entity into a given number of equal parts like DIVIDE. Instead, MEASURE allows you to place markers along the object at specified intervals.

1 Enter the **MEASURE** command and select one of the horizontal lines in the rectangle.

2 In reply to " <Segment length>," enter **.7** unit.

AutoCAD should space point entities .7 unit apart.

3 Further experiment with MEASURE on other parts of your rectangle and circle.

4 When you're finished, enter **END** to save your work and exit the Drawing Editor.

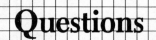

Questions

1. What AutoCAD command is used to find coordinate points while in the Drawing Editor?

   _____

2. What information is produced with the AREA command?

   _____

3. What information is produced with the LIST command?

   _____

   _____

4. Describe the difference between LIST and DBLIST.

   _____

   _____

5. How do you stop the scrolling of information when executing DBLIST?

   _____

6. How do you calculate the perimeter of a polygon?

   _____

7. How do you find the circumference of a circle?

   _____

8. Explain the difference between the DIVIDE and MEASURE commands.

   _____

   _____

   _____

9. Explain how the appearance of point entities is controlled.

   _____

   _____

   _____

   _____

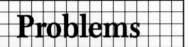

Problems

Draw the objects found in the following problems at any convenient size, omitting all letters. Then perform the inquiry commands listed above the objects. Write their values in the blanks provided.

1. ID of point A? _____

   DIST between points A and B? _____

   AREA of the polygon? _____

   Perimeter of the polygon? _____

PRB 26-1

2. DIST between A and B? _____

   DIST between B and C? _____

   AREA of circle? _____

   Circumference of circle? _____

   AREA of polygon? _____

   Perimeter of polygon? _____

   Area of polygon minus the circle? _____

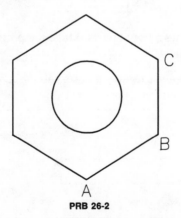

PRB 26-2

213

3. LIST information on arc A?

_____

_____

_____

_____

LIST information on line B?

_____

_____

_____

_____

DBLIST information for entire screen?

_____

_____

_____

_____

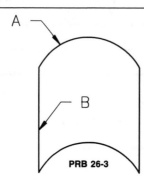

PRB 26-3

4. On the above object, divide line B into 5 equal parts. Make the point entities visible by changing the system variable.

5. On arc A above, place markers along the arc at intervals of .25 unit. If the markers are invisible, make them visible.

Unit 27 Building Blocks

■ OBJECTIVE:

To apply the BLOCK, INSERT, MINSERT, EXPLODE, RENAME, PURGE, and WBLOCK commands

If CAD systems are managed properly, their users should never have to draw the same objects twice. This is a primary reason why CAD is beneficial. Success, however, depends on the techniques by which the drawings are created, stored, documented, and retrieved.

This unit focuses on the commands that enable you to create, store, and reuse the symbols, drawings, and details that you need repeatedly.

9.1

BLOCK Command _____

The BLOCK command allows you to combine several entities into one, store it, and retrieve it at a later time. Let's work with the BLOCK command.

1 Load AutoCAD and Begin a New Drawing. Name it **BLKS**.

2 Obtain help on the **BLOCK** command and read it over.

Now that you know what a Block is, let's create one.

9.1.3

3 On layer 0, draw the following object. Approximate its size, but make it small.

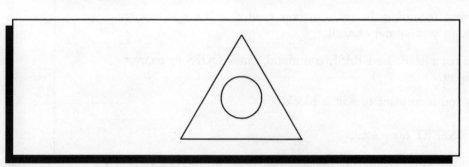

4 Enter the **BLOCK** command.

5 Create the Block based on the following information.

— Name the Block **MENTAL**.
— Specify the lower left corner of the object as the insertion base point.
— Select all four entities.
— And press **RETURN**.

After completing the above, the object should disappear. If it did, then you have successfully created a Block.

215

Your MENTAL Block is now stored in your current drawing file for subsequent insertion.

─────── NOTE: ───────

You can enter OOPS to make the individual entities reappear.

INSERT Command _____

Let's insert the Block.

1. Enter the **INSERT** command and specify the Block name **MENTAL**.

9.1.4

It should appear on the screen.

2. Insert the MENTAL Block using the following information.

— Insert near the lower left corner of your screen.
— Specify the scale at **.75** on both the X and Y axes.
— Rotate the Block 45 degrees counterclockwise by entering **45**.

It should appear in the position you indicated. If it didn't, try again.

3. Attempt to erase the circle from the Block.

The entire object, including the circle, is now treated as a single element called a Block, so you cannot erase it.

4. If you completed the ERASE command, enter **OOPS** to recover the object.

In the future, you may want to edit a Block.

1. Enter **INSERT** once again.

2. This time, when typing the Block name, place an asterisk (✳) before it: **✳MENTAL**.

9.1.4.9

3. Step through the entire INSERT command and enter whatever scale and rotation factor you wish.

4. After it appears on the screen, try to erase the circle from the Block.

Did it work? What can you conclude about the ✳ option?

MINSERT Command _____

9.1.6

MINSERT, short for Multiple Insert, allows you to insert a rectangular array of Blocks. The MINSERT command is sort of a combination of the INSERT and ARRAY commands. Let's apply it.

216

**AutoCAD®
Reference
Manual**

1 Enter **MINSERT** and then enter **MENTAL**.

2 For the insertion point, pick an open space near the lower left corner of the screen.

3 Enter **.25** for both the X and Y scale factors and **0** for the rotation angle.

4 In reply to "Number of rows," enter **3**, and enter **5** for the "Number of columns."

5 Enter **1** for the distance between rows and **1** for the distance between columns.

Fifteen MENTAL Blocks should appear on your screen.

Reviewing Block Names

After creating several Blocks, it's easy to forget their names. This is especially true when you edit the drawing file two or more weeks after you have created the Blocks.

1 Enter the **INSERT** command.

2 Enter **?**

NOTE:

You can also obtain a listing of Blocks by entering the BLOCK command and entering **?** in response to "Block name (or ?):".

Exploding Blocks

5.4.2

Often, you will insert Blocks without the "**∗**" option because you want to manipulate those Blocks as a single element. Examples are doors and windows in a house elevation drawing or components on an electrical schematic.

1 Insert the MENTAL Block without the "**∗**" option.

2 Enter the **EXPLODE** command and pick any point on the Block.

The EXPLODE command reverses the effect of the BLOCK command. The object is no longer a Block.

RENAME Command

3.13.1

The RENAME command lets you rename previously created Blocks. Let's do one.

1 Enter the **RENAME** command.

You should receive the following on your screen.

```
Block/LAyer/LType/Style/Ucs/VIew/VPort:
```

NOTE:

As you can see by the list, RENAME can be used to rename not only Blocks, but also Layers, Linetypes, Text Styles, User Coordinate Systems, Views, and viewports.

2 Select the **Block** option from the list of RENAME options.

3 In reply to "Old block name:" enter **MENTAL**.

4 Enter **SQUARE** for the new Block name.

5 Enter **INSERT ?** to obtain a listing of your Blocks.

6 Change the Block's name back to MENTAL.

PURGE Command

The PURGE command enables you to selectively delete any unused, named objects, including Blocks. Named objects may be purged at any time after entering the Drawing Editor until the drawing database has been modified.

1 Enter the **PURGE** command.

2 If you receive the message "The PURGE command cannot be used now," enter **END** to save your work and exit the Drawing Editor.

3 Load the same **BLKS** drawing file.

4 Enter the **PURGE** command.

The following should appear.

```
Purge unused Blocks/LAyers/LTypes/SHapes/STyles/All:
```

5 Select one type of object to be purged or reply **All** to purge all named object types.

AutoCAD prompts you with the name of each unused object of the specified type and asks whether that object should be purged.

Inserting Drawing Files

Drawing files from disk can also be inserted into your existing drawing using the INSERT command.

9.1.5

1 Enter the **INSERT** command.

2 Choose one of your *drawings* from disk, such as CALC, and type the drawing file name. Omit the .DWG extension; it's assumed.

HINT:

Use the FILES utility command if you need to review your drawing file names.

3 Specify **0,0** for the insertion point.

4 If the drawing is large, scale it down. Be aware that it may overlap with what is already on your screen.

If it did not work, try it again with another drawing file.

So you see, any drawing file contained on your disk can be inserted into your current drawing. This enables you to combine any of your drawings and create highly sophisticated drawings in a short period of time.

NOTE:

9.1.5.1

The BASE command may be useful for establishing a drawing insertion base point other than 0,0 (which is the default). For instance, if your current drawing is of a part that you expect to insert into other drawings, you can specify the base point for such insertions using the BASE command.

WBLOCK Command

You understand that all drawing files are accessible for insertion in any drawing. But what about Blocks? Is there a method of making the Block(s) available to other drawings? Yes, with the WBLOCK (short for Write Block) command.

1 Enter **WBLOCK**.

9.1.7

2 Name the file **MENT**, and use the Block named **MENTAL**.

Note the light on your disk drive as you complete the command. The computer created a new file called MENT with the contents of MENTAL.

Let's review the MENT.DWG file.

3 Enter the **FILES** command and list all drawing files.

You should see MENT.DWG.

Now that the MENTAL Block is in a drawing file format, it can be inserted into any other drawing file. If you keep track of it, you'll never need to draw it again.

4 For practice, create another Block and store it as a drawing file using WBLOCK.

NOTE:

The ∗ option, when used with the WBLOCK command, creates a new drawing file of the current drawing, similarly to the SAVE command. However, views, User Coordinate Systems, viewport configurations, and any unreferenced Block definitions, layers, linetypes, and text styles are not written. Consider the following.

Command: WBLOCK
File Name: BK
Block Name: ∗

5 When you're finished, enter END to save your work and exit the Drawing Editor.

Questions

1. Briefly describe the purpose of Blocks.

   _____

   _____

2. Explain how the INSERT command is used.

   _____

   _____

3. How can you list all defined Blocks contained within a drawing file?

   _____

   _____

4. A Block can be inserted with or without an asterisk preceding the name. Describe the difference between the two.

   _____

   _____

5. Explain how WBLOCK works.

   _____

   _____

6. When would WBLOCK be useful?

   _____

   _____

7. What is "exploding a Block," and what is its purpose?

   _____

   _____

8. How are Blocks renamed?

   _____

9. Explain the function of the MINSERT command.

   _____

   _____

10. Explain the PURGE command.

    _____

    _____

Problems

1. Begin a New Drawing named LIVROOM. Draw the furniture representations and store each as a separate Block. Then draw the living room outline. Don't worry about exact sizes or locations, and omit the text. Insert each piece of furniture into the living room at the appropriate size and rotation angle. Feel free to create additional furniture and to use each piece of furniture more than once.

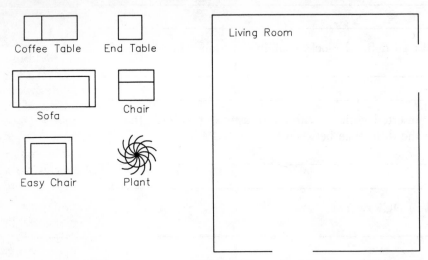

PRB 27-1

2. After creating the Blocks, write two of them (of your choice) to disk using WBLOCK.

3. Using MINSERT, create a lecture room full of chairs arranged in a rectangular pattern.

4. Explode the PLANT Block and erase every fourth arc contained in it. Then store the PLANT again as a Block.

5. Rename two of your furniture Blocks.

6. Purge unused objects.

AUTOCAD® AT WORK

Convenience Store Chain Discovers the Convenience of CAD

Southland Corporation, best known for its 7-Eleven convenience store chain, uses AutoCAD to prepare customized drawing packets for contractors' use in building new stores. Southland uses generic store layouts, but only up to a point—no two building sites are the same, nor are they in locations with identical traffic flow patterns and building codes. As a result, the company's three standardized store plans are inevitably modified extensively, in terms of floor plans, electrical and plumbing diagrams, and exterior views.

With AutoCAD, Southland's drafters can create and edit any type of drawing to any scale. They can also move, erase, rotate, duplicate, and mirror drawings.

The CAD system's layering capability has proven crucial to Southland's drafters. It enables them, for example, to call up an electrical layout while simultaneously viewing architectural layers on the display screen. According to Paul Sarrett, an area construction manager for Southland's western region, there's simply no comparison between computerized layering and the method formerly used at Southland—holding two drawings up to a window and hoping the sunlight would be strong enough to create transparencies.

With the BLOCK command, drafters can insert previously drawn office and store fixtures from a standard template library of equipment symbols, including desks, chairs, sales counters, shelving units, and refrigerator cabinets.

CAD has also simplified the design of 7-Eleven's parking lots. To ensure that parking lots and driveways are properly laid out, drafters select a car or truck from the custom block menu on the computer screen and employ the dynamic drag function to simulate the parking lot's traffic flow.

Although ninety percent of new 7-Eleven stores can be built from variations of the three standard store layouts, the remaining ten percent must be designed from scratch. It is in designing these special stores, Sarrett believes, that the drafting software truly shines. "In a single session," he says, "we can now accomplish what used to take four to six weeks of meetings, drawing revisions, and more meetings. Everyone gathers around a CAD workstation and designs the store directly on the screen. At the end of the meeting, we plot out a final design that can be approved and initialed on the spot."

Based on the success of Southland's foray into PC-based CAD, Sarrett expects that AutoCAD will soon be used at the company's remaining thirteen divisional construction departments as well. "For the cost of a single mainframe CAD workstation, we can set up AutoCAD workstations that will do the job in all of our construction departments —and still have enough left over for a round of Slurpees."

Courtesy of CalComp

Unit 28 — Symbol Library Creation

■ OBJECTIVE:

To create and use a library of symbols and details

The purpose of this unit is to create a group of symbols and details and to store them in a library. The library will then be applied in a new drawing.

The following is a collection of electrical substation schematic symbols contained within an AutoCAD drawing file that was named LIBRARY1. Each of the symbols was stored as a single Block and given a Block name. (In this particular case, numbers were used for Block names rather than words.) The crosses, which show the Blocks' insertion base points, and the numbers were drawn on a separate layer and frozen when the Blocks were created. They are not part of the Blocks; they are used for reference and retrieval purposes only.

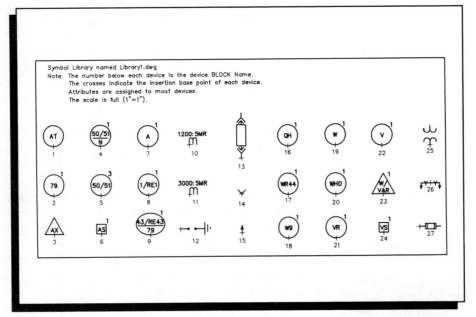

Courtesy of City of Fort Collins, Light & Power Utility

After the symbols were developed and stored in LIBRARY1, the LIBRARY1 file was inserted into a new drawing for creation of the electrical schematic shown on the following page.

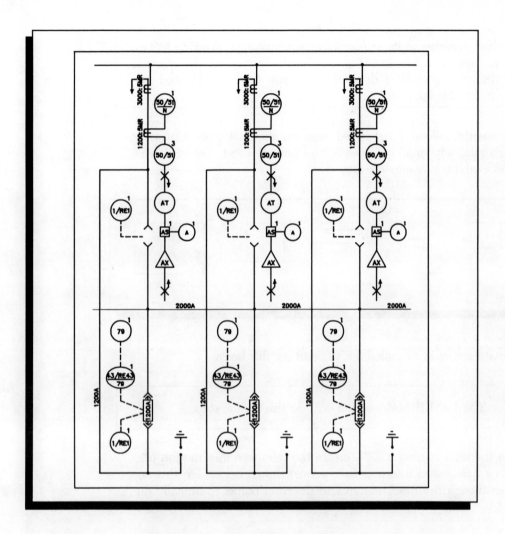

The Blocks were inserted into the new drawing along with other LIBRARY1
elements. They were then inserted into their proper locations, and lines were
used to connect them. Hence, approximately 80 percent of the work was
completed before the drawing was started. This is the primary advantage of
grouping Blocks in symbol libraries.

Creating a Library

Let's step through a simple version of the procedures just described.

1. Load AutoCAD and Begin a New Drawing. Name it **LIB1** (short
   for LIBRARY1).

NOTE:

As described in earlier units, you should use a prototype drawing to save time when creating a new drawing. But for the purpose of this exercise, do not specify a prototype drawing since you have not created one specifically for this application.

2 Create the following simplified representations of tools. Construct each relatively small on layer 0, and omit the text. Use of Snap and Ortho is recommended.

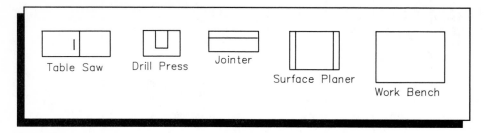

3 Create a new layer called TEXT, and set this layer.

HINT:

The LAYER Make option will do this in one step.

4 On the layer named TEXT, create the reference information (*i.e.*, Block names and insertion base points) shown below. Do this now even though the Block names and insertion points technically do not yet exist.

HINT:

Create a small cross (+) and store it as a Block. Make the center of the cross its insertion point. Insert the cross at each of the components' insertion points as indicated below.

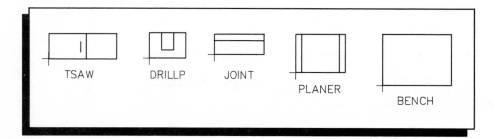

5 After you have placed the crosses and text on the layer called TEXT, set layer 0 and freeze layer TEXT.

The Block names and crosses (insertion points) should have disappeared.

6 Store each of the tool representations as a Block using the same Block names and insertion points you used above.

NOTE:

A Block can be made up of entities from different layers, with different colors and linetypes. The layer, color, and linetype information of each entity is preserved in the Block. When the Block is inserted, each entity is drawn on its original layer, with its original color and linetype, no matter what the *current* drawing layer, entity color, and entity linetype are.

A Block created on layer 0 and inserted onto another layer will inherit the color and linetype of the layer on which it is inserted and will reside on this layer. This is why it was important to create the tools on layer 0. Other options exist, but they can cause confusion. Therefore Block creation on layer 0 is generally recommended if you want the Block to take on the characteristics of the layer on which it was inserted.

Your screen should now be empty.

7 Thaw the layer called TEXT.

The Block names and crosses (insertion points) should have reappeared.

8 To restore each of the tools, insert the Blocks into their exact locations according to their insertion points.

9 Assign color number 1 (red) to layer 0 and color number 2 (yellow) to layer TEXT.

10 Enter **END** to save your work and to exit to the Main Menu.

Your symbol library is now complete.

11 If you know how to plot drawings, plot LIB1. You could use a thick black pen for color 1 and a thin colored pen for color 2. The hard copy should be saved for future reference.

Using the Library

We're going to use the new LIB1 symbol library for creation of the workshop drawing on the following page.

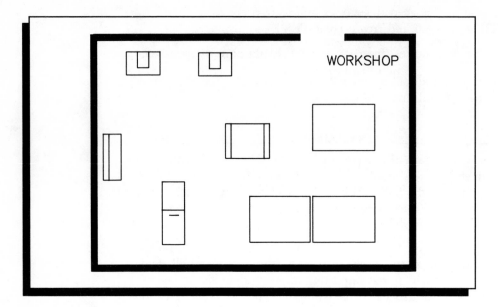

1 Begin a New Drawing and name it **WORKSHOP**.

2 Using **PLINE**, create the outline of the workshop as shown above. Make the starting and ending width **.1** unit, and make the workshop outline large enough to fill most of your screen.

Let's load and use the symbol library named LIB1.

3 Enter the **INSERT** command.

4 Enter the drawing file named **LIB1**. Do not complete the rest of the steps in the command.

IMPORTANT: When AutoCAD asks for the insertion point, cancel (press **CTRL C**). Continue, and you'll see why.

5 Enter the **INSERT** command again and do a listing of all Blocks.

All Blocks contained in LIB1 should be present.

So now you see why we inserted LIB1 and why we canceled the insertion before LIB1 was drawn on the screen. What we want from LIB1 are the Block definitions contained in LIB1, not the graphics themselves. Now that the Block definitions are present in our current drawing (WORKSHOP), we can insert each as we wish.

6 Insert each of the symbols in a similar arrangement to the drawing shown on the preceding page. Rotate each as necessary.

Because you had access to a previously created symbol library, you have just created a drawing in a fraction of the time it would otherwise have taken. Now that you know how to do it, the next time will be even faster.

HINT:

It is good practice to continuously add to the library file by storing new symbols, shapes, and details in it. Plot the library file and place it in a notebook or on the wall near your CAD system. Eventually, you will want to create new libraries for other specialized applications.

7 Enter **END** to save your work and exit the Drawing Editor.

NOTE:

If you are using AutoCAD's tablet menu, notice the empty portion at the top of the overlay. This area is available for items such as your library of symbols. Unit 43 will discuss the steps involved in adding new menu items to this area of the tablet menu.

Questions

1. What is the primary purpose of creating a library of symbols and details?

2. When creating a library, what layer is recommended for creating and storing the Blocks? Why?

3. In the symbol libraries discussed in this unit, Block names and insertion points are stored on another layer. Why is this information important, and why store it on a separate layer?

4. When inserting a symbol library, at what point do you cancel and why?

5. Identify one application for creating and using a library of symbols and details.

Problems

1. Based on steps described in this unit, create an entirely new symbol library specific to your area of application. For example, if you practice architectural drawing, create a library of doors and windows. First create and/or specify a prototype drawing (such as the prototype drawing outlined in Unit 20, if it's appropriate).

2. After you have completed the library symbols and details, Begin a New Drawing and insert the new library file as you did before. Then, create a drawing using the symbols and details.

AUTOCAD® AT WORK

Computer-Aided Drafting Plays in Peoria

For 30 years, the Central Illinois Light Company (CILCO) of Peoria, Illinois, struggled to keep its electric construction standards book up to date...and lost. This book, containing 250 pages of important drawings and specifications for use by design engineers and field construction people, had been drafted by hand in the 1950s and maintained by hand ever since. It had become obsolete, but according to Senior Electric Engineer Craig D. Frommelt, "It would take so many man-hours to redo that it simply never was redone."

Frommelt and others at CILCO felt that updating the standards book was a perfect job for a computer-aided drafting (CAD) system. They chose AutoCAD as their drafting program. Now CILCO is experiencing a productivity gain of about 2:1 in creating new drawings for the standards book and expects gains of 4:1 or 5:1 when it comes to maintaining the book in the future.

CILCO achieved these gains by using AutoCAD to create custom libraries of symbols for commonly used parts such as transformers. Using these libraries, an engineer can rapidly create a new drawing by selecting the proper symbols and indicating where on the new drawing they should be placed.

The power to customize features of the CAD program, such as the symbol libraries, also pays off in another project now beginning—the drafting and design of electric utility substations. Frommelt expects CAD to be a great timesaver on this project because CILCO must keep many drawings for each substation: site layouts, architectural drawings of buildings, electrical schematics, and mechanical drawings used to verify clearances when replacing machines.

CILCO chose to begin the project with electrical schematics because those drawings use the same symbols repeatedly. Starting with the symbols used in the standards book, CILCO's engineers created a custom CAD library of close to 1000 schematic symbols. They then created custom menus showing those symbols, in order to make the cut-and-paste process as simple as possible. "We are able to get anywhere from a 5:1 to 10:1 productivity advantage in making schematic diagrams," says Frommelt.

CILCO is considering other applications for its newfound CAD power. One is facilities mapping, which involves first digitizing the map of a service area (converting it into a computer-readable form) and then superimposing symbols for poles, transformers, and other equipment to make a complete geographic inventory. Using the CAD system, a person could assign attributes, such as model numbers and descriptions, to each symbol on a map. Then if it appeared that a particular model of transformer, for example, was likely to fail after ten years, an engineer could have the program identify all transformers of that model and age and highlight them in red. Those transformers could then be replaced quickly for better schedule maintenance.

Courtesy of CILCO

Unit 29 Remarkable Attributes

■ OBJECTIVE:

To create and display Attributes with the ATTDEF, ATTDISP, and ATTEDIT commands

The purpose of this unit is to experiment with AutoCAD's powerful Attribute feature.

Attributes are text information stored within Blocks. The information describes certain aspects of a Block, such as size, material, model number, cost, etc., depending upon the nature of the Block. The Attribute information can be made visible, but in most cases, you do not want the information to appear on the drawing. Therefore it usually remains invisible, particularly during plotting. Later, the Attribute information can be extracted to form a report such as a bill of materials.

The following electrical schematic contains Attribute information, even though you cannot see it. It's invisible. (The numbers you see in the components are not the Attributes.)

9.2

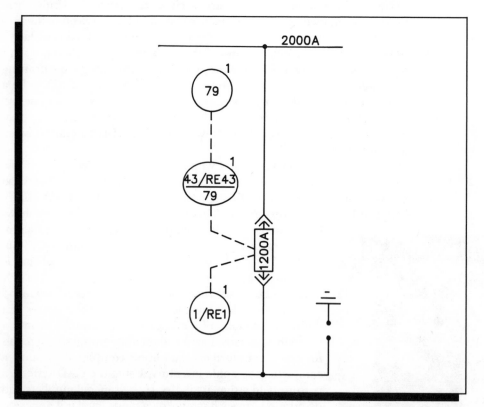

Courtesy of City of Fort Collins, Light & Power Utility

The following example shows a zoomed view of one of the schematic components. Notice that in this example the Attribute information is displayed near the top of the component.

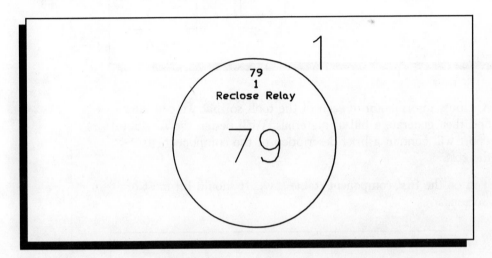

All of the Attributes contained in this schematic were compiled into a file and placed into a program for report generation. The following report (bill of materials) was generated directly from the electrical schematic drawing.

DESCRIPTION	DEVICE	QUANTITY/UNIT
Recloser Cut-out Switch	43/RE43/79	1
Reclose Relay	79	1
Lightning Arrestor	--	3
Breaker Control Switch	1/RE1	1
1200 Amp Circuit Breaker	52	1

Creating Attributes

Attributes can be extracted, and reports produced, from any type of drawing, not just electrical.

1. Load AutoCAD and bring up the library drawing called **LIB1**. It should look somewhat like the one on the next page.

NOTE:

If, for some reason, you do not have LIB1 on file, quickly create it using the steps outlined in the previous unit.

233

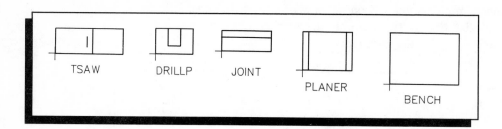

Let's assign Attribute information to each of the tools so that we can later insert them and then generate a bill of materials. We'll design the Attributes so that the report will contain a brief description of the component, its model, and the cost.

2 Zoom in on the first component (table saw). It should fill most of your screen.

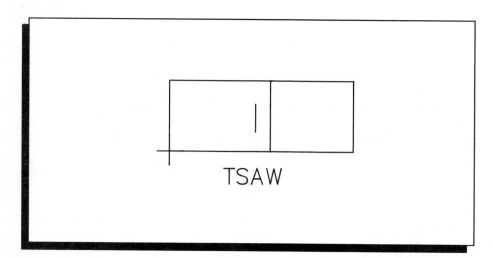

Now you're ready to assign Attributes to the table saw.

3 Enter the **ATTDEF** (Attribute Definition) command found in the BLOCKS submenu.

9.2.2

4 Set the Attribute modes as follows, and then press **RETURN**.

Invisible: Y
Constant: Y
Verify: Y
Preset: N

HINT: The modes can be changed from Yes to No or from No to Yes by simply typing the first letter of each mode. For example, if you want to change Invisible to Yes, type the letter I and press RETURN.

5 Type the word **DESCRIPTION** (in upper- or lowercase letters) for the Attribute tag and press **RETURN**.

6 Type **Table Saw** (exactly as you see it here) for the Attribute value and press **RETURN**.

7 Place the information inside the tool, near the top. Be sure to make it small. When placing the information, use the same technique used with the TEXT command.

The word DESCRIPTION should appear. If it extends outside the table saw representation, that's okay.

8 Press the **space bar** to repeat the ATTDEF command.

9 The Attribute modes should remain the same, so press **RETURN**.

10 This time, enter **MODEL** for the Attribute tag and **1A2B** for the Attribute value. Press **RETURN** at the "Start point or..." prompt.

The word MODEL should now appear on the screen.

11 Repeat Steps 8, 9, and 10, but enter **COST** for the tag and **$625.00** for the value.

You are now finished entering the table saw Attributes. That's all there is to it.

Storing Attributes

Now let's store the Attributes in the Block.

1 Using the **BLOCK** command, create a new Block of the table saw under a new name such as TSAW2. To select the Block, place a window around the entire table saw and Attribute information but omit the cross and text information.

Your Attribute information should now be stored within the Block.

2 Insert the Block in the same location where the table saw was before. The Attribute tags should not appear.

3 Edit the text so that it corresponds to the new Block name (TSAW2). Be sure to place it on layer TEXT, and consider using the CHANGE command.

Displaying Attributes

Let's display the Attribute values using the ATTDISP (Attribute Display) command.

1 Enter **ATTDISP** and specify **On**.

You should see the Attribute values, similar to the drawing below.

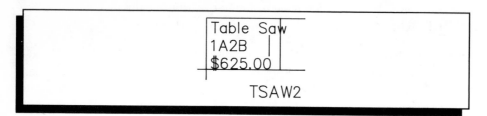

2 Enter **ATTDISP** again and specify **Normal**.

The Attribute values should again be invisible.

Practicing What You've Learned

Now, let's assign Attributes to the rest of the power tools and components.

1 Using the **ATTDEF** command, assign Attributes to each of the other four components using the following information. Then create the new Blocks and insert them in the same locations as their predecessors.

Description	Model	Cost
Jointer	902-42A	$750.00
Drill Press	7C-234	$590.00
Surface Planer	789453	$2070.00
Work Bench	31-1982	$825.00

2 When you're finished assigning Attributes, recreating the Blocks, and inserting them, display the Attribute values to make sure they are complete.

3 Last, enter **END** to save your work and exit the Drawing Editor.

Your symbol library, LIB1, now contains Attributes. When LIB1 is inserted into a new drawing and tools are inserted, the Attributes will be contained in the Blocks.

The following unit will involve the extraction of the Attributes and the generation of a bill of materials.

Variable Attributes

Thus far, you have experienced the use of fixed Attribute values. With variable Attributes, you have the freedom of changing the Attribute values as you insert the Block. Let's step through the process.

1. Begin a New Drawing and name it **WINDOW=PROTO1**. (By entering the name in this manner, you will be using your PROTO1.DWG prototype drawing.)

2. Zoom in on the lower left corner of your display, set layer **0** and set your snap resolution to **2"**.

3. Draw the following architectural window symbol to the dimensions shown, but do not place dimensions on the drawing. (The symbol represents a double-hung window for use in architectural floor plans.)

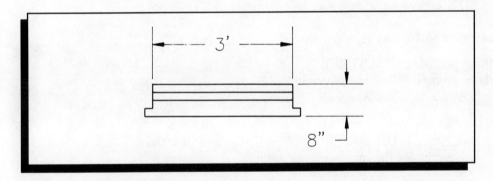

4. Enter the **ATTDEF** command, set the following modes, and press RETURN when you're finished.

   Invisible: Y
   Constant: N
   Verify: N
   Preset: N

Notice that, unlike before, the Constant and Verify modes are set at "No." Attribute values that are not Constant, called variable Attributes, can be edited. In the following section titled "Attribute Editing," we will practice editing variable Attributes. But for now, let's continue.

5. Enter **TYPE** for the Attribute tag.

You should now have "Attribute prompt:" on your screen. As you may recall, you did not receive this statement before when the Constant mode was set at "Yes."

6 In reply to "Attribute prompt:", enter **What type of window?** and press **RETURN**.

You will see what this is for when we go to insert the Block.

7 Enter **Double Hung** for the default Attribute value.

8 Center the Attribute over the top of the window and leave space for two more Attributes. (Make the Attribute text small.)

Did the word TYPE appear on your screen?

9 Press the **space bar** to reenter ATTDEF and leave the Attribute modes as they are.

10 Enter **SIZE** for the Attribute tag, **What size?** for the Attribute prompt, and **3' x 4'** for the default Attribute value.

11 At the "Start point or ..." prompt, press **RETURN**.

Did the word SIZE appear on your screen below the word TYPE?

12 Repeat Steps 9, 10, and 11, using the following information.

Attribute tag: **MANUFACTURER**
Attribute prompt: **What manufacturer?**
Default Attribute value: **Andersen**

13 Store the window symbol and Attributes using the **BLOCK** command. Name it **DH** (short for Double Hung) and pick the lower left corner for the insertion base point.

Inserting Variable Attributes _____

1 Insert the Block **DH**.

What's different about this Block insertion?

2 Press **RETURN** to use the default manufacturer, Andersen.

3 Enter **3' x 5'** for the size.

4 Press **RETURN** in reply to "What type of window?"

The window should appear.

5 Enter **ATTDISP** and specify **On**.

Did the correct Attribute values appear?

NOTE:

You also have the option of using the Attribute mode "Preset." It allows creation of Attributes that are variable but are not requested during Block insertion. In other words, when you insert a Block containing a preset Attribute, the Attribute value is not requested but rather is set automatically to its default value.

Attribute Editing

One very simple way of editing Attributes is to first insert the Block using the "*" option. As you know, this brings in the object as pieces and not as a Block. The Attributes contained in the object are also pieces (entities) and any of them can be erased. Using ATTDEF, new Attributes can be added, and using the BLOCK command, the object can be redefined as a Block.

Use of ATTEDIT, short for Attribute Edit, is a more powerful, but more complicated, method for editing Attributes. It allows you either to edit Attributes one at a time, changing any or all of their properties, or to do a global edit on a selected set of Attributes, changing only their value strings.

You should currently have something similar to the following on your screen.

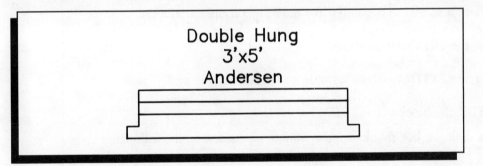

Make sure ATTDISP is On.

1 Enter the **ATTEDIT** command.

2 Default (press **RETURN**) at each of the following prompts, but stop at "Select Attributes:".

    Edit attributes one at a time?   Y
    Block name specification < * > :
    Attribute tag specification < * > :
    Attribute value specification < * > :

3 Pick the Attribute value **Andersen**. It will appear as though nothing happened. Then press **RETURN**.

The following list of options should appear on your screen. Also notice the "X" at the word Andersen.

```
Value/Position/Height/Angle/Style/Layer/Color/Next <N>:
```

4 Select the Value option and press **RETURN**.

5 Enter the **Replace** option.

6 In reply to "New attribute value:" enter **Pella** and press **RETURN** again.

Now Pella is contained in the DH Block definition in place of Andersen.

7 Practice editing other Attribute values contained in your window symbol.

Attribute Entry Dialogue Box _____

AutoCAD offers a special dialogue box for entering variable attributes.

1 Enter the **SETVAR** command.

2 Enter the **ATTDIA** system variable and enter a value of 1.

3 **INSERT** the Block named **DH**.

An Attribute dialogue box should appear similar to the one in the following illustration.

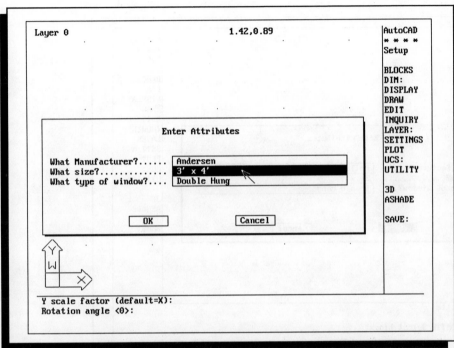

4 Move the arrow pointer to one of the Attribute values and type in a new value or leave the values as they are.

5 Pick the **OK** box when you are finished.

Attribute Editing Dialogue Box _____

9.2.6

The DDATTE command is provided for dialogue-oriented Attribute editing.

1 Enter the **DDATTE** command.

2 Pick one of the Blocks contained on your screen.

The following dialogue box should appear.

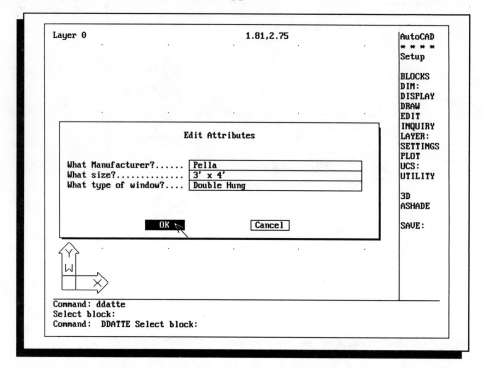

3 Move the arrow pointer to one of the Attribute values and type in a new value.

4 When you're finished, enter **END** to save your work and exit the Drawing Editor.

Questions

1. Explain the purpose of creating and storing Attributes.

_____

_____

2. Briefly define each of the following commands.

   ATTDEF _____

   ATTDISP _____

   ATTEDIT _____

3. What are Attribute tags?

_____

_____

4. What are Attribute values?

_____

_____

_____

5. Explain the Attribute modes Invisible, Constant, Verify, and Preset.

HINT: See 9.2.2 of the *Reference Manual*.

_____

_____

_____

_____

6. What advantage do variable Attribute values have over fixed Attribute values?

_____

_____

Problem

Call up the drawing containing the furniture representations you created for Unit 27. If this file is not on disk, create a similar drawing. Outline a simple plan for assigning Attributes to each of the components contained in the drawing. Create the Attributes and redefine each of the Blocks so that the Attributes are stored within the Blocks.

AUTOCAD® AT WORK

Getting the Picture: Movie Cameras Designed with CAD

Dennis Smith works in the movie industry, but he's neither behind the camera nor in front of it. Smith, a design engineer based in Hollywood, designs and manufactures the camera.

Smith works with Ultracam Inc., a company that produces 35-mm motion picture cameras and lenses. Ultracam, a subsidiary of Leonetti Cine Rentals, is one of only two companies in the United States that make "sound cameras"—cameras that generate little or no noise when in operation—for rentals to film production companies.

In 1982 Ultracam began using AutoCAD. "The drafting aspect of our work," notes Smith, "radically changed." Instead of drawing by hand on vellum, drafters now create their designs on a microcomputer. The company's two plotters then plot directly on vellum. "We redid our schematics using CAD," says Smith. The advantages include shorter drafting time and ease of revision.

In addition to its use as a standard drafting tool, AutoCAD is used at Ultracam to determine optimum designs. When he designs a lens, Smith explains, he stacks as many as 20 separate housing elements atop one another.

By laying out hypothetical geometric arrangements of the lens elements, he can see whether the various pieces of glass will match up rather than interfere with each other's operation—all without actually going to the work of creating a finished design. Since every camera Ultracam makes generally has a set of seven lenses, and each lens can have as many as 20 separate housing elements surrounding the lens glass, what-if scenarios play a major role in the camera's design.

The Ultracam camera has been used to date on about 50 movies, among them *Poltergeist*, *Jagged Edge*, and *Weird Science*, and on more than 30 television series. According to Smith, working in the film industry isn't particularly glamorous. Dropping in on a production, he says, is merely "a change of pace." For Smith, what matters is fine-tuning a camera design and creating accurate and precise blueprints from which to manufacture the camera. The rest is just show business.

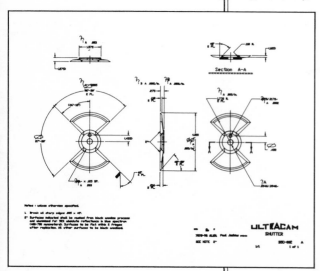

Courtesy of Ultracam Inc. and Autodesk, Inc.

Unit 30 Bill of Materials Generation

■ OBJECTIVE:

To practice report generation using ATTEXT, BASIC, and ATTEXT.BAS

After finishing the Attribute assignment process (Unit 29), you are ready to create a report such as a bill of materials. The first step in this process involves extracting the Attribute information and storing it in a file that can be read by another computer program.

■ *Attribute Extraction* _____

1. Load AutoCAD and Begin a New Drawing. Name it **EXTRACT**.

2. Insert your latest version of the LIB1 library containing Attributes.

HINT: Use the INSERT command. At the "Insertion point:" prompt, cancel by pressing CTRL C.

3. Reenter the **INSERT** command and do a listing of Blocks.

Block names of the tools should be present.

4. Insert each of the Blocks in a comparable arrangement to what you see in the drawing below.

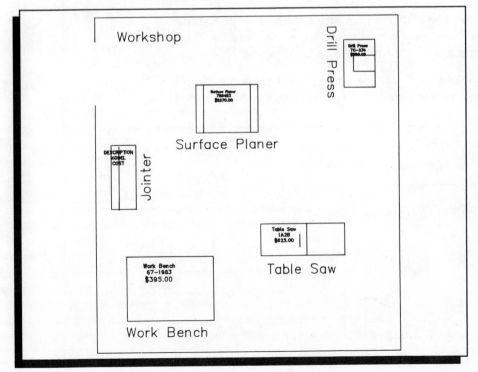

Each of the tools should contain Attributes as shown in the drawing. ATTDISP can be on so that you can see the Attributes. You may need to zoom in order to read them.

5 Enter the **ATTEXT** (short for Attribute Extraction) command.

6 Specify **DXF**.

NOTE:

This file type can be read by other computer programs.

7 Press **RETURN**. This will make the extract file name the same as your current drawing file name (but without the .DWG extension).

Your Attributes are now in a form that can be manipulated by other programs for report generation.

Attribute Reporting ──────────────────────

Now let's load the new extract file into the BASIC program called ATTEXT.BAS. This will require exiting AutoCAD.

1 Enter **END**.

2 When you are in the Main Menu, select task **0**, "Exit AutoCAD."

You should now have the DOS prompt (such as C>) on the screen.

The next few steps will involve disk preparation. This preparation is necessary before you can proceed with the bill of materials generation. You can find information about copying files in Appendix F.

1 Locate your DOS directory or diskette containing the BASIC Program Editor called BASIC.COM.

HINT:

BASIC.COM is usually contained with the other DOS files on your hard disk or on your DOS diskette.

2 Locate the AutoCAD file ATTEXT.BAS.

NOTE:

Your Release 10 package may not contain the ATTEXT.BAS file. However, this file was shipped on the Sample Drawings diskette with AutoCAD 9, 2.6x, 2.5x, and 2.1x. Therefore you can obtain ATTEXT.BAS from one of these earlier versions if you have access to one of them. Or, ATTEXT.BAS can be obtained by purchasing the optional *Applying AutoCAD* companion diskette from Glencoe Publishing Company.

3 Copy ATTEXT.BAS, BASIC.COM, and EXTRACT.DXX (your new extract file) to a single directory. Combining these three files is not mandatory, but having them together will simplify your work.

Now you're ready to create a bill of materials.

1 At the DOS prompt, type **BASIC** and press **RETURN**.

This will bring up the BASIC Program Editor.

2 Then type **LOAD"ATTEXT** and press **RETURN** to load the ATTEXT.BAS program.

The message "OK" will appear if the program loads properly.

3 Type **RUN** and press **RETURN** to run the ATTEXT program.

4 When the program asks you for the extract file name, type **EXTRACT** and press **RETURN**.

NOTE:

Be sure to indicate the directory and drive (such as A:) if the extract file EXTRACT.DXX is located in another location.

At this time, the BASIC program will generate the bill of materials. Your report should look very similar to the one below.

COST	DESCRIPTION	MODEL
$750.00	Jointer	902-42A
$590.00	Drill Press	7C-234
$2070.00	Surface Planer	789453
$825.00	Work Bench	31-1982
$625.00	Table Saw	1A2B

⑤ To print the report, use your computer's keyboard print-screen feature.

⑥ To return to DOS (*e.g.*, C >), type **SYSTEM** and press **RETURN**.

_____ NOTE: _____

You can list the contents of EXTRACT.DXX with the DOS TYPE command. Consider the following example:

C > TYPE EXTRACT.DXX

The following gives a sampling of what should appear. This is the raw data read by the ATTEXT.BAS FILE.

```
         Ø
     INSERT
         8
     OBJ
        66
             1
         2
     TSAW2
        1Ø
     1.Ø
        2Ø
     4.25
        3Ø
     Ø.Ø
         Ø
     ATTRIB
         8
     Ø
         1
     $625.ØØ
         2
     COST
        7Ø
```

Questions

1. Describe the purpose of AutoCAD's ATTEXT command.

   _____

   _____

2. What type of AutoCAD file can be read and manipulated by other computer programs?

   _____

3. Explain the process of bringing up the BASIC Program Editor when generating a report.

   _____

   _____

   _____

4. Explain the process of loading and running AutoCAD's BASIC program called ATTEXT.BAS.

   _____

   _____

   _____

5. What command is used to exit the BASIC Program Editor and return to DOS?

   _____

Problem

Load the drawing that contains furniture representations. Using the steps outlined in this unit, create a bill of materials.

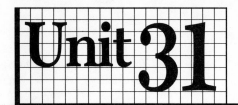

Unit 31 Dressing Your Drawings

■ OBJECTIVE:

To apply the HATCH and SKETCH commands

This unit covers the application of hatching using the numerous patterns made available by AutoCAD. Sketching is also practiced using the SKETCH command and subcommands.

Some drawings make use of hatching and sketching to accurately and correctly communicate, as illustrated in the drawing below.

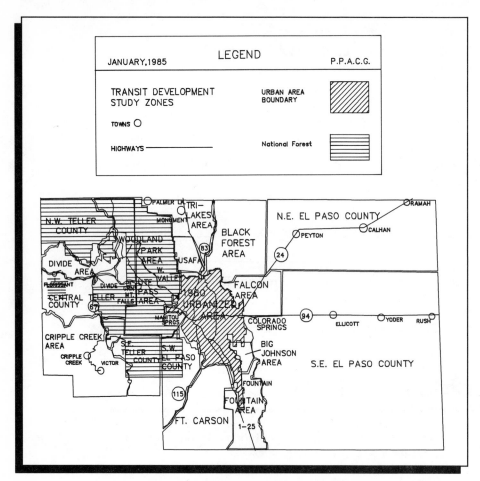

Courtesy of David Salamon, Pikes Peak Area Council of Governments

Both hatching and sketching can enhance the quality of drawings greatly, but both consume lots of memory. Therefore both hatching and sketching should be used only when necessary. Be aware of their memory requirements to avoid a system crash when storing your drawings on floppy diskettes.

AutoCAD®
Reference
Manual
10.2.3

■ HATCH Command _____

Let's see what AutoCAD's HATCH command can do.

1 Load AutoCAD and Begin a New Drawing. Name it **HATCH**.

2 Draw the following, but don't worry about exact sizes and locations. Include the text and outside rectangle as well.

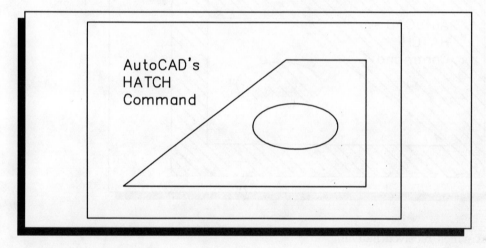

AutoCAD's
HATCH
Command

3 Enter the **HATCH** command.

You should now have the following at the bottom of your screen.

```
Command: HATCH
Pattern (? or name/U,style):
```

4 Do a listing of all hatch patterns by entering ?.

As you can see, AutoCAD provides many hatch patterns—over forty, in fact. Let's use one of them on our drawing.

5 Enter the **HATCH** command again, and this time type the hatch pattern **ANSI31** (the standard cross-hatching pattern).

6 Specify a scale of 1.

NOTE: _____

Like DIMSCALE, the "Scale for pattern" should be set at the reciprocal of the plot scale so that the hatch pattern size corresponds with your drawing scale.

7 Specify an angle of **0**.

8 To define the hatch boundary, place a window around your entire drawing, including the rectangle, and press **RETURN**.

Does your drawing look like the one below? If not, try again.

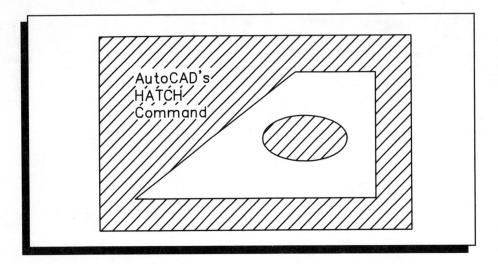

Note the areas which received hatching.

9 Erase the hatching by picking any one of the hatch lines.

HINT: The entire hatch pattern is treated as one object when editing. If you want the freedom to edit small pieces from the hatch pattern, precede the hatch pattern name with an asterisk (*). This is similar to inserting Blocks with an asterisk (see Unit 27).

10 Hatch the outermost areas only by using the O option. (When you enter the name of a pattern, follow it with a comma and O, as in CLAY,O.)

Did it work?

11 Undo your last operation and then use the I option (as in CLAY,I) to Ignore the internal structures.

The hatch pattern should cover the internal areas.

12 Construct other enclosed objects and experiment with several of the remaining patterns.

Hatch Pattern Dialogue Box _____

AutoCAD provides a visual means of selecting hatch patterns with the hatch pattern dialogue box.

1 Construct one or more enclosed objects.

2 Select the **Draw** pull-down menu.

3 Select the "**Hatch** ..." menu item.

The hatch pattern dialogue box should display as shown below.

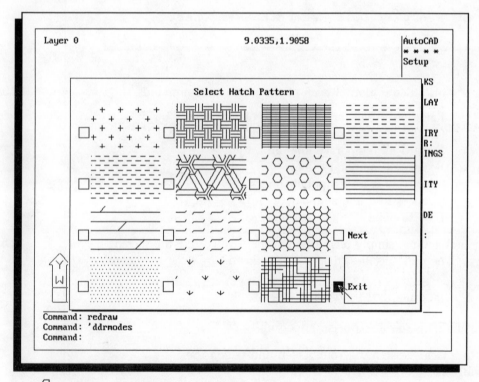

4 Pick the "**Next**" item contained in the dialogue box.

5 Pick the "**Next**" item again to view the remaining hatch patterns.

6 Pick one of the hatch patterns from the dialogue box and hatch one of the enclosed objects on your screen.

SKETCH Command _____

Now let's try some freehand sketching.

1 First, clear a small area of your screen so that you'll have room for the sketch.

2 Enter the **SKETCH** command.

3 Specify .1 unit for the Record increment.

You should now have the following at the bottom of your screen.

```
Sketch.   Pen eXit Quit Record Erase Connect .
```

The following is a brief description of each of the above subcommands.

Pen	Raise/lower pen (or toggle with pick button)
eXit	Record all temporary lines and exit
Quit	Discard all temporary lines and exit
Record	Record all temporary lines
Erase	Selectively erase temporary lines
Connect	Connect to a line endpoint
. (period)	Line to point

4 To begin sketching, simply pick a point where you'd like the sketch to begin. The pick specifies (toggles) "pen down."

5 Move your pointing device to sketch a short line.

6 Pick again. This specifies (toggles) "pen up."

7 Move to a clear location on your screen and sketch the following lake.

_____ NOTE: _____

If you make a mistake or need to back up, toggle "pen up" and enter ERASE from the SKETCH submenu (or type E). Then reverse the order of your crosshairs until you have erased that which needed to be removed; press the pick button.

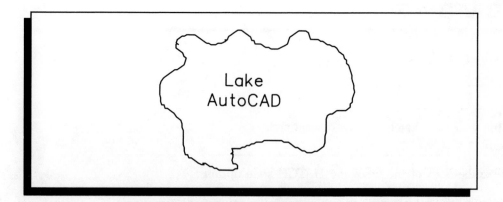

It's okay if your sketch doesn't look exactly like the one above.

⑧ When you're finished sketching the lake, enter either **Record** or **eXit** to record and finalize your temporary lines.

NOTE:

If you select Record, you now have the option to sketch additional lines or to Quit.

⑨ Practice sketching by using the remaining SKETCH subcommands. Draw anything you'd like.

CAUTION:

If you are storing your drawing on a floppy diskette and your drawing appears to be getting somewhat large, you may want to erase some of your screen to avoid a system crash.

⑩ When you're finished, enter **END** to save and exit.

Questions

1. Explain why hatch patterns are useful.

   _____

   _____

2. How is the scale of a hatch pattern determined?

   _____

3. Briefly describe both of the following HATCH style options.

   O _____

   I _____

4. Briefly describe the purpose of each of the following SKETCH subcommands.

   Pen _____

   eXit _____

   Quit _____

   Record _____

   Erase _____

   Connect _____

   . (period) _____

5. SKETCH requires a Record increment. What does it determine?

   _____

HINT:
Specify a coarse increment such as .5 or 1 and notice the appearance of the sketch lines.

Problems

Construct each of the following drawings. Use the HATCH and SKETCH commands where appropriate, and don't worry about specific sizes. The hatch patterns to be used are indicated below each of the drawings.

In PRB31-2 and PRB31-3, use the SKETCH and LINE commands to define temporary boundaries for the hatch patterns. Place the boundaries on a separate layer and freeze that layer after you are finished hatching.

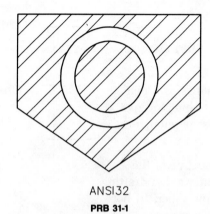

ANSI32

PRB 31-1

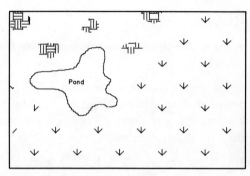

EARTH AND GRASS

PRB 31-2

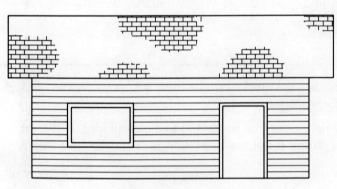

BRICK AND LINE

PRB 31-3

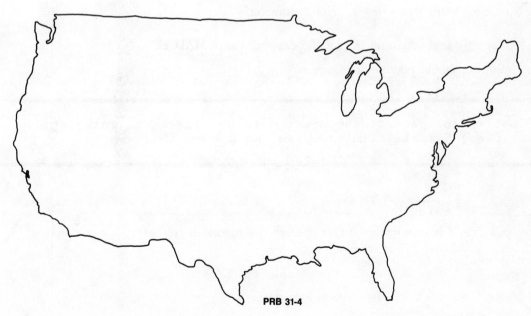

PRB 31-4

AutoCAD Drawing Courtesy of Autodesk, Inc.

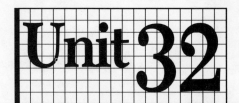

Unit 32 From Display to Paper

■ OBJECTIVE:

To practice the plotting procedure and use the PLOT and PRPLOT commands

This unit covers the steps necessary to properly send drawings to a pen plotter or matrix printer. Emphasis is given to setting and changing plot parameters for pen plotting since pen plotters are the most popular for creating hardcopy output.

Until plotting occurs, all AutoCAD work is done electronically via the computer display. Plotting makes it easier to relate computer-aided drafting to traditional drafting because both involve placing lines on paper. In both cases, the goal is to end up with a drawing of proper scale, correct linetypes/thicknesses, and good quality. With AutoCAD, you have this capability.

Ch. 13

■ *A Fast Plot*

First, let's plot a drawing the quickest and easiest way possible, even though it may not be exactly what you want.

Your computer may or may not be connected to a pen plotter. If it's not, connect it now. If a plotter is not available, step through the following anyway.

1 Load AutoCAD and bring up the Main Menu.

2 Select Main Menu task 3, "Plot a drawing."

3 Specify that you want to plot the drawing called **HATCH**.

The following should now be on your screen:

```
Specify the part of the drawing to be plotted by entering:
Display, Extents, Limits, View, or Window <D>:
```

4 Specify **Display**.

Now you should have a screen similar (though not identical) to the following. Read over this information carefully.

```
Plot will NOT be written to a selected file
Sizes are in Inches
Plot origin is at (0.00,0.00)
Plotting area is 10.50 wide by 8.00 high (A size)
Plot is NOT rotated 90 degrees
Pen width is 0.010
Area fill will NOT be adjusted for pen width
Hidden lines will NOT be removed
Plot will be scaled to fit available area

Do you want to change anything? <N>
```

5 Respond to the question by specifying "No." (Since N is the default response, just press **RETURN**.)

NOTE:

If your computer is connected to a plotter, be sure it is turned on and everything is set properly, including the paper size, plotter pens, and paper.

6 Last, press **RETURN** to activate the plotter.

Now, just sit back and enjoy.

NOTE:

You may have to press RETURN again for certain hardware configurations. Also note that your drawing is not scaled, but remember, we plotted without making changes in the plot settings.

7 To stop the plotting at any time, press **CTRL C**. Then press **RETURN** to go back to the Main Menu. Do this now if your computer is not connected to a plotter.

Tailoring Your Plot

The following plot procedure becomes much more involved. It utilizes the capabilities AutoCAD has provided for customizing the plot according to your specific drawing requirements.

Let's plot a drawing that contains at least two layers, such as one of your dimensioning drawings from a previous unit.

1 Load the drawing (*e.g.*, DIMEN) and do a layer listing.

259

② If you do not yet have the two layers OBJ and DIM, create them now.

Be sure that your object is contained on layer OBJ and your dimensions on layer DIM.

HINT:
The CHANGE and CHPROP commands can help you to move objects to another layer.

③ Assign color 1 to OBJ and color 2 to DIM. Do this regardless of your monitor type (color or monochrome).

HINT:
The layer colors correspond directly to the plotter pen numbers.

This time, let's plot directly from the Drawing Editor.

① Enter the **PLOT** command, and specify that you want to plot the Limits of the drawing.

Do you remember the drawing limits of DIMEN? Unless you have changed them, they should be the default limits 0,0 and 12 units,9 units. This information is important when plotting the limits because the limits represent your scaled units.

Proceed as you did before by reading over the information now on your screen.

② This time, reply with a Yes because we do want to make at least one change.

As a result, you should have something very similar to the following on your screen. (See next page.) Read over this information.

```
Entity      Pen   Line  Pen      Entity      Pen   Line  Pen
Color       No.   Type  Speed    Color       No.   Type  Speed
1 (red)     1     Ø     32       9           1     Ø     32
2 (yellow)  1     Ø     32       10          1     Ø     32
3 (green)   1     Ø     32       11          1     Ø     32
4 (cyan)    1     Ø     32       12          1     Ø     32
5 (blue)    1     Ø     32       13          1     Ø     32
6 (magenta) 1     Ø     32       14          1     Ø     32
7 (white)   1     Ø     32       15          1     Ø     32
8           1     Ø     32
Line types: Ø = continuous line        Pen speed codes:
            1 = .................
            2 = .  .  .  .  .  .  .       Inches/Second:
            3 = -------------------          1, 2, 4, 8, 16, 24, 32
            4 = - - - - - - - - - -
            5 = -- -- -- -- -- -- -       Cm/Second:
            6 = --- --- --- --- ---          3, 5, 1Ø, 2Ø, 4Ø, 6Ø, 8Ø
            7 = -- - -- - -- - -- -
            8 = __--__--__--__--__-

Enter line types, pen numbers, pen speed codes
blank=go to next, Cn=go to Color n, S=Show current choices, X=Exit
Do you want to change any of the above parameters? <N>
```

3 Reply with a Yes—you do want to make changes to the above.

NOTE:

Ignore the Linetype category since it is recommended to specify all linetypes while in the Drawing Editor.

Now let's make changes so that your settings look identical to the following. (Directions on next page.)

```
Entity      Pen   Line  Pen      Entity      Pen   Line  Pen
Color       No.   Type  Speed    Color       No.   Type  Speed
1 (red)     1     Ø     4        9           1     Ø     16
2 (yellow)  2     Ø     4        10          1     Ø     16
3 (green)   2     Ø     4        11          1     Ø     16
4 (cyan)    1     Ø     4        12          1     Ø     16
5 (blue)    1     Ø     4        13          1     Ø     16
6 (magenta) 6     Ø     2Ø       14          1     Ø     16
7 (white)   7     Ø     2Ø       15          1     Ø     16
8           8     Ø     2Ø
```

4 Assign pen 1 to color 1; hence, press **RETURN**.

5 Leave the linetype at 0; hence, press **RETURN**.

6 Type **4** (4 inches per second) for the pen speed and press **RETURN**.

HINT:

If you make a mistake and need to return to color 1, simply type C1 and press RETURN.

7 Assign pen 2 to color 2 by entering **2** and press **RETURN**.

8 Leave the linetype at 0 and press **RETURN**.

9 Enter **4** for the pen speed and press **RETURN**.

Since our drawing uses only colors 1 and 2, we're finished. However, if you'd like to practice, make the remaining changes as indicated in the settings on the previous page.

10 Check your new settings by typing **S** (for Show) and press **RETURN**.

Are the changes correct? If not, correct them now.

11 Enter **X** to exit and move on.

12 Enter No—you do not want to write the plot to a file.

NOTE:

A "Yes" reply would send the plot output to a file rather than to a plotter. Once a plot file is created, you can use a utility program (not supplied with AutoCAD) to send it to the plotter.

13 In reply to "Size units," enter Inches.

14 Leave the plot origin at 0.00, 0.00.

15 Specify a **B** size (approximately 15″ × 10″) for the plotting size. If your plotter does not accommodate this size, enter either A or C size.

16 Do *not* rotate your drawing 90 degrees.

17 If you are using standard pens of average width (.3 mm to .7 mm), then specify a width of 0.010.

18 Enter No in reply to "Adjust area fill boundaries for pen width?".

This question refers to using unusually thick or thin pens with solid-filled objects.

19 Enter No in response to "Remove hidden lines?" since our drawing is not a 3-D model and it contains no hidden lines.

20 For the plot scale, enter 1=1.

21 Ready your plotter and press **RETURN** to begin the plotting.

22 Last, return to the Drawing Editor and enter **END** to save your changes and return to the Main Menu.

A Printer Plot

13.7

After completing the above, let's do a printer plot; that is, if you have a matrix printer supported by AutoCAD and connected to your computer. If not, you can step through the process just the same.

1 Select Main Menu task 4, "Printer Plot a drawing."

NOTE:

"Printer Plot" can also be entered at the Drawing Editor with the PRPLOT command.

2 Choose any drawing you'd like.

The next steps are very much like the steps involved with pen plotting...

3 ...therefore step through the process on your own.

NOTE:

Most matrix printers offer only one color, black. Therefore entity/color assignments are omitted.

Questions

1. Briefly describe each of the components in the following plot prompt:

   What to plot—Display, Extents, Limits, View, or Window <D>:

   Display _____

   Extents _____

   Limits _____

   View _____

   Window _____

2. Explain the relationship between the entity color and the pen number.

   _____

   _____

3. In preparation for plotting, explain why it is important to draw certain components of your drawing on certain layers with certain colors.

   _____

   _____

4. If a drawing plot scale is set at 1=4″, what exactly does this mean? In other words, what does the 1 represent, and what does the 4″ represent?

   _____

   _____

5. What AutoCAD command allows you to print drawings on a printer?

   _____

Problems

In problems 1 and 2, prepare to plot a drawing using the given plot settings. Make up any name; it doesn't matter since you will not actually be plotting the drawing.

1. Specify the part of the drawing to be plotted by entering:
   Display, Extents, Limits, View, or Window <L>: L

   Plot will NOT be written to a selected file
   Sizes are in Inches
   Plot origin is at (0.00,0.00)
   Plotting area is 10.50 wide by 8.00 high (A size)
   2D Plots are rotated 90 degrees clockwise
   Pen width is 0.015
   Area fill will be adjusted for pen width
   Hidden lines will be removed
   Scale is 1=48

Entity Color	Pen No.	Line Type	Pen Speed	Entity Color	Pen No.	Line Type	Pen Speed
1 (red)	1	0	10	9	1	0	16
2 (yellow)	1	0	10	10	1	0	16
3 (green)	1	0	10	11	1	0	16
4 (cyan)	1	0	10	12	1	0	16
5 (blue)	1	0	10	13	1	0	16
6 (magenta)	1	0	10	14	1	0	16
7 (white)	1	0	10	15	1	0	16
8	1	0	10				

2. Specify the part of the drawing to be plotted by entering:
   Display, Extents, Limits, View, or Window <L>: L

   Plot will be written to a selected file
   Sizes are in Millimeters
   Plot origin is at (0.00,0.00)
   Plotting area is 1188.72 wide by 883.92 high (MAX size)
   Plot is NOT rotated 90 degrees
   Pen width is 0.38
   Area fill will be adjusted for pen width
   Hidden lines will NOT be removed
   Scale is 1=10

Entity Color	Pen No.	Line Type	Pen Speed	Entity Color	Pen No.	Line Type	Pen Speed
1 (red)	1	0	16	9	1	0	16
2 (yellow)	2	0	16	10	1	0	16
3 (green)	3	0	16	11	1	0	16
4 (cyan)	1	0	20	12	1	0	16
5 (blue)	1	0	20	13	1	0	16
6 (magenta)	1	0	20	14	1	0	16
7 (white)	1	0	20	15	1	0	16
8	1	0	20				

3. Choose at least two of your previously created drawings for which you provided a scale, paper size, units, limits, ltscale, dimscale, new layers, color, and linetype assignments. Plot each. Set each of the plot options so that the drawings properly plot to the scale you intended.

AUTOCAD® AT WORK

Landscaping with AutoCAD

For 150 years, a typical landscape designer's work tools—a drafting table, pen and pencil, paper, and templates—remained virtually the same. But the introduction of CAD changed the profession. Nowadays landscape architects who don't use CAD are at a serious disadvantage. Layouts that traditionally took two days to prepare by hand can now be completed by CAD in a few hours.

Landscape architecture focuses on everything above the ground and outside a building, including vegetation, fountains, sculptures, and roads. In working with their clients, landscape architects must draw up detailed plans that can be adapted quickly and easily, and the special features of CAD programs such as AutoCAD complement the professional nicely.

By using the layering feature, the architect can plot buildings, roads, boundaries, irrigation systems, and recreation areas on separate layers. Or the architect can combine any of the layers to use for presentations to clients or for construction plans for engineers and work crews.

AutoCAD's symbol library capability is especially useful. It can be utilized to store symbols, such as a tree, and data about materials and costs. Use of symbols increases drawing speed, and the data can be used to generate reports.

By using a telecommunications link, a landscape architect in one city and a client in another can view a proposed drawing and make immediate modifications. Also, the architect can exchange information with other professionals working on the project, and field personnel—such as surveyors—can make on-site suggestions.

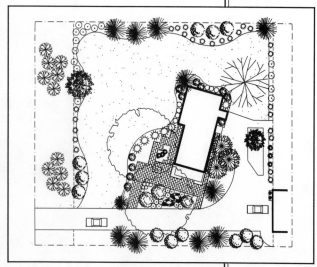

Courtesy of Mill Brothers Landscape and Nursery, Inc.

Unit 33 — Isometrics: Creating Objects from a New Angle

AutoCAD® Reference Manual

■ OBJECTIVE:

To apply AutoCAD's isometric drawing capabilities using the SNAP and ISOPLANE commands

The purpose of this unit is to practice the construction of simple isometric drawings.

Isometric drawing is one of two ways to obtain a pictorial representation of an object using AutoCAD. Below is an example of an isometric drawing created with AutoCAD.

Ch. 8

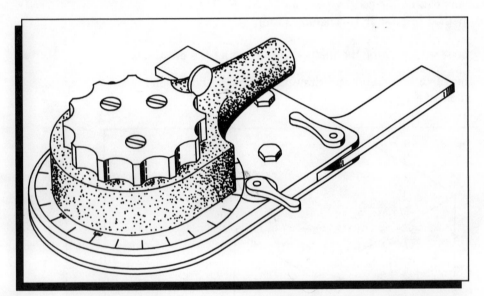

AutoCAD Drawing Courtesy of CAD Northwest, Inc.

■ *Isometric Drawing*

Let's do some simple isometric drawing.

1 Load AutoCAD and Begin a New Drawing. Name it **ISO.**

2 Set the grid at 1 unit and the snap resolution at **.5** unit.

AutoCAD isometric drawing is accomplished by changing the snap style to isometric using the SNAP command...

3 ...therefore enter the **SNAP** command, select the Style option, and press **RETURN.**

8.1

4 Select the Isometric option by entering **I**, and set the vertical spacing at **.5** unit (the default).

You should now be in the isometric drawing mode, with the crosshairs set for one of the three (Left, Top, or Right) isometric planes.

5 Move your crosshairs and notice how they run parallel to the isometric grid.

6 Enter the **ISOPLANE** command.

The crosshairs can now be changed from one plane to another by entering L, R, or T.

Another method of changing the crosshairs is to simply press RETURN while the ISOPLANE command is entered.

Last, the crosshairs can be toggled by pressing CTRL E. This is the recommended method because it is generally faster.

7 Experiment with each of the methods of changing the crosshairs.

8 Enter the **LINE** command and draw the following box. Don't worry about specific sizes.

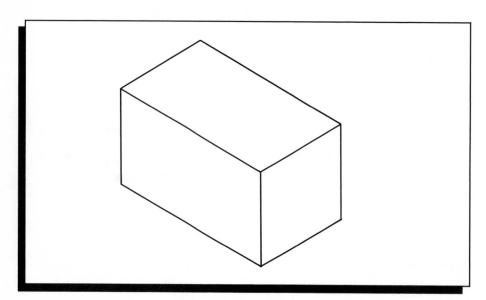

9 Now alter the box so that it looks similar to the one on the next page, using the **LINE**, **BREAK**, and **ERASE** commands.

NOTE:

You are able to use all AutoCAD commands while constructing isometric drawings.

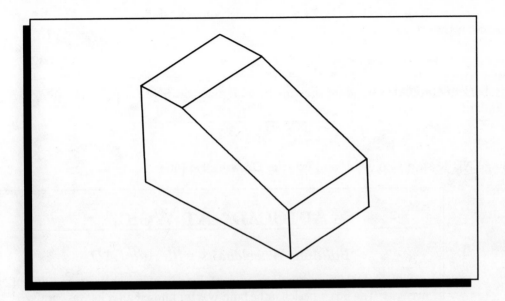

10 Further alter the object so that it looks similar to the following. Use the **ELLIPSE** command to draw the isometric circle.

HINT: Since the ellipse is to be drawn on the top isometric plane, toggle (change) your crosshairs to reflect this plane. Then choose the ELLIPSE command's Isocircle option.

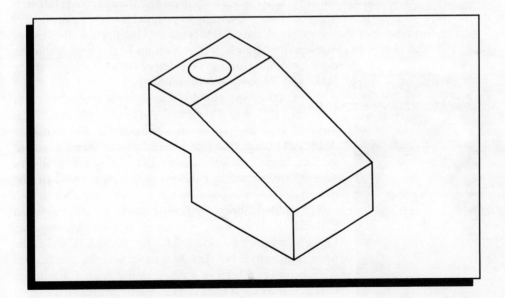

11 Further experiment with AutoCAD's isometric drawing capability by constructing other isometric objects.

——————— NOTE: ———————

To change back to AutoCAD's standard drawing format, enter the SNAP, Style, Standard sequence.

12 Enter **END** to save your work and exit the Drawing Editor.

AUTOCAD® AT WORK

Building Wheelchairs with AutoCAD

Ralf Hotchkiss' occupation as a builder of wheelchairs came out of necessity. The first wheelchair he built was for himself after he was paralyzed from the waist down in a motorcycle accident nearly twenty years ago.

Recently Hotchkiss started using AutoCAD to help him design wheelchairs for Third World countries. Unpaved roads in underdeveloped countries place special demands on wheelchair riders, who must maneuver through mud and rocks and around chuckholes. Using AutoCAD, Hotchkiss hopes to design a chair that is durable, compact, lightweight, and inexpensive. And AutoCAD's design features are helping him find ways to solve his biggest design challenge for the Third World: electric-powered wheelchairs for those people who are unable to operate them manually.

Hotchkiss contends that CAD technology gives him the advantage he needs to accomplish his goals. "I do my design work much faster. I can modify and combine drawings, check the clearances of moving parts on the screen, and plot publication-quality drawings in a fraction of the time it took to do it by hand. Tracing is a thing of the past—my drafting table and T-square are in mothballs."

AutoCAD allows Hotchkiss to sketch a design, see it in 3-D from different views, and make changes until he is satisfied that he can begin a working model. Another AutoCAD feature that Hotchkiss frequently uses is a custom symbol library, which allows him to create a file of wheelchair parts that can be easily incorporated in any drawing.

The symbol library feature is especially helpful when Hotchkiss looks for ways to overcome the everyday obstacles faced by wheelchair riders. Says Hotchkiss, "Wheelchairs must be able to move close to a table, withstand collisions with curbs, and turn in a small radius with a minimum of effort. If a design fails, then I have to go back to the computer to make adjustments—and that's where drafting with AutoCAD really shines."

Questions

1. Explain how to change from AutoCAD's standard drawing format to isometric drawing.

   _____

   _____

2. Describe the purpose of the ISOPLANE command.

   _____

3. Describe two methods of changing the isometric crosshairs from one plane to another.

   _____

   _____

   _____

4. Explain how accurate isometric circles can be created.

   _____

   _____

5. How do you change from isometric drawing to AutoCAD's standard drawing format?

   _____

Problems

Create each object in PRB33-1 through PRB33-4 using AutoCAD's isometric capability. Don't worry about their exact sizes.

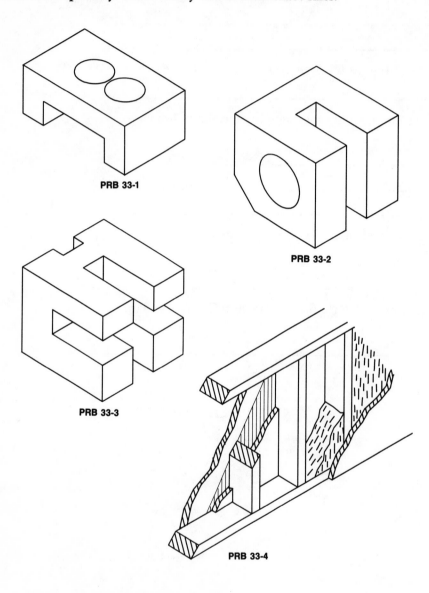

PRB 33-1

PRB 33-2

PRB 33-3

PRB 33-4

AutoCAD Drawing Courtesy of Autodesk, Inc.

(continued on next page)

In PRB33-5 accurately draw an isometric representation of the orthographic views. Draw the isometric according to the dimensions provided.

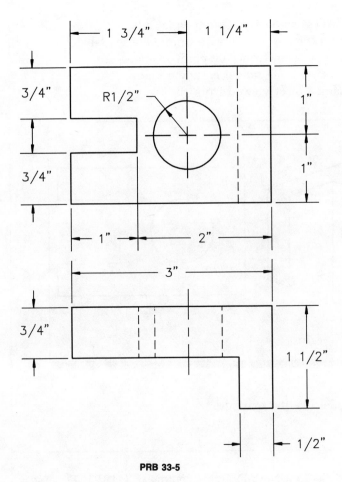

PRB 33-5

273

Unit 34 The Third Dimension

■ OBJECTIVE:

To apply AutoCAD's 3D modeling capability using the ELEV, VPOINT, and HIDE commands

This unit introduces AutoCAD's three-dimensional capability with three easy-to-use commands. They permit you to create simple 3D models (boxes, cylinders, etc.) and view them from any point in space. An example of an AutoCAD-generated 3D model is shown below, left. The model on the right is the same object viewed from the top.

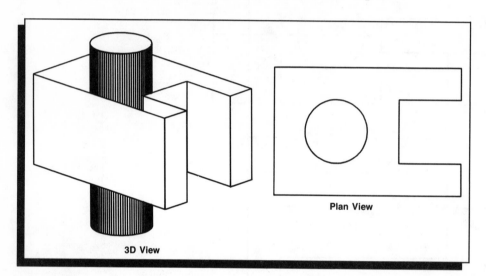

3D View

Plan View

Let's draw a simple 3D model like the one here.

■ *ELEV Command*

1 Load AutoCAD and Begin a New Drawing. Name it **THREE-D**.

2 Enter the **ELEV** command and set the elevation at 1 and the thickness at 3.

7.11

___ NOTE: ___

With these settings, all objects drawn will have a thickness on the Z-axis of 3 units. This is called the extrusion thickness.

3 Draw the top (plan) view of the object using the **LINE** command. Construct the object as shown above, right, but omit the circle (cylinder) at this time. Don't worry about exact sizes.

**AutoCAD®
Reference
Manual**

VPOINT and HIDE Commands _____

Now let's view the object in 3D.

1 Select **DISPLAY** from the root page of the screen menu.

2 Select the **VPOINT** command, and then select the **axes** option from the submenu.

6.6.1

3 Move your pointing device and watch what happens.

4 Place the small crosshairs inside the globe representation as shown below and pick that approximate point.

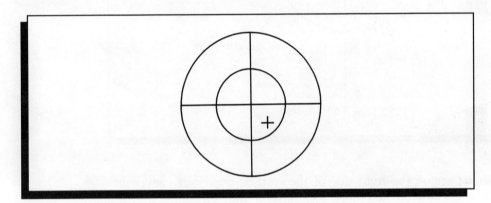

Did a 3D model of the object appear on your screen?

Study the globe representation on the next page carefully. The placement of your crosshairs on the globe indicates the exact position of your viewpoint. Placement of the crosshairs inside the inner ring (called the equator) will result in viewing the object from above. Placing the crosshairs outside the inner ring will result in a look underneath the object.

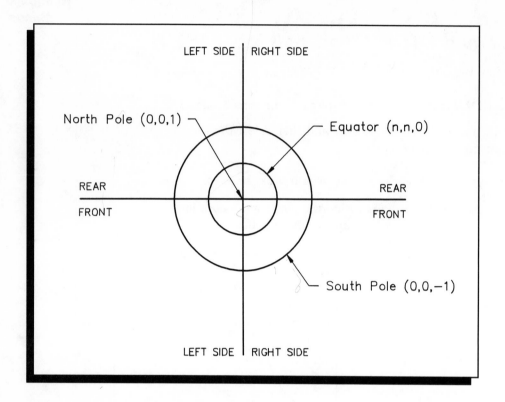

If your crosshairs are on the right side of the vertical line, your viewpoint will be on the right side of the object. Similarly, if your crosshairs are in front of the horizontal line, then your viewpoint will be in front of the object.

Your object should look somewhat like the one below.

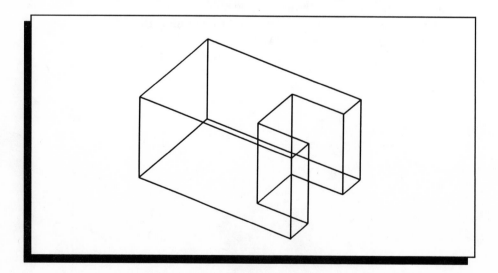

**AutoCAD®
Reference
Manual
6.6.4**

5 After viewing the object in 3D, enter the **HIDE** command to remove the hidden lines.

Your object should now look similar to the following.

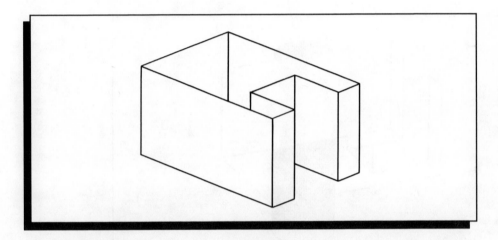

6 Return to your plan view (0,0,1) of the object by entering **VPOINT** and then selecting **plan** from the screen menu. Or, you may enter 0,0,1 instead of selecting plan.

7 **ZOOM All** to obtain the original plan view of the model.

Adding Objects of Different Elevation and Thickness

Now, let's add the cylinder to the model at a new elevation and thickness.

1 Enter the **ELEV** command and set the elevation at −1 and the thickness at 6.

2 Draw a circle in the center of your model as shown on page 274.

Visualize how the cylinder will appear in relation to the existing object.

3 Enter **VPOINT** and **axes**, and place the crosshairs in approximately the same location as before.

Does your model appear as you had visualized it?

4 Remove the hidden lines by entering the **HIDE** command. The computer may take a few seconds to remove the hidden lines.

Does your model now look similar to the one shown at the beginning of this unit? It should.

5 Now, experiment with VPOINT to obtain a look from different points in space.

6 Attempt creating a 3D view of the model as shown in the following.

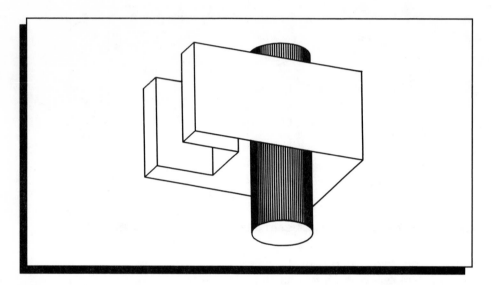

7 Enter **END** to save your last 3D view and exit the Drawing Editor.

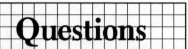

Questions

1. Describe the purpose of the VPOINT command.

   _____

   _____

2. What is the viewpoint (*i.e.*, the X, Y, and Z coordinates) when viewing the plan view of a 3D model?

   _____

3. The extrusion thickness of your object is specified with what command?

   _____

4. Briefly explain the process by which you create objects (within the same model) at different elevations and thicknesses.

   _____

   _____

   _____

   _____

5. When the small crosshairs are in the exact center of the globe, what is the location of the viewpoint in relation to the object?

   _____

6. With what command are hidden lines removed from 3D objects?

   _____

7. Indicate on the globe below where the small crosshairs would be placed in order to view an object from the rear and underneath.

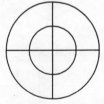

8. Match the following globe representations with the objects. The first one has been completed to give you a starting point.

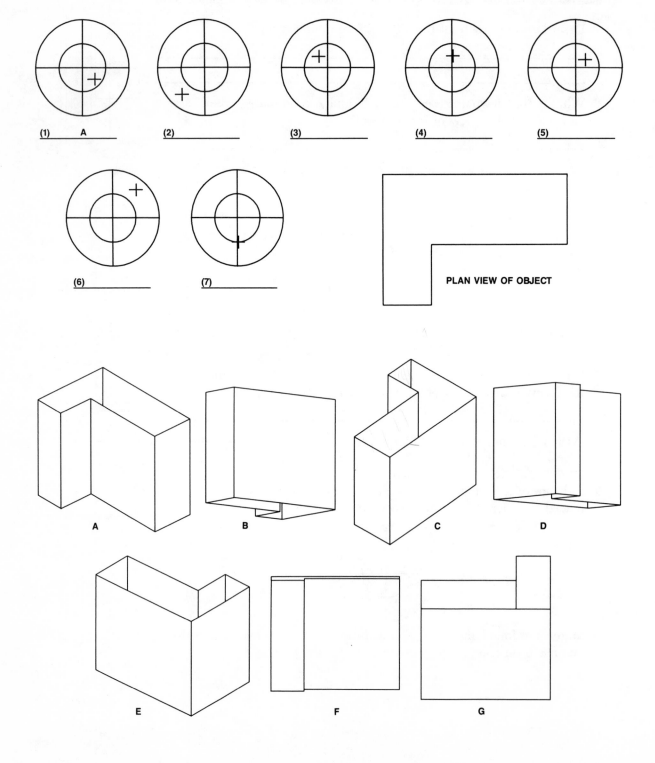

(1) A _____

(2) _____

(3) _____

(4) _____

(5) _____

(6) _____

(7) _____

PLAN VIEW OF OBJECT

A

B

C

D

E

F

G

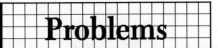

Problems

Draw the following objects and generate a 3D model of each.

1. In PRB34-1 set the elevation at 1 inch.

2. In PRB34-2 set the elevation for the inner cylinder at 0.

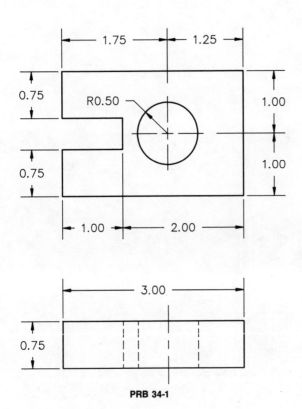

PRB 34-1

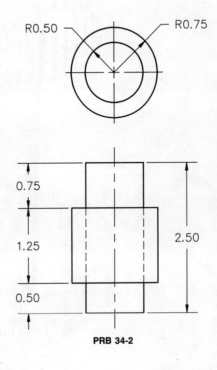

PRB 34-2

3. In PRB34-3 try as best you can to draw a similar object.

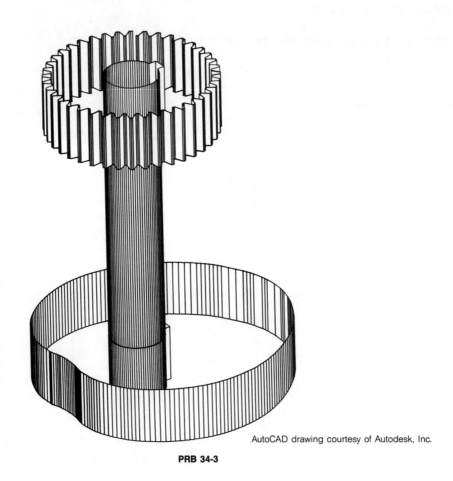

AutoCAD drawing courtesy of Autodesk, Inc.

PRB 34-3

AUTOCAD® AT WORK

Facilities Planning: CAD Standards in the Foodservice Industry

One of today's growth areas is the foodservice industry. Those millions of burgers and chicken dinners and egg rolls we consume are produced with a variety of specialized equipment. Typically, the commercial kitchen contains between 50 and 150 pieces of equipment that may come from two manufacturers or twenty. Many of the manufacturers, as well as foodservice consultants and equipment dealers, use AutoCAD or work with clients and vendors who do. For these firms, standardized symbols for equipment would improve communication and productivity.

Naturally, setting CAD standards among these different groups presents a challenge. A major turning point for the foodservice industry came in 1985 with the voluntary adoption of an industry-wide standard for microCAD running on an IBM-AT. Approximately four months later, the Foodservice Equipment Dealers Association (FEDA) developed a recommended layering system for AutoCAD foodservice drawings and symbols.

The National Association of Foodservice Equipment Manufacturers (NAFEM) responded favorably because the establishment of standards allowed manufacturers to develop a set of CAD symbol libraries on a cost-effective basis.

There are 18 recommended layers, in 7 colors and 7 linetypes, and a suggested linetype scale. No recommended line widths are given. Some of these layers contain valuable information that can aid in the layout and engineering work but isn't plotted in the final drawings.

In general, the actual electrical and mechanical connection points are shown only on the plan view because this view is used for rough-in plans.

The standard insertion point for a plan view is the upper left corner of the item or the clearance lines if there are any. This automatically gives the designer the clearance requirements when inserting the item of foodservice equipment.

Kochman Consultants of Morton Grove, Illinois, creates symbol libraries for the foodservice industry. The AutoCAD symbol libraries they create are supplements to manufacturer's catalogs. The manufacturers normally provide their libraries at no charge to firms that specify and/or sell their products.

Many firms that have other CAD systems can import the AutoCAD foodservice symbol libraries Kochman created. Kochman's symbol libraries are a good example of how standardization can benefit an industry.

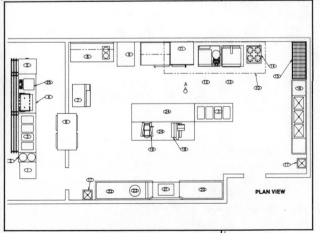

PLAN VIEW

Based on a story in *CADENCE* magazine, Vol 2, No. 5.

 **X/Y/Z Point Filters**

■ OBJECTIVE:

To apply AutoCAD's 3D X/Y/Z point filters using the 3DFACE command

AutoCAD® Reference Manual

8.8

This unit continues with AutoCAD's 3D modeling facility. With the LINE (3DLINE) and 3DFACE commands, you are able to create lines and surfaces in three-dimensional space using X, Y, *and* Z coordinates. For instance, inclined and oblique surfaces, such as a roof on a building, can be created. AutoCAD is also capable of creating cones, domes, spheres, and other 3D objects with commands presented in the following units.

■ *3DFACE Command* _____

4.8

The 3DFACE command creates a three-dimensional object similar in many respects to a two-dimensional SOLID entity. The 3DFACE prompt sequence is identical to that of the SOLID command. However, unlike the SOLID command, points are entered in a natural clockwise or counterclockwise order to create a normal 3D face. Z coordinates are specified for the corner points of a 3D Face, forming a section of a plane in space. Let's try it.

1 Load the drawing named **THREE-D**.

_____ NOTE: _____

If you want to keep THREE-D as it is, make a copy of it and give it a new name, such as THREE-D2, using the DOS REName command (see Appendix F). Then load it instead of your original THREE-D. Or, use THREE-D as a prototype drawing, *e.g.*, THREE-D2=THREE-D.

2 If you don't already have the plan view on the screen, obtain it by entering **VPOINT** and **plan**, then **ZOOM ALL**.

3 Erase the cylinder (circle) from the 3D model, and set the Snap at **.25** unit.

4 Select **3D** from the root page of the screen menu.

5 Select the **3DFACE** command from the menu.

6 Also from the screen menu, select **.xy** because you are about to pick an x,y point.

HINT:
You can also enter .xy—as you see it here—at the keyboard. Be sure to include the period before the letters. Or, you can pick .xy from the FILTERS menu found in the Tools pull-down menu.

7 Approximate the x,y position of point 1 in the following illustration and pick that point. (Point 1 is about .5 unit from the corner of the object.)

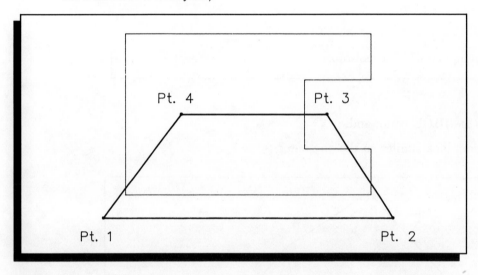

As shown on the prompt line, the first point also requires a Z coordinate. Therefore. . .

8 . . .enter a Z coordinate of **3.5**.

This method of entering 3D points is referred to as X/Y/Z filtering.

9 In reply to "Second point:" select .xy from the screen menu or enter .xy at the keyboard and pick point 2 as shown in the illustration.

10 Enter **3.5** for the Z coordinate.

11 Repeat these steps for points 3 and 4, but enter **7** for the Z coordinate of these points.

12 Press **RETURN** when you're finished.

Do you know what you've just created? If not, try to visualize its position in relation to the object. In case you may not yet know, it's an inclined surface resembling a portion of a roof. Let's make the opposite portion.

1 Enter the **MIRROR** command and select the 3D Face entity you just created.

2 Place the mirror line so that the two sections of the roof meet at the middle of the object.

Now let's view the object in 3D.

8.8

③ Enter the **VPOINT** command and the **axes** option.

④ Pick a point on the globe so that you view the object from above, front, and right side.

HINT:
See page 276 for assistance.

⑤ Enter the **HIDE** command.

Does your model look similar to the one here?

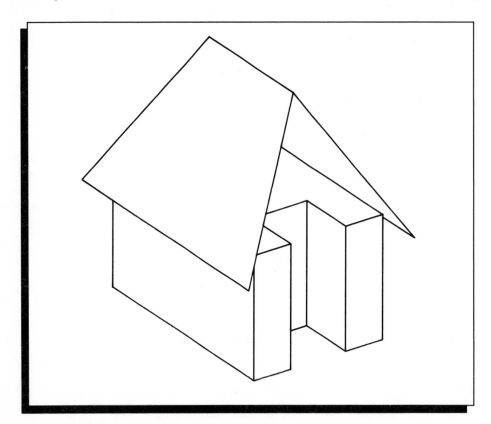

Let's finish the roof so that it looks similar to the following.

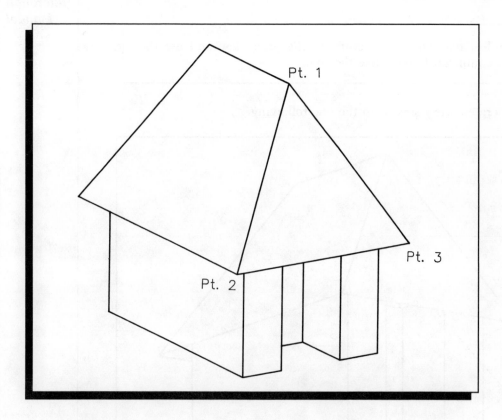

1 With your current 3D view remaining on the screen, enter the **3DFACE** command and then enter the **END**point Object Snap mode.

2 Snap to point 1, shown in the preceding illustration.

3 Enter the **END**point mode again and snap to point 2.

4 Enter **END**point and snap to point 3.

5 Enter **END**point once more and snap to point 1 to complete the surface boundary.

6 Press **RETURN** to exit the 3DFACE command.

7 Enter the **HIDE** command.

8 View the object from above, front, and left side using the **VPOINT** command and **axes** option.

9 Create the remaining portion of the roof using the 3DFACE command and Object Snap facility.

HINT:

You may choose to return to the plan view and use the MIRROR command to complete the roof.

10 Generate a view similar to the one following.

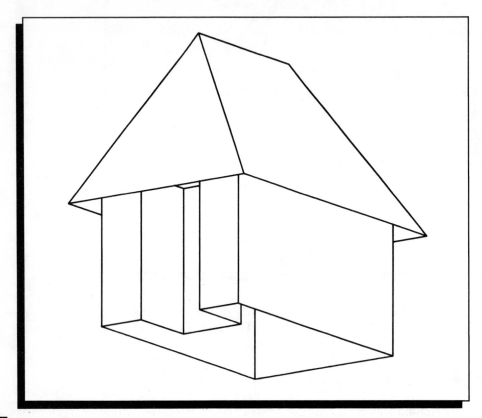

Invisible Option

4.8

3D Faces can define visible and invisible edges. Consider the following steps in constructing a pentagon.

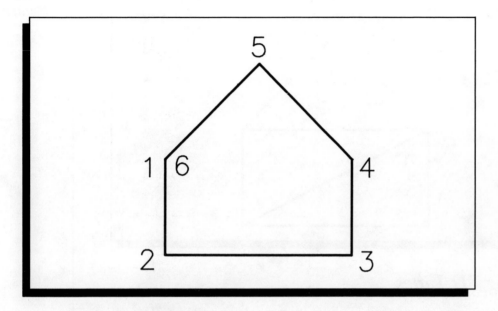

Command: 3DFACE
First point: (pick point 1)
Second point: (pick point 2)
Third point: (pick point 3)
Fourth point (enter I and pick point 4)
Third point: (pick point 5)
Fourth point: (enter I and pick point 6)
Third point: (press RETURN)

The invisible option is also useful when connecting two or more 3D faces together to create a 3D model.

The system variable SPLFRAME controls the display of invisible edges in 3D Faces. When set to a nonzero value, invisible edges are displayed. This allows you to edit them as you would a visible 3D Face.

Shown on the next page is the same pentagon with SPLFRAME set at a nonzero value.

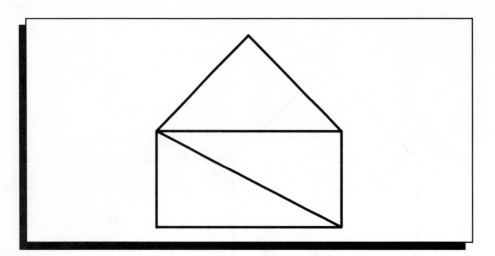

Creating 3D Lines

The LINE command creates full 3D lines in space. Let's create a 3D property line around the building using LINE.

1 Enter the **VPOINT** command and **plan** option, and then **ZOOM** All.

2 Enter the **ELEV** command and change the elevation to **1** and the thickness to **0**.

3 Enter the **LINE** command and pick one of the four corners of the property line shown in the following illustration. (Approximate its location.)

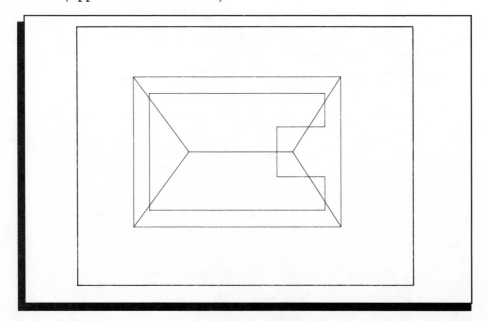

4 Approximate the location of the remaining corners and press
RETURN when you are finished.

5 Obtain a view similar to the following using the **VPOINT**
command.

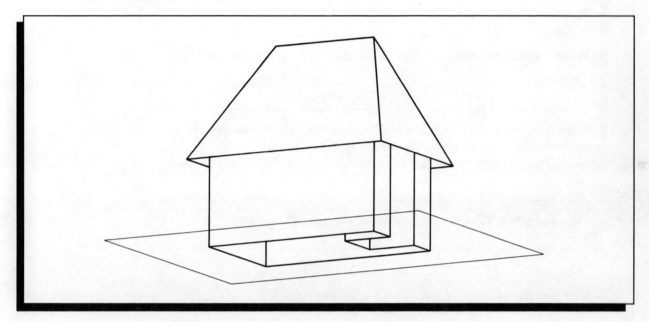

6 Further experiment with the LINE and 3DFACE commands.

NOTE:

A VPOINT "Rotate" option is available. It lets you specify VPOINT in
terms of two angles: one with respect to the X-axis (in the X-Y plane)
and another "up" from the X-Y plane. Experiment with this option on
your own.

7 Enter **END** to save your work and exit the Drawing Editor.

Questions

1. Describe a 3D Face entity.

   _____

   _____

2. What basic AutoCAD command is the 3DFACE command most like?

   _____

   _____

3. What can be created with the 3DFACE command that cannot be created with the LINE command? Be specific.

   _____

   _____

4. Describe the X/Y/Z filtering process of entering 3D points.

   _____

   _____

5. Describe the purpose of the VPOINT Rotate option.

   _____

   _____

6. What is the primary benefit of using X/Y/Z point filters?

   _____

   _____

Problems

1. Using AutoCAD's 3D modeling facilities, add a door, window, and fireplace chimney to the object you created earlier. When finished, your drawing should look similar to the one here.

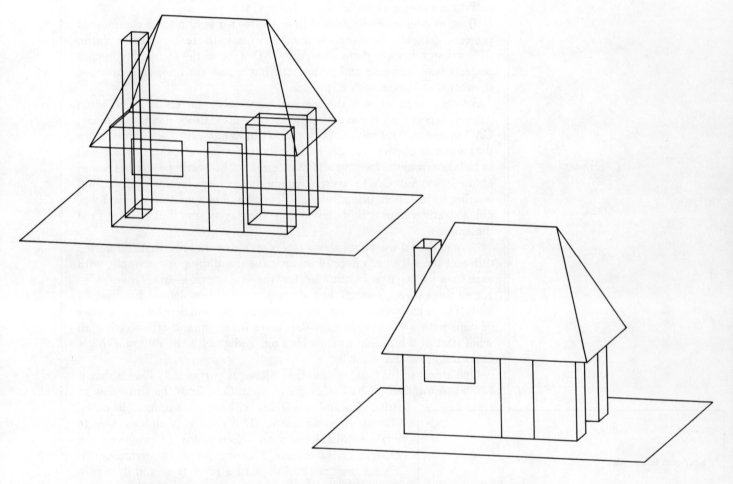

2. Embellish the drawing further by adding other details to the building. Save the finished drawing as PRB35-1.

AUTOCAD® AT WORK

CAD Gives Small Business Its Competitive Edge

When you're a relatively small business, you need whatever edge you can get. For Trusco Industries Ltd., a family business with 20 employees located in Prince George, Canada, that edge is CAD.

Trusco manufactures roof and floor trusses for housing and commercial projects, generally building wood web trusses with steel connector plates. All its design work is done with AutoCAD. One of the company's biggest projects was designing and manufacturing trusses for temporary wooden structures at Vancouver's Expo '86.

Another large job was the married personnel quarters at a Canadian Armed Forces base. "It was entirely in metric," notes Bruce Richards, Trusco's CAD operator, "but with CAD you don't have to worry about units, since the computer doesn't care. Because the footings were offset, dimensions had to be taken from the footings and transferred to the bearing walls and beams above. I used AutoCAD's layering capability to isolate footings, beams, and bearing walls. Then, using AutoCAD's copy and change commands, I was able to transfer lines within drawings to other layers, and thus arrive at final dimensions.

"Typically, I'd use about thirty layers on a drawing like that. I'd have a different layer for each floor of an apartment building, for example, with each floor having its own sublayers for truss layout and beams. Once you've got all those layers, though, how do you remember which ones to turn on and off? I've designed a macro (a customized command that initiates a series of steps with a single keystroke) that turns layers on and off according to what part of a building I'm working on. I play with the program to get CAD doing what I want."

One aspect of his CAD system that Richards particularly likes is that it can be customized. "I had an engineering student from the University of British Columbia working with me one summer," he notes. "He caught on to AutoCAD very quickly and was able to write AutoLISP programs. Now, AutoLISP programs can generate cross sections of buildings for us. For example, we'll ask for the span and slope of a given truss and its depth. Automatically, the program creates a totally dimensioned building cross section."

In a further customization, Richards' brother Bryan has written a DXF (drawing interchange file) program that automatically draws flat trusses (used for flat roofs and floors) and converts them to a file that can be read by AutoCAD.

Trusco has found CAD to be a sound investment. Says Richards, "It's fast and it's accurate. I like the fact that everything you draw consistently fits together and that you don't have to draw objects more than once. Those capabilities are worth a lot of money in manufacturing."

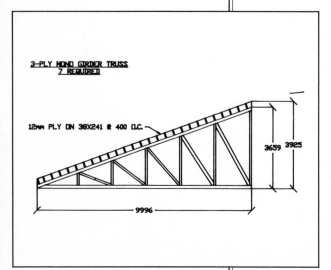

3-PLY MONO GIRDER TRUSS
7 REQUIRED

12mm PLY ON 38X241 @ 400 O.C.

3659 3925

9996

Courtesy of Trusco Industries Ltd. and Autodesk, Inc.

■ OBJECTIVE:

To learn about the user-definable User Coordinate System (UCS) and apply it to the construction of 3D wireframe models

As you know, AutoCAD uses a coordinate system; points in a drawing are located by their X,Y,Z coordinates. When you call up the Drawing Editor, the default coordinate system is the World Coordinate System (WCS). In this system, the X-axis is horizontal on your screen, the Y-axis is vertical, and the Z-axis is at right angles to the XY plane (the plane defined by the X and Y axes). The WCS is indicated in the lower left corner of your screen by the following coordinate system icon.

AutoCAD® Reference Manual

1.2.1
2.7.1.4
8.6

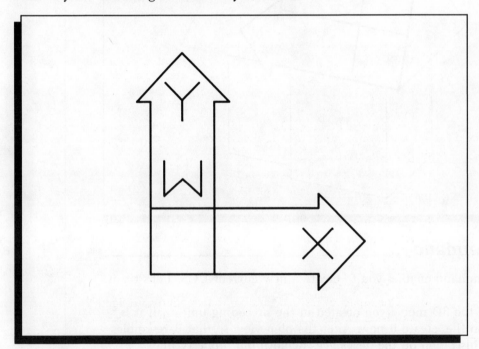

You may create drawings in the World Coordinate System, or you may define your own User Coordinate System (UCS). The advantage of a UCS is that its origin is not fixed. You can specify it to be located anywhere within the world coordinate system. Thus the axes of the UCS can be rotated or tilted in relation to the axes of the WCS. This is a useful feature when you're drawing a three-dimensional model.

1.2.1
8.6

Consider the following 3D model. A UCS is defined to match the inclined plane of the roof as indicated by the arrows. Once established, all new objects constructed lie in the same plane as the roof.

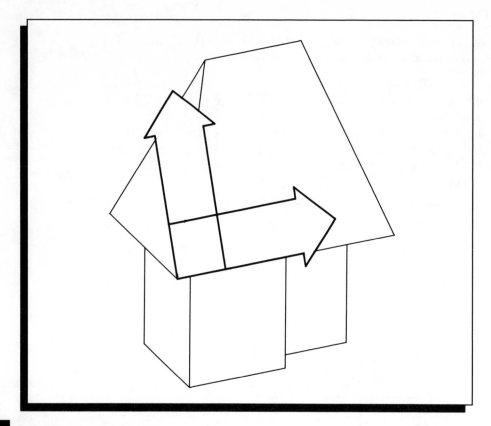

■ *UCS Command*_____

The UCS command enables you to create a new current UCS. Let's try it.

1 Load the 3D model you created in the preceding unit or, if it is not on file, create it now. Alter the plan view so that it resembles the illustration on the next page. Remove the property line around the model.

HINT:
Be sure to set the elevation at 1 and the thickness at 3 before drawing new lines.

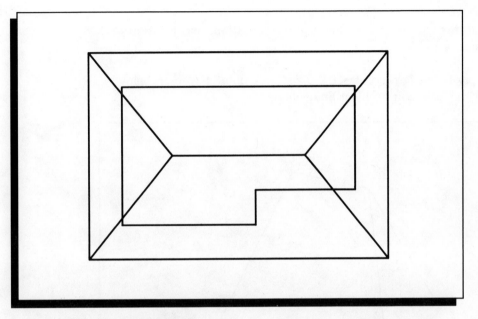

2 Using the **VPOINT** command, obtain a view similar to the one shown on the preceding page.

HINT:
With reference to the globe (see page 276), place your viewpoint in front, above, and to the left.

3 Enter the **UCS** command either from the keyboard or from the screen menu.

NOTE:

Do not use the pull-down menu to enter the UCS command because it may cause confusion as you step through the following. After you learn to use the UCS command, experiment with the pull-down option on your own.

You should see the following list of options.

```
Origin/ZAxis/3point/Entity/View/X/Y/Z/Prev/Restore/Save/
Del/?/<World>:
```

4 Enter the 3point option.

This option allows you to specify the origin, orientation, and rotation of the XY plane in a UCS.

5 In reply to "Origin point <0,0,0>:" pick point 1 (shown below) using the **END**point Object Snap mode.

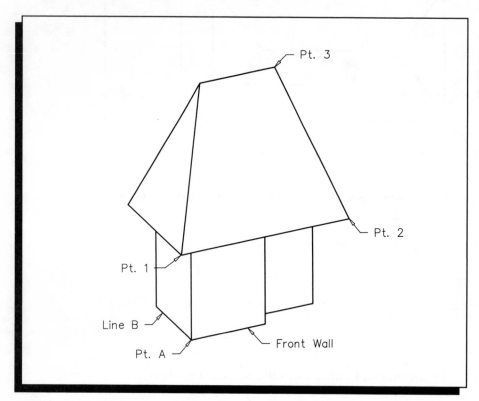

6 In reply to the next prompt, snap to point 2.

This defines the positive X direction from your first point.

7 In reply to the next prompt, snap to point 3. Point 3 lies in the new XY plane and has a positive Y coordinate.

Note that the drawing on your screen does not change. However, your crosshairs, grid, and coordinate system icon do shift to reflect the new UCS.

**AutoCAD®
Reference
Manual**

1.2.1
8.6.3

The coordinate system icon indicates the positive directions of the X and Y axes. A "W" appears in the icon if the current UCS is the World Coordinate System. If the icon is located at the origin of the current UCS, a "+" is displayed at the base of the icon. A box is formed at the base of the icon if you're viewing the UCS from above. The box is absent if you are viewing the UCS from below.

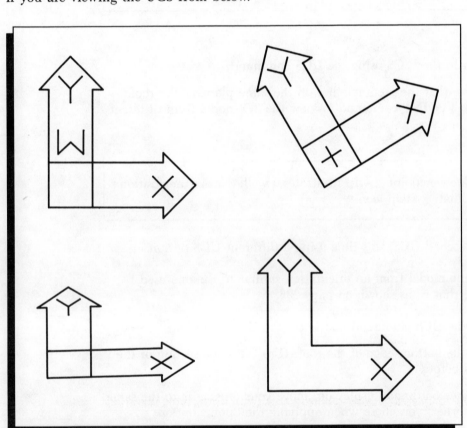

8 With the coordinate display on, notice the X and Y values in the status line as you move your crosshairs to each of the three points you selected.

9 Save your current UCS by selecting the Save option. Name it **FRTROOF**.

Using the UCS

Suppose you want to construct the line of intersection between the roof and a chimney passing through the roof.

1 Change both the elevation and thickness values to **0**.

2 With the **LINE** command, approximate the line of intersection by creating a rectangle at any convenient location on the roof.

HINT:

Turn on Ortho if it isn't on already.

3 Return to the WCS using the **UCS** command.

4 To prove that the rectangle lies on the same plane as the roof, use the **VPOINT** command to view the 3D model from different points in space.

HINT:

The viewpoint 4, −.1,1 illustrates it well. (Notice the position of the coordinate system icon.)

Let's create a second UCS, this time using a different UCS option.

1 View the model from an orientation similar to the one used before; that is, as shown on page 298.

2 Enter the **UCS** command and select the Entity option.

3 Select the bottom edge of the roof. (Use the same section of the roof as before.)

4 With the coordinate display on, move your crosshairs to the same three corners you chose when applying the 3point option.

Notice that the Entity option created an identical UCS.

You are likely to use the 3point and Entity options for most applications, at least at first. However, other UCS creation options are available.

1 Enter the **UCS** command and choose the **ZA**xis option.

2 Snap to point A (see the illustration on page 298) in reply to "Origin point <0,0,0>:".

3 In reply to the next prompt, pick any point on line B.

This point specifies the positive Z direction of the UCS. AutoCAD then determines the directions of the X and Y axes using an arbitrary but consistent method.

The new UCS should be on the same vertical plane as the front wall of the building. In relation to the wall, notice the positive X, Y, and Z directions that make up the UCS, and notice the UCS coordinate system icon.

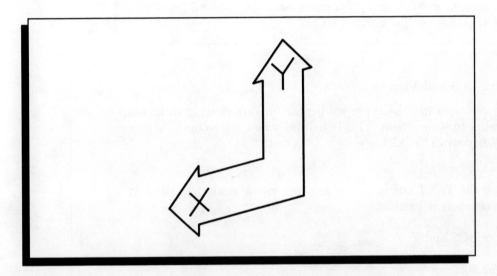

4 Enter **UCS** and **Prev.**

This restores the previous UCS. AutoCAD saves the last ten User Coordinate Systems in a stack, so you can step back through these systems with repeated UCS Previous operations.

5 Enter **UCS** and **Restore.**

This lets you restore a previously saved UCS.

6 Enter **?**.

The screen should display data about the FRTROOF coordinate system, which you saved earlier.

7 Enter **FRTROOF** to restore that UCS.

8 Enter **UCS World**—the default action of the UCS command.

This restores the World Coordinate System. Notice that W (for World) appears in the coordinate system icon.

NOTE:

If you are in a UCS and you want to place a point in the WCS, you can do so by entering an asterisk prior to the coordinates (*e.g.*, ∗7.5,4). During line construction, for example, you can also place relative coordinates (*e.g.*, @ ∗5,3) and polar coordinates (*e.g.*, @ ∗3.5<90) in the WCS regardless of the current UCS.

⑨ Enter **UCS** and **View**.

This option creates a new UCS perpendicular to your viewing direction; that is, parallel to your screen. This is helpful when you want to annotate (add notes to) your 3D model.

⑩ Using the **TEXT** command, place your name near the model at any convenient location.

⑪ Enter **UCS** and **Z**.

⑫ Enter **30**.

Did the current UCS icon rotate 30 degrees about the Z axis?

⑬ Use the X and Y options to rotate the current UCS about the X and Y axes.

HINT:

You may choose to apply UCS View prior to experimenting with the X and Y options so that you can more easily see their effects.

UCS Del lets you delete one or more saved User Coordinate Systems. UCS Origin defines a new UCS by moving the origin of the current UCS, leaving the orientation of its axis unchanged.

PLAN Command

6.6.3

The PLAN command enables you to easily generate the plan view of any User Coordinate System including the WCS.

① Enter the **PLAN** command.

② Press **RETURN** to generate the plan view of the current UCS.

**AutoCAD®
Reference
Manual**
8.6.3

NOTE:

A "broken pencil" icon, shown below, will replace the coordinate system icon whenever the XY plane of the current coordinate system is perpendicular to the computer screen. This indicates that drawing and selecting objects is limited in this situation.

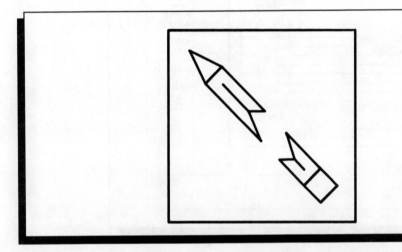

③ Enter the **PLAN** command again and enter the World option.

The plan view of the World Coordinate System should be present.

If you want to display the plan view of previously saved User Coordinate Systems, enter the PLAN U option.

NOTE:

If you want AutoCAD to automatically generate a plan view whenever you change from one UCS to another, you can accomplish this by setting the system variable UCSFOLLOW to 1 (on) with the SETVAR command. Changing from one UCS to another does not change the view of the model unless UCSFOLLOW is on.

6.6.3

UCS Dialogue Box

8.6.2

If you choose the "UCS Dialogue..." item found in the Settings pull-down menu, the following will appear.

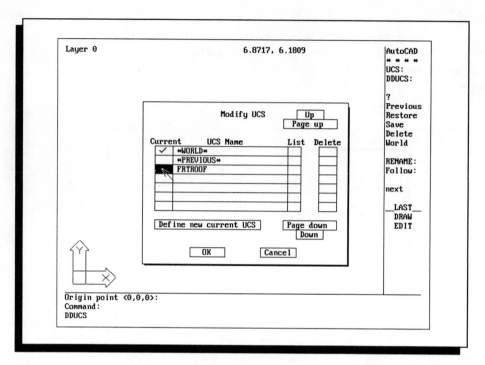

The use of the dialogue box is self-explanatory.

Selection of the "UCS Options..." item, also contained in the Settings pull-down menu, will display the following.

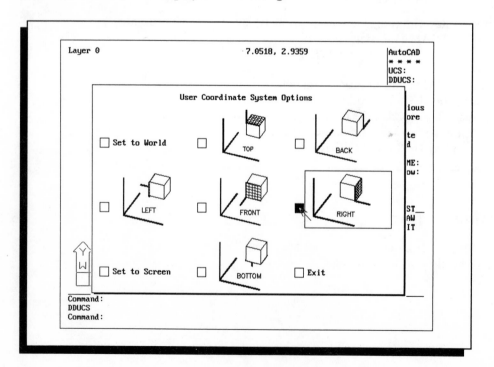

This dialogue box enables you to create new User Coordinate Systems around a 3D cube.

14 Enter **END** to save your work and exit the Drawing Editor.

Questions

1. What is the purpose and benefit of the User Coordinate System (UCS)?

   _____

   _____

   _____

2. Describe the UCS 3point option.

   _____

   _____

3. What purpose does the coordinate system icon serve?

   _____

   _____

4. When the "W" appears within the coordinate system icon, what does it represent?

   _____

5. If a box is formed at the base of the coordinate system icon, what does this mean?

   _____

6. What command and option do you select to obtain the previous UCS?

   _____

7. Describe, briefly, the UCS View option.

   _____

Problems

1. With the UCS 3point option, create a UCS using one of the walls that make up the building found in this unit. Save the UCS using a name of your choice. With this as the current UCS, add a door and window to the building. Save this drawing as PRB36-1.

2. Using the VPOINT command, obtain a 3D wireframe model of the building contained in this unit. With the UCS View option, create a UCS. At any convenient location and size, create a border and title block for your 3D model. Include your name, date, file name, etc., in the title block. Save your work as PRB36-2.

AUTOCAD® AT WORK

*A Technical Illustrator's Story**

Dick Clark is an Engineering Specialist at NEC Information Systems, Inc. He creates illustrations for use in maintenance/repair manuals and user manuals. While he started his career using pencils, templates, and Leroy pens, today his main drawing tool is AutoCAD.

Dick works closely with the hardware technical writers during the writing of maintenance guides for both field and depot level. His main task is creating the Illustrated Parts Breakdown (IPB) for these guides. Since usable master drawings are seldom available, this process often means dismantling a complex piece of computer equipment or peripheral hardware down to the component and base assembly level to obtain the parts to be drawn and also to understand the assembly/reassembly process that is to be shown. Complex electromechanical assemblies and subassemblies are reduced to the Smallest Replaceable Unit (SRU) level and technically illustrated for the generation of the IPB. Each object is measured prior to drawing, and the final drawing is appropriately scaled to match those dimensions.

To create national or local advertisements, data sheets and brochures, Dick works with the marketing staff, providing the technically correct drawings they need.

Dick does most of his drawing in isometric and 3D views on AutoCAD. For prints, he first plots the drawing, then has the plot photographically reduced to an 8½″ × 11″ size. When incorporating these drawings into manuals, the photoreduced plot is digitized back into an Interleaf publishing system, using a scanner. This technique provides a very high-resolution image in that proper photo reduction improves apparent (but not actual) resolution, allowing the scanner to digitize the image to its maximum potential. Interleaf then incorporates the image with documentation to produce brochures or booklets.

The technical illustrator can wear many hats, from company space planner to advertisement production. One of Dick's special projects is the design of NEC's show booth. In addition to playing with booth layout, he provides a detailed presentation image of it. "My day is not always filled up entirely with production drawings," says Dick, "but if you're doing something new and challenging, and you love drawing, it's a joy. 'Can it be done?' is my favorite professional question."

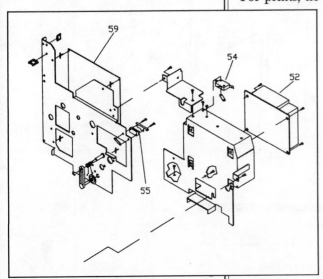

*Based on a story in *CADENCE* magazine, Vol. 3, No. 8.

Unit 37 — Dynamic View Facility

■ OBJECTIVE:

To practice using AutoCAD's powerful dynamic view facility in connection with 3D wireframe modeling

The VPOINT command lets you view 3D models from any angle in space. The DVIEW command also lets you view models from various angles in space, but in a dynamic way. It also provides a range of 3D viewing features and enables you to generate 3D perspective projections—as opposed to parallel projections—of your 3D work.

Other benefits of the dynamic view facility are its exceptionally fast dynamic zooming and panning capability and fast hidden line removal. Plus, you are able to create front and back *clipping planes* of your 3D models.

Consider the following two views of the building from the previous unit. Both views are from the same point in space. However, the one on the left is shown in standard parallel projection. The lines are parallel and do not converge toward one or more vanishing points. The right view is a true perspective projection. Parts of the building that are farther away appear smaller—the same as in a real-life photograph.

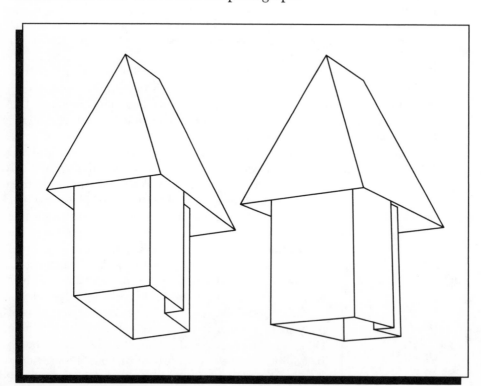

Perspective Projections _____

Using the dynamic view facility, let's generate a 3D perspective projection.

**AutoCAD®
Reference
Manual**

1 Load the 3D building named **THREE-D.**

_____ **NOTE:** _____

If THREE-D.DWG is not on file, create it quickly. Refer to the illustrations and instructions in the previous three units and approximate all dimensions.

2 Using the **VPOINT** command, create a view similar to the parallel projection shown in the preceding illustration.

HINT:

Using the VPOINT Axes option, position the viewpoint below, to the left, and slightly in front of the model. Refer to the globe on page 276. Use the HIDE command to remove hidden lines.

3 Enter the **DVIEW** command. (Do not use the pull-down menu.)

4 In response to "Select objects:" select the entire model.

_____ **NOTE:** _____

The entities you select will be those you preview as you perform the DVIEW options. If you select too many entities, dragging and updating of the image will be slow. However, choosing too few entities may not provide an adequate preview.

The following options should appear.

```
CAmera/TArget/Distance/POints/PAn/Zoom/TWist/
CLip/Hide/Off/Undo/<eXit>:
```

5 Enter the **Distance** option.

A *slider bar* should appear at the top of the screen.

6.6.2.1

The DVIEW command uses a camera and target metaphor. The slider bar is labeled from 0x to 16x, with 1x representing the current distance. Moving the slider bar cursor to the right increases the distance between the camera and the target. Moving the cursor to the left moves the camera closer to the target.

6 With your pointing device, slowly move the slider bar cursor to the right and then to the left and notice the changes in the drawing.

7 Position the slider bar cursor so the model is approximately the same size as before and press the pick button on your pointing device.

The model is now in perspective projection as indicated by the perspective icon found at the lower left corner of the screen.

8 Enter the DVIEW **Hide** option.

Notice that hidden lines are removed the same as when the HIDE command is applied. But, two things are different. First, you are currently in the DVIEW command. Second, you are viewing the model in perspective projection—not parallel projection—with hidden lines removed.

9 Press **RETURN** to exit the DVIEW command and to obtain the "Command:" prompt.

Notice that the hidden lines reappear but the perspective view remains.

10 Enter **DVIEW**, select the model, and select the **Off** option to turn off the perspective projection.

11 Experiment further with the DVIEW **Distance** option and press **RETURN** when you are finished.

Other DVIEW Options

Use of the camera/target metaphor helps you view the 3D model as it appears from any point in space. The line of sight (also referred to as the viewing direction) is the line between the camera and the target.

1 Enter the **DVIEW** command and select the model once again.

2 Enter the **Off** option and then the **CA**mera option.

A slider bar should appear at the right side of the screen.

3 Move the slider bar cursor up and down slowly and notice its effect.

The slider bar enables you to specify the angle of the camera up or down relative to the XY plane of the current UCS. For instance, a camera angle of 0 degrees means you are looking parallel to the XY plane of the UCS. An angle of 90 degrees means you're looking straight down from above, and −90 degrees means you're looking straight up from below. The *status line* reflects the position of the slider bar cursor.

4 Position the 3D model on the screen and press the pick button on your pointing device.

A horizontal slider bar should appear on the screen. It lets you rotate the camera around the target. The camera moves to the left as you move the slider bar cursor to the left, and to the right as you move the cursor to the right.

5 Slowly move the horizontal slider bar cursor and notice its effect.

6 Position the model on the screen and press the pick button.

NOTE:

The DVIEW Undo option is available in case you need to undo your last operation.

So you see, the Camera option rotates the camera—that is, the point you are looking *from*—around the target point.

The Target option is similar to the Camera option, but it rotates the target point—that is, the point you are looking *at*—around the camera.

7 Experiment with the DVIEW **TA**rget option on your own.

NOTE:

The DVIEW Points option is available if you want to define new camera and target points using X, Y, and Z coordinates.

As a result of using the Target option, the model may appear partially off the screen.

8 Enter the DVIEW **PA**n option to dynamically shift the model to a new location.

HINT:

Place the first point (that is, the displacement base point) on or near the model. Drag the model to the second point.

⑨ Enter the DVIEW Zoom option.

This enables you to dynamically zoom in and out on the model.

⑩ Adjust the slider bar cursor until you are satisfied with the new zoom magnification.

The Twist option lets you rotate the model around the line of sight. It is similar to using the ROTATE command in a 2D environment.

⑪ Enter the DVIEW TWist option, move your crosshairs, and pick a point at any convenient location.

Clipping Planes

6.6.2

The DVIEW Clip option enables you to create front and back *clipping planes*. It lets you view the interior of your model in much the same way as conventional sectional views.

① Using the various DVIEW options, position the model so that it is similar to the ones at the beginning of this unit.

② Enter the DVIEW CLip option and then choose the Front option.

③ Slowly move the slider bar cursor and pay particular attention to how the model changes.

④ Attempt to display only half of the model and then press the pick button.

⑤ Enter the DVIEW Hide option.

The Clip Front option should remove the front portion of the model—that is, the portion between you and the clipping plane—and leave a drawing similar to the following.

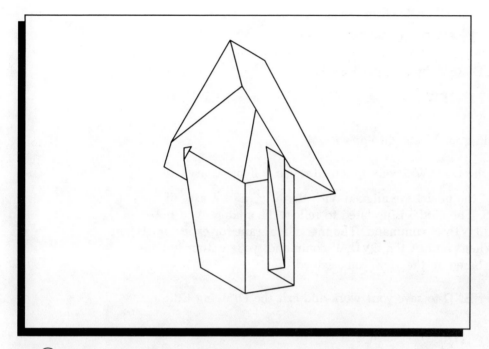

6 Experiment with the DVIEW **CL**ip **B**ack option.

7 Enter the DVIEW **H**ide option to realize the effect of the Clip Back option.

Does your view look similar to the following? Notice that both front and back clipping planes are in effect.

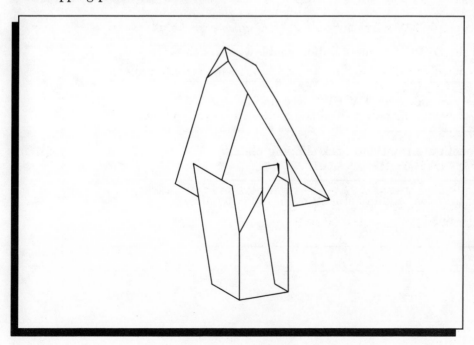

⑧ Enter the DVIEW **CLip Off** option.

Did the model return to its previous form?

⑨ Exit DVIEW by pressing **RETURN**.

⑩ Enter **DVIEW** and give a null response (press **RETURN**) in reply to "Select objects:".

A new building model should appear.

⑪ Use the DVIEW **Z**oom option to resize it if necessary.

The edges of the model are aligned with the X, Y, and Z axes of the current UCS. The model is updated to reflect the changes you make while in the DVIEW command. The model is meant for experimentation purposes. When you exit the DVIEW command, your entire drawing regenerates, based on the view you selected.

⑫ Enter **END** to save your work and exit the Drawing Editor.

Questions

1. How are 3D perspective projections generated?

_____

2. What does the DVIEW Camera option enable you to do?

_____

3. What is the purpose of the DVIEW Twist option?

_____

4. Of what benefit are front and back clipping planes?

_____

5. Describe at least two additional features of the dynamic view (DVIEW) facility.

_____

_____

Problems

1. While in the WCS plan view, create an array of lines. Create them in both the X and Y directions and place them approximately one unit apart. View the grid of lines at an arbitrary point in space using the VPOINT command. Create a perspective projection of the view using the DVIEW command. Use other dynamic view options to view the grid at various orientations and sizes in space. Save your grid as PRB37-1.

2. Obtain a left view of the building using either the DVIEW or VPOINT commands. Use a front clipping plane to create a full cross section of the model. Save this drawing as PRB37-2.

AutoCAD® At Work

Young Disabled Designer Uses AutoCAD

Ron Grooms, a computer science researcher at Iowa State University in Ames, Iowa, is the director of the university's vocational training project for seriously disabled students. The purpose of the project is to teach students with disabilities to use computerized word processing, data bases, and spread sheets.

When Autodesk, Inc. heard about the project, the company donated an AutoCAD program. For one of Grooms' star pupils, 15-year-old Jeff Hanson, AutoCAD opened the door to his talents as a graphic artist.

Although Jeff was born without hands or lower forearms, he has always been a talented artist. Jeff could draw and paint pictures by grasping a pen or brush between his forearms. The results were professional looking, but the process was slow and difficult. Grooms began to look for ways to make drawing easier for Jeff.

Grooms, who has backgrounds in electrical engineering, mathematics, and computer science, solved the problem by pairing AutoCAD with a Texas Instruments Professional computer that has voice recognition capability. Now Jeff speaks commands into the computer instead of typing them on a keyboard. His physical limitations no longer inhibit his ability to draw.

First Jeff learned the spoken commands he needed to operate AutoCAD. Then he and Grooms added voice commands that allowed Jeff to draw basic shapes, such as rectangles and ellipses. Next Jeff programmed the computer to respond to his voice by storing his voiceprints in the computer.

When Jeff speaks a command into the specially adapted mouthpiece, the computer scans its memory for the correct voiceprint. Once the computer finds the voiceprint, it translates the command to AutoCAD. Thus, when Jeff speaks the word circle, a circle appears on the computer screen. By using the zoom feature, Jeff can change the diameter of the circle to fit his drawing. By using voice recognition and AutoCAD, Jeff hopes to eventually fulfill his dream of becoming a graphic artist or a designer in the aerospace industry.

Unit 38   3D Revolutions

■ OBJECTIVE:

To apply REVSURF and RULESURF commands to the construction of curved surfaces in 3D space

The REVSURF command enables you to create a surface of revolution by rotating a path curve (or profile) around a selected axis. The RULESURF command lets you create a polygon mesh representing the ruled surface between two curves.

The following 3D model represents a table lamp. The lamp's base was created with the REVSURF command, while the lamp shade was created with the RULESURF command.

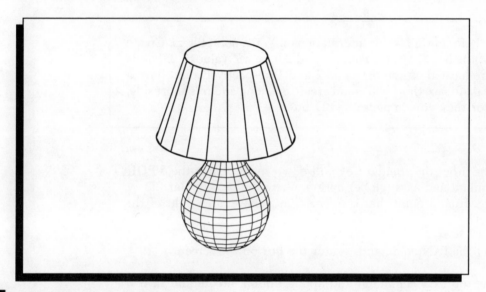

3D Prototype Drawing _____

In preparation for creating a lamp similar to the one shown above, let's create a prototype drawing. The prototype drawing will apply to subsequent 3D exercises in this unit and following units. Its purpose is to help you orient yourself as you create 3D models.

1   Load AutoCAD and Begin a New Drawing. Name it **3DPROTO**.

2   Set the Grid at **1** unit and Snap at **.5** unit; make sure they are both on.

3   Create the following three layers:

Layer name	Layer Color
BOX	**White**
3DOBJ	**Yellow**
OBJ2	**Blue**

The right margin column reads:

AutoCAD® Reference Manual

4.9.4
4.9.2

317

4 Set the layer named **BOX**.

5 Construct a rectangle in the center of the screen using the 3DFACE command and X/Y/Z point filters. Make it 4 units on the X-axis by 3 units on the Y-axis, by 2 units on the Z-axis.

HINT:

Refer to Unit 35 for information on X/Y/Z point filters. Create one side of the box at a time. Points 1 and 2 have a Z value of 2. Points 3 and 4 are located on top of points 2 and 1, respectively, and have a Z value of 0. To save time, you could create one long and one short side, then mirror these to complete the 3D box.

6 Using either the standard or pull-down menu, enter the **VPOINT** command and **axes** (globe) option. View the rectangular 3D model from a point that is to the front, above, and right of the object.

7 Using the **PAN** command, center the box on the screen.

8 Using the **UCS** command and 3point option, create and save each of the six User Coordinate Systems as indicated in the following illustration. Remember, the 3point option lets you specify the origin, orientation, and rotation of the XY plane.

HINT:

On the following illustration, each UCS name lies on its respective UCS. Likewise, each leader points to its respective UCS origin (0,0,0).

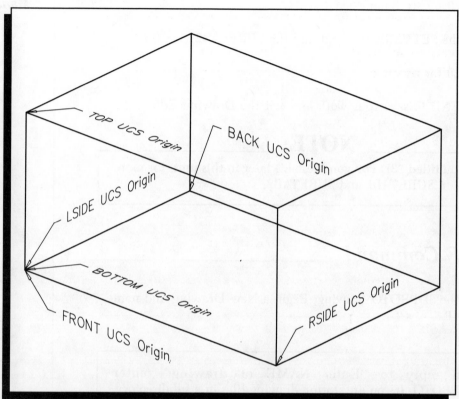

⑨ Set layer **3DOBJ**.

SURFTAB1 and SURFTAB2

The system variables SURFTAB1 and SURFTAB2 control the density
(resolution) of 3D meshes created by 3D commands such as RULESURF
and REVSURF.

4.9
4.9.2
4.9.4

① Enter the **SETVAR** command and the system variable
SURFTAB1.

HINT:
         Pick 3D in the root page of the standard screen menu and
you will find the system variables SURFTAB1 and SURFTAB2, written
as Surftb1 and Surftb2. They are also found by picking the "3D
Construction..." item from the Draw pull-down menu.

2 Enter **20** for its value.

3 Enter the **SETVAR** command and the **SURFTAB2** variable.

4 Enter **20** for its value.

5 Enter **END** to save your work and exit the Drawing Editor.

_____ NOTE: _____

See the section titled "3D Polygon Meshes", later in this unit, for more information on SURFTAB1 and SURFTAB2.

REVSURF Command _____

1 Using the 3DPROTO drawing, Begin a New Drawing and name it **LAMP**.

HINT:

In reply to "Enter NAME of drawing:" enter LAMP=3DPROTO. If you are storing drawing files in a subdirectory, include the name of the subdirectory. For example, enter USER\LAMP=USER\3DPROTO.

2 Enter the **UCS** command and Restore the **FRONT** UCS.

3 Enter the **HIDE** command to remove hidden lines.

4 Using the front, right corner of the rectangular 3D model as the starting point, create (approximately) the following shape with the **PLINE** command and the **Arc** option.

HINT:

Use PLINE's Undo option if you need to redo segments of the Polyline.

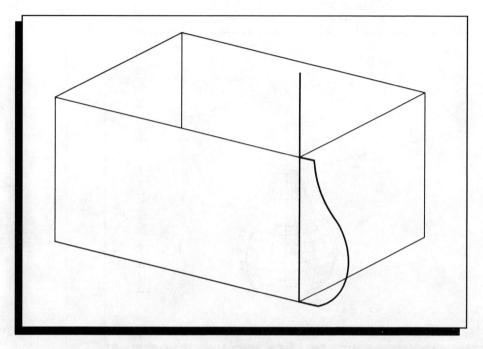

5 With the **LINE** command, draw a line that passes through the corner of the rectangular model and extends upward as indicated.

6 Enter the **REVSURF** command.

7 Pick the Polyline in reply to "Select path curve:".

8 Pick the line in reply to "Select axis of revolution:".

9 Enter **0** (the default) in reply to "Start angle:".

10 Enter **360** (the default, "Full circle") in reply to "Included angle:".

A 3D model of the lamp base should appear on your screen.

11 Enter the **HIDE** command to remove hidden lines.

___ NOTE: ___

The HIDE operation could take several minutes if you are working on a relatively slow computer (*e.g.*, a CPU clock speed of less than 16 megahertz).

Your lamp base should be similar to the one here.

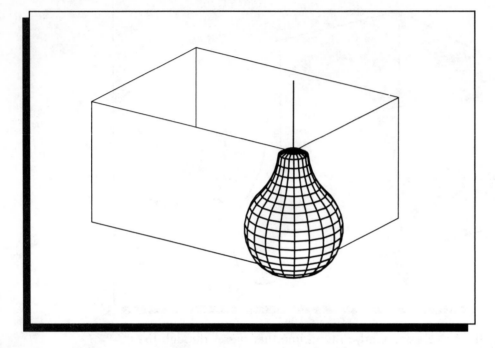

RULESURF Command

Now let's create the lamp shade.

1 Set the layer **OBJ2**.

2 Enter the **UCS** command and **Restore** the **TOP** UCS.

3 Enter the **CIRCLE** command.

4 Pick the upper, front, right corner of the rectangular model for the circle's center point. (Refer to the illustration on the next page.)

5 Enter **1.25** units for the radius of the circle.

This circle lies in the TOP UCS, and it will remain on this plane.

6 Create another circle using the same center but enter a radius of **.75**.

This circle also lies in the TOP UCS, but it will be moved upward in Step 8.

7 Change the current UCS to **FRONT**.

This will allow you to move the circle upward in the next step.

8 With Ortho and Snap modes on, use the **MOVE** command to move the smaller circle up **1.5** units.

This circle is now 1.5 units above the TOP UCS.

Your 3D model should now look similar to this one.

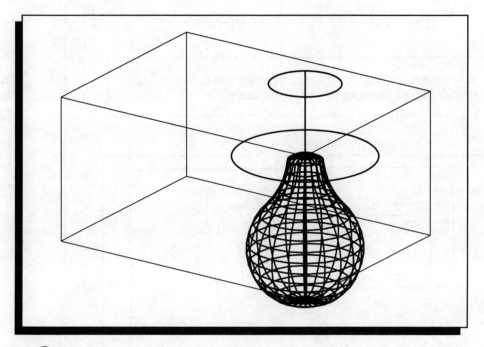

9 Enter the **RULESURF** command.

10 Pick one of the two circles in reply to "Select first defining curve:".

HINT:
You may have to turn Snap off.

11 Pick the remaining circle in reply to "Select second defining curve:".

Did the lamp shade appear as you envisioned it?

12 Freeze layer **BOX**.

13 Enter the **HIDE** command.

Your 3D model should look similar to the one found at the beginning of this unit.

14 Enter the **DVIEW** command and view the lamp from various orientations in space.

15 Enter **END** to save your work and exit the Drawing Editor.

HINT:
When constructing 3D models, consider using the multiple viewports facility. The following provides an example.

6.6.1
6.7

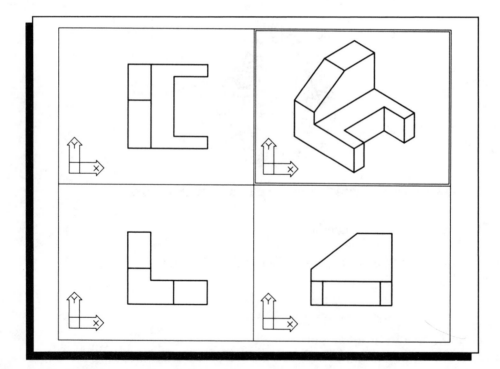

3D Polygon Meshes

4.9

A polygon mesh is defined in terms of *M x N* vertices. Envision the vertices as a grid consisting of columns and rows, with *M* and *N* specifying the column and row position of any given vertex.

The system variables SURFTAB1 and SURFTAB2 control the density (or resolution) of the 3D mesh. Specifically, the system variable SURFTAB 1 controls the *N*-direction of a polygon mesh. An example is the resolution of the lamp shade created by the RULESURF command.

Consider the lamp base. Both SURFTAB1 and SURFTAB2 come into play because both *M* and *N* vertices are applied by the REVSURF command.

If you increase the values of these two system variables, the appearance of 3D models may improve. But the model will require more time to regenerate on the screen. The HIDE command especially will consume more time. If you decrease the numbers excessively, the model will regenerate quickly on the screen, but the 3D model may not adequately represent your design.

NOTE:

3D meshes can be edited using the PEDIT command. You can also EXPLODE a mesh.

5.4.1.3
5.4.2

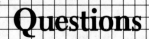

Questions

1. What is the purpose of the REVSURF command?

_____

_____

2. Describe the use of the RULESURF command.

_____

_____

3. How are the User Coordinate Systems beneficial when using the REVSURF and RULESURF commands?

_____

_____

4. Explain the purpose of the SURFTAB1 and SURFTAB2 system variables.

_____

_____

5. What are the consequences of entering high values for the SURFTAB1 and SURFTAB2 variables?

_____

6. What are the consequences of entering low values for SURFTAB1 and SURFTAB2?

_____

7. In AutoCAD terms, 3D polygon meshes are made up of what?

_____

Problems

Using the 3D facilities covered in this unit, create each of the following 3D models. Approximate all sizes.

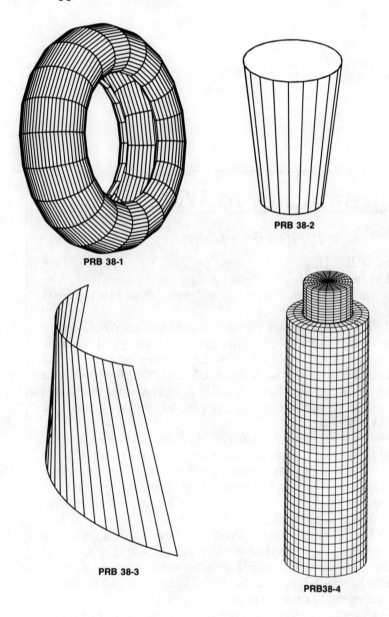

PRB 38-1

PRB 38-2

PRB 38-3

PRB38-4

AUTOCAD® AT WORK

*It Fits Like a Glove**

Glovemaker Wells Lamont had a vexing problem. Glove styles change annually, which means each year Wells Lamont had to draw new styles mechanically, cut the patterns out of tin, and refine them in a painfully slow way.

In its quest to modernize both design and manufacturing, Wells Lamont turned to Conversion Graphics, Inc., a Chicago-area scanning and data conversion service bureau. CGI used CAD Overlay software to scan the glove patterns and convert them for use in AutoCAD. CAD Overlay (developed by Image Systems Technology, Inc., Troy, NY) combines raster and vector technologies within AutoCAD to provide low-cost drawing conversion with complete CAD capabilities.

Every few weeks, CGI receives a batch of tin patterns that are reproduced photographically, several to a page, and then scanned into AutoCAD as a single image. The working file information is then translated and supplied in Wells Lamont's working file format. Wells Lamont can open these files on its computer system and manipulate the graphic information to restyle the glove and numerically cut a new pattern.

Use of CAD Overlay has resulted in several significant savings, according to Randy Worozaken, Vice President of Sales and Marketing at CGI. "It has streamlined our operation by eliminating the vectorizing process, a 2-6 hour step, and enhancing editing time by about 25 percent. It also eliminates the guesswork involved in drawing conversion by giving us a true image."

In addition to assisting glovemakers and other manufacturers requiring CAD/CAM pattern manipulation, CAD Overlay is well suited to other applications. In fact, CGI is using it to enter drawings for projects involving illustrations, schematics, mapping, architecture, shop floor display, logo design, red lining, and archiving. CGI can output data to most mainframe and micro CAD packages.

*Based on a story in *CADENCE* magazine, Vol. 3, No. 6.

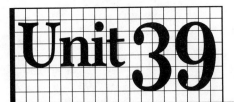

Unit 39 Advanced 3D Modeling

AutoCAD®
Reference
Manual

■ OBJECTIVE:

To practice the 3D modeling capabilities of the TABSURF, EDGESURF, and 3DMESH commands

AutoCAD's TABSURF command enables you to create a polygon mesh representing a tabulated surface defined by a *path* (profile) and *direction vector*. The EDGESURF command lets you construct a *Coons surface* patch from four adjoining edges. The most basic of the 3D-specific commands is 3DMESH. It enables you to define a 3D polygon mesh by specifying its size (in terms of *M* and *N*) and the location of each vertex in the mesh.

4.9.3

4.9.5

4.9.1

The following shows basic 3D models created by each of these three commands.

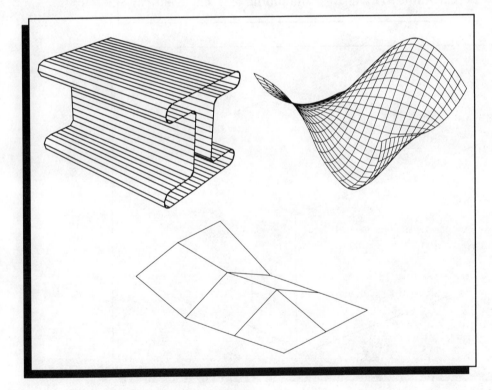

Let's create each of these 3D models.

■ *TABSURF Command*

4.9.3

We'll use the TABSURF command to construct the I-beam shown above.

1 Load AutoCAD and Begin a New Drawing.

2 Name the file **I-BEAM** and use the prototype drawing named 3DPROTO.

3 Enter the **UCS** command and **Restore** the **RSIDE** UCS.

4 Using the **PLINE** command and Arc and Line options, approximate the following figure. It represents one-quarter of the I-beam profile.

_____ NOTE: _____

It's important to use the PLINE rather than the LINE and ARC commands so that AutoCAD will treat the profile as a single entity.

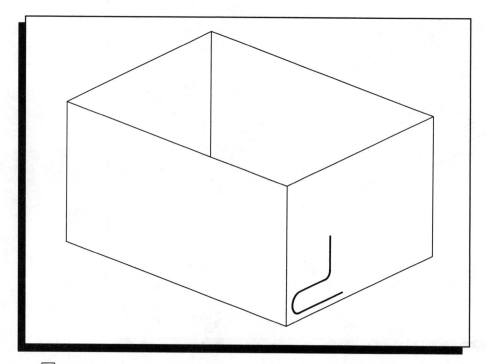

5 Complete the I-beam profile so that it looks like the next illustration.

HINT:

After creating one-quarter of the object, mirror it to complete half of the object. Then mirror that to complete the entire object.

**AutoCAD®
Reference
Manual**

6 Enter the **UCS** command and **Restore** the **TOP** UCS.

7 Set layer **OBJ2**.

8 Beginning at the RSIDE UCS as shown in the following
illustration, draw a line approximately **3** units long.

HINT:

Turn on the Snap mode. It should already be set to .5 unit.

The line provides the *direction vector* for use with the TABSURF
command.

4.9.3

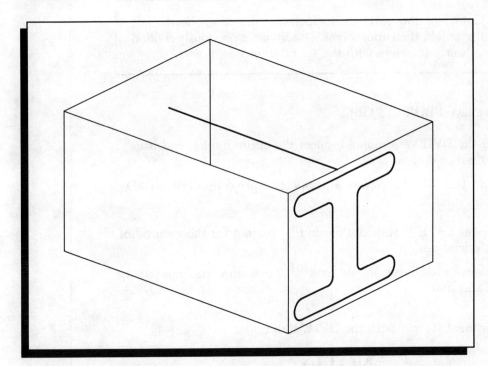

9 Set layer **3DOBJ**.

10 Enter the **TABSURF** command.

11 In reply to "Select path curve:" pick a point on the lower right
quadrant of the I-beam profile.

HINT:

You may need to turn off the Snap mode.

12 Pick a point on the line in reply to "Select direction vector:". The point *must* be closer to the right endpoint of the line than the left endpoint in order for the tabulated surface to extend in the desired direction.

One-quarter of the I-beam should appear.

13 Complete the remaining parts of the I-beam using the TABSURF command.

HINT:

Complete the parts in a clockwise direction—lower left quadrant, upper left, then upper right. Otherwise, a previously created polygon mesh may interfere with the selection of new points.

14 Freeze layers **BOX** and **OBJ2**.

15 Enter the **DVIEW** command, select the entire model, and issue the **D**istance option.

As discussed in Unit 37, this creates a perspective projection of your 3D model.

16 Enter the DVIEW **H**ide option and be patient for the removal of the hidden lines.

Your 3D model of the I-beam should look similar to the one found at the beginning of this unit.

17 Experiment further with the **DVIEW** options.

NOTE:

System variable SURFTAB1 controls the density of the tabulated surface.

4.9.3

18 Enter **END** to save your work and exit the Drawing Editor.

**AutoCAD®
Reference
Manual**

4.9.5

EDGESURF Command

The EDGESURF command is used to construct a *Coons surface patch*. A Coons patch is a 3D surface mesh interpolated (approximated) between four adjoining edges. Coons surface patches are used to define complex, irregular surfaces such as land formations (topography) and manufactured products such as car bodies.

Let's apply the EDGESURF command to the creation of a topological figure similar to the one shown at the beginning of this unit.

1 Using the 3DPROTO prototype drawing, Begin a New Drawing. Name it **CONTOUR**.

2 Enter the **UCS** command and **Restore** the **FRONT** UCS.

3 Using the **PLINE** command and **Arc** option, approximate the construction of Polyline A as shown in the following illustration.

NOTE:

When picking the first and last points of the Polyline, use the NEArest object snap mode. This will snap these points onto the vertical edges of the 3D face. If you do not do this, the Polyline endpoints will not meet accurately. If they do not meet, the EDGESURF command will not work.

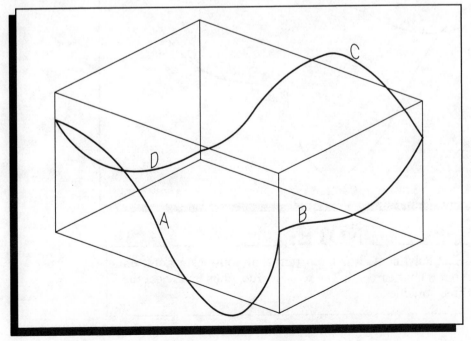

4 Enter the **UCS** command and Restore the **RSIDE** UCS.

5 Using the **PLINE** command and Arc option, approximate the construction of Polyline B as shown in the previous illustration. Use the ENDpoint and NEArest Object Snap modes for the first and last endpoints of the Polyline.

6 Restore the **BACK** UCS and construct Polyline C using the same procedure described in the preceding step.

7 Restore the **LSIDE** UCS and construct Polyline D. Use the ENDpoint Object Snap mode to connect Polyline D to Polyline A.

8 Freeze layer **BOX**.

9 Enter the **EDGESURF** command.

10 In reply to "Select edge 1:" pick a point on Polyline A and near corner 1. (Refer to the following illustration.)

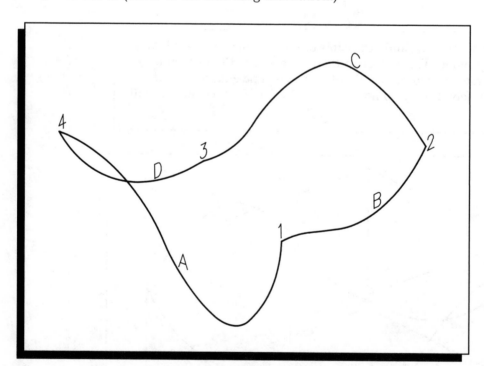

NOTE:

When you select Polyline A, it is important that you pick a point on the Polyline that is near corner 1. The same is true when you select the remaining three Polylines.

11 In reply to "Select edge 2:" pick a point on Polyline B and near corner 2.

12 Select Polylines C and D in the same fashion.

A contour should appear similar to the one shown at the beginning of this unit.

13 Enter the **HIDE** command.

This may take minutes if the speed of your computer is slow.

14 View the contour from various orientations in space using the **DVIEW** and **VPOINT** commands.

15 Enter **END** to save your work and exit the Drawing Editor.

3DMESH Command

4.9.1

1 Begin a New Drawing using the **3DPROTO** prototype drawing. Name it **3DMESH**.

2 Enter the **3DMESH** command.

3 Enter 4 in reply to "Mesh M size:".

4 Enter 3 in reply to "Mesh N size:".

5 Enter the following in reply to the series of "Vertex" prompts. Be sure to include the decimal points.

Vertex (0,0): **5,4,.2**
Vertex (0,1): **5,4.5,.3**
Vertex (0,2): **5,5,.3**
Vertex (1,0): **5.5,4,0**
Vertex (1,1): **5.5,4.5,.2**
Vertex (1,2): **5.5,5,0**
Vertex (2,0): **6,4,0**
Vertex (2,1): **6,4.5,.2**
Vertex (2,2): **6,5,0**
Vertex (3,0): **6.5,4,0**
Vertex (3,1): **6.5,4.5,0**
Vertex (3,2): **6.5,5,0**

Your mesh should look similar to the one at the beginning of this unit.

6 If the mesh does not appear, **ZOOM** All.

As you can see, specifying even a small three-dimensional polygon mesh is very tedious. The 3DMESH command is meant to be used primarily with AutoLISP and not in the fashion presented above.

7 Freeze layer **BOX**.

Editing 3D Polygon Meshes

The vertices of the mesh can be edited with the PEDIT command in a manner similar to editing a Polyline.

1 Enter the **PEDIT** command, pick the mesh, and enter the Edit vertex option.

An "X" should appear at one corner of the mesh.

2 Press **RETURN** four times. This will move the "X" to four consecutive vertices.

3 Enter the Move option and pick a new location for the vertex.

4 Enter eXit twice to exit the PEDIT command.

Types of Mesh Surfaces

3D polygon meshes can be viewed in any one of these surface types.

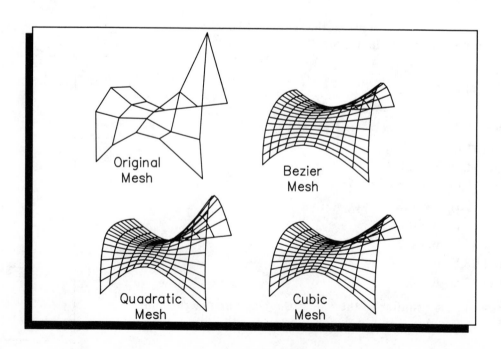

Original Mesh

Bezier Mesh

Quadratic Mesh

Cubic Mesh

Let's create one of them from our original mesh. First, we must specify the mesh type.

1 Enter the **SETVAR** command and the **SURFTYPE** system variable.

2 Enter **5** for the new value. This specifies the quadratic B-spline surface.

NOTE:

A SURFTYPE value of 6 specifies the cubic B-spline surface, and a value of 8 specifies the Bezier surface.

3 Enter the **PEDIT** command, pick the mesh, and enter the Smooth surface option.

Your 3D polygon mesh should change to a quadratic B-spline surface.

NOTE:

System variables SURFU and SURFV control the accuracy of the surface approximation by changing the surface density in the M and N directions.

4 Enter the eXit option to exit the PEDIT command.

3D Construction Dialogue Box

A.3.2.2

AutoCAD's pull-down menu offers an item called "3D Construction..." found under the Draw menu. If you choose it, the dialogue box shown on the following page will be displayed.

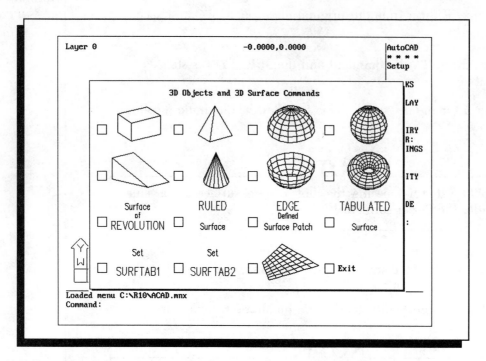

It uses AutoLISP to create 3D objects and also offers an alternative method of entering some of the commands covered in this and the previous unit.

1 Experiment with the 3D Construction dialogue box on your own.

2 Enter **END** to save your work and exit the Drawing Editor.

Questions

1. Describe the steps in using the TABSURF command.

   _____

   _____

2. In connection with the TABSURF command, what is the purpose of the direction vector?

   _____

   _____

3. Describe the EDGESURF command.

   _____

   _____

4. How are User Coordinate Systems used in conjunction with the EDGESURF command?

   _____

   _____

5. Why is use of the 3DMESH command not generally recommended for even the simplest 3D meshes?

   _____

Problems

Using the commands and techniques presented in this unit, construct the following 3D models. Approximate all sizes.

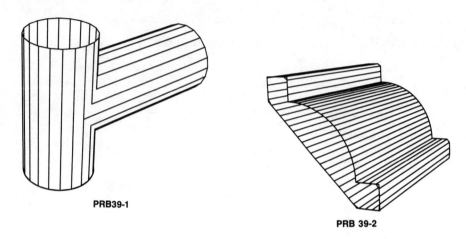

PRB39-1

PRB 39-2

PRB 39-3

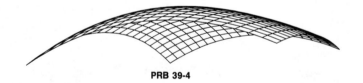

PRB 39-4

AUTOCAD® AT WORK

CAD Brings Unexpected Benefits

An improvement in one area can sometimes result in a host of unexpected benefits in other areas. Consider the case of Advanced Micro Devices (AMD), which recently incorporated micro-based CAD into its design process.

The Manufacturing Services Division of AMD, a semiconductor manufacturer in San Jose, California, designs and produces packages for all of AMD's semiconductor devices. The packages protect fragile electronic circuits from contamination. The strategic planning manager for the division, Mark Brodsky, realized AMD engineers needed a quicker way to modify piece-part drawings used in package assembly.

The division already had—and intended to keep—a dedicated drafting system called Pegasys. But AMD still needed a way for its engineering staff to modify documentation quickly and accurately as it shuttled between the engineers and the vendor. To accomplish this goal, AMD purchased the AutoCAD software package plus a file server and network to run with the program. In addition to serving a front-end function for the existing drafting stations, the system also could allow the Manufacturing Services Division to integrate their office automation procedures. These rewards greatly exceeded those commonly associated with a CAD system.

In looking for micro-based software, Brodsky had sought a program that featured simplicity and ease of use, as well as the ability to work with all the other constraints. "We found AutoCAD to be the most applicable for general-purpose drawings, and the simplest to use," Brodsky said. "We also found that AutoCAD's DXF (Drawing Interchange File) was becoming the major format standard." The company that originated Pegasys was preparing translation software that would convert Pegasys to DXF. Thus choosing AutoCAD meant that all the work done by the drafters on Pegasys would be compatible with the new system, and vice versa.

As soon as the division's staff had satisfied their drafting needs, they were able to explore other benefits of their new system. Brodsky describes one of them: "We've asked vendors of our piece parts to provide us with electronic copies of our drawings. This eliminates the tedious task of our vendors having to redraw an AMD drawing in order to set up their photo plot equipment. Two major vendors will begin transferring drawings to AMD in AutoCAD's DXF format. DXF, we now realize, is the most widely used translator for all of our vendors' inhouse CAD systems." When the vendors' work is complete, they provide AMD with a disk of the finished product. "We can load the disk on AutoCAD, send it through our network to the Pegasys system, and, with very little modification, offer translation into Pegasys format and then print out an official AMD drawing ready for signoff," explains Brodsky. "It's a good sign that we are already using CAD for purposes beyond our original goals," he adds. "We anticipate that, over time, we'll find still other uses."

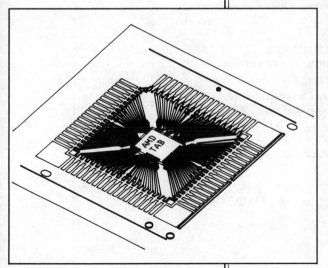

Courtesy of Advanced Micro Devices and Autodesk, Inc.

Unit 40

An Internal Peek at AutoCAD's Menus

AutoCAD®
Reference
Manual

A.3

■ OBJECTIVE:

To examine and understand the contents of AutoCAD's menu file ACAD.MNU

This unit concentrates on the components which make up the ACAD.MNU file. It reviews the file in its raw form: the components you don't see when you're in the Drawing Editor. Later, you will learn to modify and create your own menu, one as simple or as sophisticated as you'd like.

The following steps do not require a word processor, but it is desirable to use one. In a later exercise (when you actually create a custom menu), a word processor or text editor is highly recommended.

The Raw Menu

1 Start your computer system and obtain your DOS prompt (*e.g.*, C < or C:\ >).

2 Make the AutoCAD ACAD.MNU file resident in your current directory.

HINT:

ACAD.MNU contains the accessible source code of your screen menu. This file is contained in a disk directory called SOURCE. If you cannot locate this directory and file on your hard disk, then review your AutoCAD "Support" diskette. After you have located ACAD.MNU, copy it to your hard disk. See Appendix G for details on changing directories and Appendix F for details on copying files.

NOTE:

Note the file ACAD.MNX contained with your other AutoCAD system files. This file is ACAD.MNU in its compiled form. The compiled .MNX file is compact and fast. AutoCAD uses this file to display the screen menus found in the Drawing Editor. You are unable to review and edit the contents of compiled menu files such as ACAD.MNX. Therefore ACAD.MNU is made available.

3 Using the DOS "TYPE" command, list the contents of ACAD.MNU.

Example: C:\ACAD\SOURCE>**TYPE ACAD.MNU** (and press **RETURN**)

NOTE:

The file will scroll off the screen before you can read it. To stop the scrolling, quickly press CTRL S. To resume scrolling, press any key.

You may want to press CTRL C and start over so that you can see the first portion of the file. Function key F3 reenters your last entry at the DOS prompt.

4 Quickly stop the scrolling so that you have the first portion of the file on your screen.

Your screen should have information similar to the following.

```
***BUTTONS                                  ***POP2
;                                           [Draw]
$p1=*                                       [Line]*^C^C$S=X $s=line line
^c^c                                        [Arc]*^C^C$S=X $s=poparc arc
^B                                          [Circle]*^C^C$S=X $s=popcircl circle
^O                                          [Polyline]*^C^C$S=X $s=pline pline
^G                                          [3D Polyline]*^C^C$S=X $S=3dpoly 3dpoly
^D                                          [Insert]^C^Csetvar attdia 1 $S=X $s=insert insert
^E                                          [Dtext]*^C^C$S=X $s=Dtext Dtext
^T                                          [Hatch...]^C^C$i=hatch1 $i=*
***AUX1                                     [3D Construction...]$i=3dobjects $i=*
;
$p1=*                                       ***POP3
^C^C                                        [Modify]
^B                                          [Erase]*^C^C$S=X $s=erase erase si auto
^O                                          [Move]*^C^C$S=X $s=move move si auto
^G                                          [Copy]*^C^C$S=X $s=copy copy si auto
^D                                          [Properties]*^C^C$S=X $S=chprop chprop si auto
^E                                          [Break]*^C^C$S=X $S=break break
^T                                          [Fillet]*^C^C$S=X $S=fillet fillet
                                            [Mirror]*^C^C$S=X $s=mirror mirror auto
***POP1                                     [Trim]*^C^C$S=X $s=trim trim auto
[Tools]                                     [Extend]*^C^C$S=X $s=extend extend auto
[OSNAP]^C^C$p1= $p1=* OSNAP \               [Stretch]*^C^C$S=X $s=stretch stretch crossing
CENter                                      [Edit Polylines]^C^C^P+
ENDpoint
INSert
[INTersection]INT
MIDpoint
NEArest
NODe
[PERpendicular]PER
QUAdrant
[QUICK,]QUICK,^Z$p1=*
TANgent
NONE
[~--]
[FILTERS...   ]$p1=filters $p1=*
[Cancel]^C^C
[U]^C^CU
[Redo]^C^CREDO
[List]^C^CLIST

**filters
[Filters]
.X
.Y
.Z
.XY
.XZ
.YZ
[TOOLS...]$p1= $p1=*
```

---

⑤ Find each of the following components in ACAD.MNU. Most should be contained within the first portion of the menu.

***BUTTONS —specifies a buttons menu for the buttons on a mouse or digitizer cursor control

***SCREEN —specifies a screen menu

***TABLET1 —specifies tablet menu area 1

***icon —an icon menu is declared by providing a ***icon item in the menu file

***pop2 —pull-down menu sections are defined using ***pop1, ***pop2, etc.

**XYZ —specifies a submenu; XYZ can be any characters, such as BL

$S=BL 3 —means to activate submenu **BL 3

$S= —means to activate the last menu

$p1=* —causes pull-down POP1 to appear

$i=fonts1 —here, the "$i=" item addresses the **fonts1 icon menu

$i=* —this special menu item displays an icon menu and allows you to make a selection from it

[BLOCK:] —the text enclosed by brackets will appear in the screen menu; in this particular case, the item "BLOCK:" will appear in the screen menu

[acad(cone)] —this addresses the cone slide image contained in the acad slide library for display as an icon

SI —short for Single; causes the command to execute immediately and does not allow for further object selection interaction

Auto —also AU; during object selection, the use of Auto enables you to apply the Window and Crossing options without the need to enter them

; —This character will tell the computer to automatically press RETURN

\ —the backslash will stop the computer, and the computer will expect input from the user

(a space) —an empty space is the same as pressing the space bar

+ —menu item continues on next line

~ —displays prompt in half-tone

-- —dashes display a separator line between pull-down menu items

* —an asterisk at the beginning of a menu item will cause the menu item to repeat until a cancel (CTRL C) is issued

^ —this character (called a caret) will automatically press the CTRL key

^C —this will issue a cancel, the same as pressing CTRL C

^O —this will activate the CTRL and O keys the same as if you were to press CTRL O to toggle the Ortho mode; ^O is used in the BUTTONS menu to assign button #6 to this function

^D	—toggles coordinates display
^E	—toggles isometric plane
^B	—toggles snap on and off
^G	—toggles grid on and off
^T	—toggles tablet mode on and off
^M	—repeats last command
^Q	—toggles printer echo on and off
^X	—deletes current command line

These individual components are combined to create menu items (also referred to as macros) that perform specific AutoCAD functions. For example, [U]^C^CU will display U in the standard screen menu, will enter cancel twice, and will enter the U command.

⑥ Examine each of the following menu items from the ACAD.MNU file.

$S=OSNAPB	— activates the **OSNAPB submenu
***POP5	— specifies pull-down menu area 5
[DRAW]$S=X $S=DR	— displays "DRAW" in the screen menu; activates the **X submenu and the **DR submenu
[* * * *]$S=OSNAPB	— displays "* * * *" in the screen menu; activates the **OSNAPB submenu
[ZOOM:]$S=X $S=ZOOM 'ZOOM	— displays "ZOOM:" in the screen menu; activates the **X and **ZOOM submenus; enters the transparent ZOOM command
[ERASE:]^C^CERASE	— displays "ERASE:" in the menu; issues cancel; issues cancel again; enters the ERASE command
[drag]$S=X $S=PARC drag	— displays "drag" in the menu; activates the **X submenu and the **PARC submenu; enters drag
[3-point:]^C^CARC \\DRAG	— displays "3-point:" in the menu; issues cancel; issues cancel again; issues the ARC command and space bar; pauses for user input again; enters drag

345

[Line]*^C^C$S=X $s=line line — displays "Line" in the menu; the asterisk causes the menu item to repeat; issues cancel; issues cancel again; activates the **X submenu; activates the **line submenu; enters the LINE command (This menu item is found in the Draw pull-down menu.)

[3D Construction . . .]$i=3dobjects $i=* — displays "3D Construction..." in the menu; addresses the 3dobjects icon menu; displays the named icon menu (This menu item is found in the Draw pull-down menu.)

[acad(ansi31)]^c^chatch ansi31 — addresses the ansi31 slide image contained in the acad slide library; issues cancel; issues cancel again; enters the HATCH command; enters the ansi31 hatch pattern (This item is found in the hatch pattern dialogue box.)

7 Attempt to locate each of the previous menu items in the ACAD.MNU file. Print the pages on which they appear.

HINT: Some text editors and word processors have a search/find function. This function will assist you in locating each of the menu items.

8 Start AutoCAD and proceed into the Drawing Editor. (Begin a New Drawing or edit an existing one.)

9 Referring to the hardcopy printouts, locate each of the above menu items in the Drawing Editor and pick each of them. Compare the printouts to how they function.

10 Enter **QUIT** to exit the Drawing Editor.

Questions

Describe what each of the following menu items will do.

[DIM:]$S=DIM ^CDIM

_____

_____

[style]S;

_____

[HELP:]^C^C? BLOCK

_____

_____

**LINE

_____

[3-point:]^CARC \\DRAG

_____

_____

window

_____

[*]*

_____

[INSERT:]^C^CINSERT

_____

[S,E,D:]^C^CARC \E \D DRAG

_____

_____

[done];

_____

Problems

1. Print a portion of the ACAD.MNU file and then start AutoCAD. Get into the Drawing Editor and experiment with different command and submenu sequences. Locate the sequences on the ACAD.MNU printout. (Because ACAD.MNU is very long, you may want to print only part of it.)

2. Locate items in the ACAD.MNU printout that you cannot fully visualize. Then find the corresponding item in the screen menu and execute it.

AUTOCAD® AT WORK

*Parametrics and AutoCAD Speed Engine Design**

If there were a real magic wand, Joe Schubeck of Eagle Engine Manufacturing would swear that its name was AutoCAD. Schubeck and his small group of technicians produce an aluminum V-8 engine for use in top fuel dragsters completely designed with AutoCAD and Synthesis, a parametric processor that works with AutoCAD.

Depending on the fuel used, the Eagle Engine can put out as much as 3,000 horsepower. Besides delivering colossal horsepower, the engine is designed to be configurable by the user. It allows interchangeable cylinders and sleeves on five-inch centers. The heads are even designed to allow from one to three spark plugs per cylinder. This flexibility lets one racer build on the basic engine block for top fuel racing while another builds on it for tractor pulls. No longer are drag racers locked into one winning design.

With Synthesis, Eagle Engine Manufacturing can make a part from the drawing and check out the formulas for that part in the dynamometer room or on the strip. When satisfied with the part, the company can use the original formulas modified with Synthesis, to make a similar part without having to bench test it.

Another advantage of Synthesis is its ability to tighten tolerances. By running a DXF file through Synthesis, a user can specify tolerances up to sixteen decimal places.

The engines built so far have been machined out-of-house from drawings produced by Eagle's printer/plotter. When the engines are in full production, most machining will be done in-house using the same drawings that created the Eagle to control the CNC processor on the machine tool.

Schubeck's biggest goal for his engine is to power a top fuel dragster past the 300 mph mark in a quarter-mile. Considering the Eagle's advantages over other competition, that goal seems easily attainable.

*Based on a story in *CADENCE* magazine, Vol. 3, No. 3.

Creating Custom Screen Menus

■ OBJECTIVE:

To create a simple AutoCAD screen menu and to apply the MENU command

This unit involves the development of an AutoCAD screen menu which incorporates several commonly used AutoCAD commands. It uses a simple approach for creating the menu and does not require a word processor or text editor, although using one is recommended.

AutoCAD users can create screen menus to include a wide range of AutoCAD commands. Furthermore, users can develop custom "macros," which automatically execute any series of inputs. For example, a simple two-item macro can be created to enter ZOOM Window in one step, thereby minimizing input from the user. ZOOM W could then be included on, and activated from, a screen menu. Sophisticated macros can be created to activate numerous AutoCAD commands and functions in a single step.

Everything that can be entered using the keyboard can be entered automatically via macros. Thus, you have the flexibility to develop a menu at any level of sophistication.

■ *Developing a Screen Menu with Macros* _____

Let's develop a short and simple screen menu.

1 Start your computer system and obtain your DOS prompt, *e.g.,*
C:\>

2 If you have been storing your files on a floppy diskette, place this diskette into the computer. (You will create and store a file named SIMPLE1.MNU on this diskette.)

HINT:
If you have a word processor or text editor, use it. Create a new file and name it SIMPLE1.MNU, and then skip to Step 4.

3 If you don't have a word processor or text editor, type the following after the DOS prompt: **COPY CON:SIMPLE1.MNU** and press **RETURN**. If you are storing on A drive, then specify A: (*e.g.,* COPY CON:A:SIMPLE1.MNU).

You have just begun a new file named SIMPLE1.MNU.

NOTE:
Your only editing capability is your backspace key, so be very careful. If you make a mistake you cannot correct, you must start over.

Your cursor should now be at the beginning of the next line.

4 Begin typing the contents of the following menu. Type it *exactly* as shown. Use either upper- or lowercase letters for the macros (the information after the second bracket).

***SCREEN (press **RETURN**)
[A] (press **RETURN**)
[SIMPLE] (press **RETURN**)
[MENU] (press **RETURN**)
(press **RETURN**)
(press **RETURN**)
[LINE]^C^Cline (press **RETURN**)
[ERAS L]^C^CERASE L (press **RETURN**)
[ZOOM W]^C^Czoom W (press **RETURN**)
[TEXT]^C^Ctext (press **RETURN**)
[*Cancel*]^C^C (press **RETURN**)
press the **F6** function key and press **RETURN**

5 When you're finished, immediately make a backup copy of this file.

6 If you haven't done so already, make this file easily accessible while in the Drawing Editor by copying it to the appropriate (ACAD) directory.

7 Load AutoCAD and bring up the Drawing Editor by selecting option 1 or 2 from the Main Menu.

You should now have the standard ACAD.MNU items on your screen, as usual.

MENU Command _____

1 Enter the **MENU** command.

3.7

2 For the menu name, enter **SIMPLE1**. (If SIMPLE1.MNU is contained in a directory other than the default directory, you must specify the path. For example, if SIMPLE1.MNU is on a directory named USER, you would enter USER\SIMPLE1.)

Your new SIMPLE1 menu should appear. SIMPLE1.MNU automatically compiled too, and a new SIMPLE1.MNX exists.

3 Select each of the commands to see whether they work.

NOTE: _____

You also have full access to all other AutoCAD commands. Just type them.

4 If you have a mouse or cursor control with more than one button, try each of them.

Do they not work as before? That's because SIMPLE1.MNX does not contain a buttons menu.

5 Enter **MENU** again, type **ACAD**, and press **RETURN**.

6 Enter **QUIT** to exit the Drawing Editor.

NOTE:

The UNDEFINE and REDEFINE commands are also available. The UNDEFINE command will delete the built-in definition of an AutoCAD command. This lets you create entirely new command definitions using the existing AutoCAD command names. If you want to restore the original built-in definition of the AutoCAD command, use the REDEFINE command.

AUTOCAD® AT WORK

Illustrating Books with AutoCAD

Before George Omura began using AutoCAD, he made book illustrations with India ink or colored drawing pens. The work was time-consuming, and sometimes Omura had to throw away a drawing after hours of painstaking work because of an error or spilled ink.

Since Omura began using CAD, however, he doesn't have to worry about such things. Any errors he makes can be corrected quickly and easily.

Easy revision is only one of the AutoCAD features that George finds useful. Other features Omura relies on are his library of frequently used shapes and objects, the zoom feature, and the layering feature, which he uses to experiment with color.

Currently Omura works mostly as an illustrator for technical manuals and textbooks. But because AutoCAD is so efficient and flexible, Omura is interested in taking on more graphic design projects, such as letterheads, logos, and brochures for individuals and small businesses. "AutoCAD takes the dreariness out of drafting work, allowing me to concentrate on the creative part," he says happily.

Questions

1. Briefly define an AutoCAD macro.

   _____

   _____

2. Why are custom macros useful?

   _____

   _____

3. The INSERT command can be included in a macro like any other command. In conjunction with a drawing name, how could this macro be useful?

   _____

   _____

4. State one useful application for developing a new AutoCAD macro, and write this macro below.

   _____

   _____

   _____

5. What AutoCAD command allows you to bring up a new screen menu?

   _____

6. What is the file extension for a noncompiled menu file? A compiled menu file?

   _____

7. What is the difference between a compiled and a noncompiled menu file?

   _____

   _____

8. What menu item specification must precede the contents of a screen menu?

   _____

1. Create the following screen menu and name it SECOND.MNU. Enter it exactly as you see it. Then load AutoCAD and Begin a New Drawing. Name it PRB41-1. Load the SECOND menu and execute each of its commands to see whether and how they work. If any of the commands do not work, edit SECOND.MNU. You'll need to use a word processor or a text editor such as EDLIN.

```
***SCREEN
[LINE]^c^cline
[ERAS W]^c^cerase w
[ZOOM W]^c^czoom w
[ZOOM P]^c^czoom p
[Comp S]^c^cstyle comp complex;;;;;;;;
[His Name]^c^ctext 6,2 .2 0 John Doe;;;Mechanical Engineer;
[My Name]^c^ctext s comp 6,3 .2 0;
[FLIPSNAP]^b
[ARCH U]^c^cunits 4;;;;;;graphscr

[FLIP T]textscr;
[*Cancel*]^c^c
```

2. Copy SECOND.MNU and rename the copy SECOND2.MNU. Modify SECOND2.MNU so that it looks exactly like the one below. You'll need to use a word processor or a text editor such as EDLIN.

```
**SECOND2
[LINE]^c^cline $S=ZZZ
[ERAS W]^c^cerase w
[ZOOM W]^c^czoom w
[ZOOM P]^c^czoom p
[COMP S]^c^cstyle comp complex;;;;;;;;
[His Name]^c^ctext 6,2 .2 0 John Doe;;;Mechanical Engineer;
[My Name]^c^ctext s comp 6,3 .2 0;
[FLIPSNAP]^b
[ARCH U]^c^cunits 4;;;;;;graphscr
[FLIP T]textscr
[*Cancel*]^c^c
[LAST MNU]$S=
[ROOT PG]$S=S

**ZZZ
[End Pt]end
[Cen Pt]cen
[Nearest]near
[More]$S=OSNAPB
```

If you attempt to use the menu in its current form, certain items will not function properly. Make a copy of the AutoCAD standard menu, ACAD.MNU, and rename it ACAD2.MNU. Add the contents of SECOND2.MNU to the beginning of ACAD2.MNU as shown by the following printout. Add the [Sample]$S=SECOND2 item at the empty space after the "Setup" item contained in the root page of the screen menu. (See printout below.) The root page portion begins at approximately the 450th line of the menu.

HINT: Use a word processor such as Volkswriter® to perform this operation. Use the word processor's "text merge" or "file read" capability.

```
**SECOND2
[LINE]^c^cline $S=ZZZ
[ERAS W]^c^cerase w
[ZOOM W]^c^czoom w
[ZOOM P]^c^czoom p
[Comp S]^c^cstyle comp complex;;;;;;;;;
[His Name]^c^ctext 6,2 .2 0 John Doe;;;Mechanical Engineer;
[My Name]^c^ctext s comp 6,3 .2 0;
[FLIPSNAP]^b
[ARCH U]^c^cunits 4;;;;;;;graphscr
[FLIP T]textscr
[*Cancel*]^c^c
[LAST MNU]$S=
[ROOT PG]$S=S

**ZZZ
[End Pt]end
[Cen Pt]cen
[Nearest]near
[More]$S=OSNAPB

***BUTTONS
;
$p1=*
^c^c
^B
^O
^G
^D
^E
^T
```

(continued next page)

```
***AUX1
;
$p1=*
^C^C

[ Join Viewports]^C^CVPORTS;J
[ Restore Saved]^C^CVPORTS;R;
[ List Saved]^C^CVPORTS;?;
[ Exit]^c^c

***SCREEN
**S
[AutoCAD]^C^C$S=X $S=S $P1=POP1 $P3=POP3
[* * * *]$S=OSNAPB
[Setup]^C^C^P(progn(prompt "Loading setup...   ")(load "setup")) ^P$S=X $S=UNITS
[ Sample]$S=SECOND2  ←
[BLOCKS]$S=X $S=BL
[DIM:]$S=X $S=DIM ^C^CDIM
[DISPLAY]$S=X $S=DS
[DRAW]$S=X $S=DR
[EDIT]$S=X $S=ED
[INQUIRY]$S=X $S=INQ
[LAYER:]$S=X $S=LAYER ^C^CLAYER
[SETTINGS]$S=X $S=SET
[PLOT]$S=X $S=PLOT
[UCS:]$S=X $S=UCS1 ^C^CUCS
[UTILITY]$S=X $S=UT

[3D]$S=X $S=3D
```

After completing the above, load AutoCAD and bring up ACAD2.MNU
into the AutoCAD Drawing Editor. See whether each menu item works
properly and be sure to select the new item called Sample.

Also, be sure to experiment with the LINE item from the Sample
submenu, and then pick each of its submenu items, including "More."

3. Develop a new custom screen menu (and buttons menu, too, if you'd
like). Make the menu as sophisticated and powerful as you'd like.

AutoCAD®
Reference
Manual

■ OBJECTIVE:

To apply the TABLET command, the tablet configuration steps, and the tablet menu development process

This unit focuses on configuring a digitizing tablet for use with a tablet menu and on creating tablet menus. You must, of course, have a digitizing tablet to complete this unit.

As you may know, part of your digitizing tablet allows for *screen menu* pointing. This enables you to select screen menu items with your pointing device instead of typing them in. Other areas of the digitizing tablet can be designated for *tablet menus*, enabling you to enter a wide variety of AutoCAD commands and functions quickly and conveniently.

12.1
B.4

Developing a Tablet Menu

The first step in designing a new tablet menu is to ask yourself what you would like included in the menu. The best way to answer this question is to sketch the tablet menu overlay on paper so that you gain some sense of the placement of each menu component. After the sketch is refined to your liking, it is used in developing the actual menu file. In this unit, a sample tablet menu overlay has been provided. Later, after you've learned the procedures, you'll be able to design your own.

The sample on the next page is a relatively simple but functional tablet menu overlay. Let's use it as the model for the following steps.

1 Make an enlarged photocopy of the tablet menu overlay so that it comes close to fitting your digitizing tablet. If your copier doesn't have enlargement capability, you may use the overlay at the same size.

___ NOTE: ___

The overlay must not extend outside the active area on your digitizer. For instance, if your active area is 11″ × 11″, then the overlay must not be larger than 11″ × 11″.

Next, let's create the menu file that holds the menu items. Notice how these menu items correspond to the items on the tablet menu overlay, starting with tablet menu 1.

2 Using COPY CON: or better yet, a word processor, enter the items on pp. 358-359. Name the file **FIRSTTAB.MNU**. Be sure to enter the items exactly as shown and press **RETURN** after each entry.

NOTE: ___

The Buttons Menu is for a three-button cursor control.

12.2
A.3.3

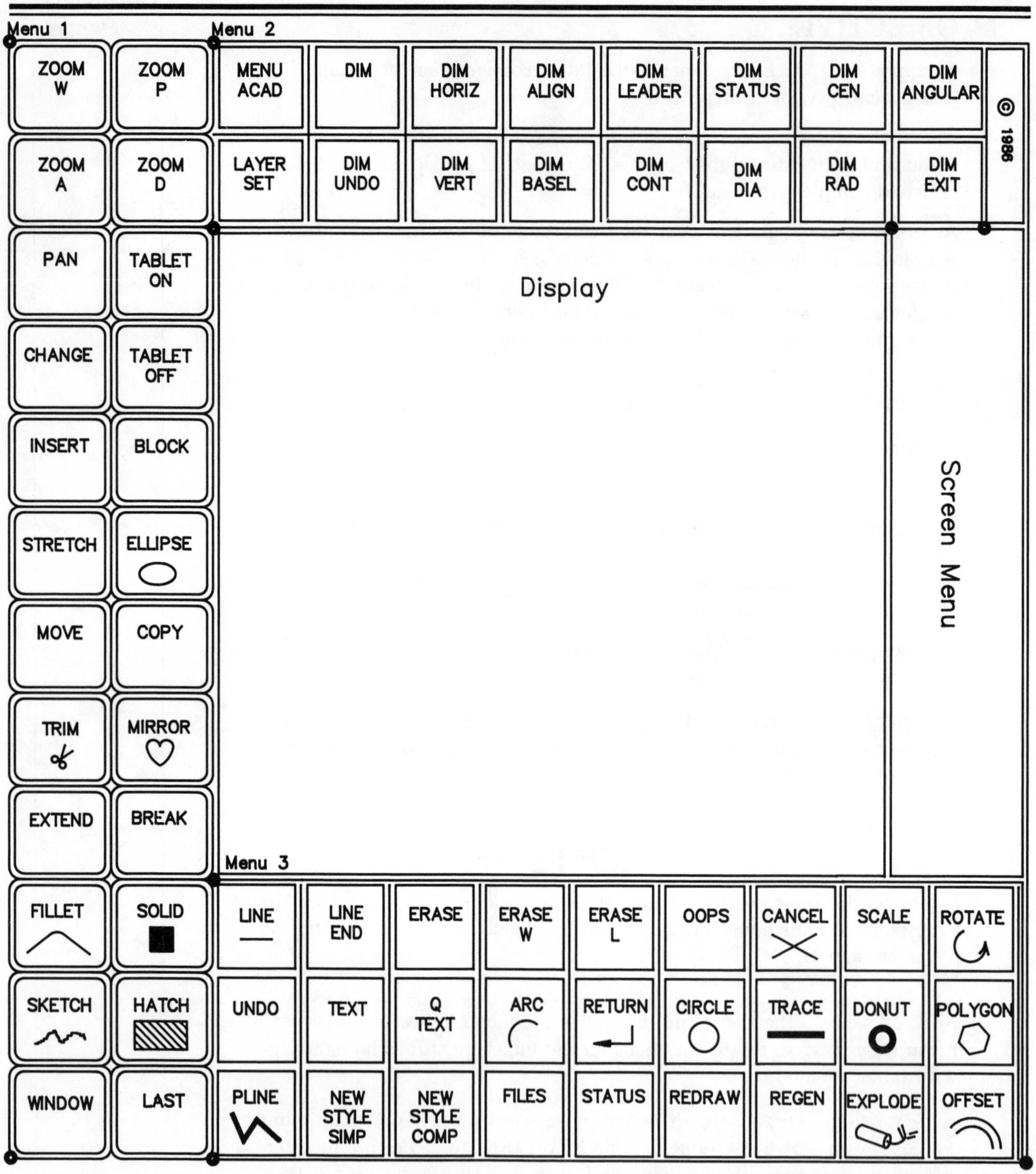

| ZOOM W | ZOOM P | MENU ACAD | DIM | DIM HORIZ | DIM ALIGN | DIM LEADER | DIM STATUS | DIM CEN | DIM ANGULAR |
| ZOOM A | ZOOM D | LAYER SET | DIM UNDO | DIM VERT | DIM BASEL | DIM CONT | DIM DIA | DIM RAD | DIM EXIT |

© 1986

PAN — TABLET ON

CHANGE — TABLET OFF

INSERT — BLOCK

STRETCH — ELLIPSE

MOVE — COPY

TRIM — MIRROR

EXTEND — BREAK

Display

Screen Menu

Menu 3

FILLET	SOLID	LINE	LINE END	ERASE	ERASE W	ERASE L	OOPS	CANCEL	SCALE	ROTATE
SKETCH	HATCH	UNDO	TEXT	Q TEXT	ARC	RETURN	CIRCLE	TRACE	DONUT	POLYGON
WINDOW	LAST	PLINE	NEW STYLE SIMP	NEW STYLE COMP	FILES	STATUS	REDRAW	REGEN	EXPLODE	OFFSET

***BUTTONS
;

^C^CREDRAW

***TABLET1
^C^Czoom w
^C^Czoom p
^C^Czoom a
^C^Czoom d
^C^Cpan
^C^Ctablet on
^C^Cchange
^C^Ctablet off
^C^Cinsert
^C^Cblock
^C^Cstretch
^C^Cellipse
^C^Cmove
^C^Ccopy
^C^Ctrim
^C^Cmirror
^C^Cextend
^C^Cbreak
^C^Cfillet
^C^Csolid
^C^Csketch
^C^Chatch
window
last

***TABLET2
^C^Cmenu acad
^C^Cdim
horizontal
aligned
leader
status
center
angular
^C^Clayer set
undo
vertical
baseline
continue
diameter
radius
^C^C

```
***TABLET3
^C^Cline
^C^Cline end
^C^Cerase
^C^Cerase w
^C^Cerase l
^C^Coops
^C^C
^C^Cscale
^C^Crotate
^C^Cundo
^C^Ctext
^C^Cqtext
^C^Carc
;
^C^Ccircle
^C^Ctrace
^C^Cdonut
^C^Cpolygon
^C^Cpline
^C^Cstyle simp simplex;;;;;;;
^C^Cstyle comp complex;;;;;;;
^C^Cfiles
^C^Cstatus
^C^Credraw
^C^Cregen
^C^Cexplode
^C^Coffset
```

③ Be sure to store the menu contents, and then copy the file to the directory containing the AutoCAD system files, if it is not there already.

④ Make a backup copy of the file.

TABLET Command ————————————————

① Secure the menu overlay to your digitizer tablet with tape.

NOTE:

Be sure that all of the overlay is inside the active pointing area of your digitizing tablet. If it is not, the tablet configuration process will not work.

② Load AutoCAD and bring up the Drawing Editor by selecting item 1 or 2 from the Main Menu.

**AutoCAD®
Reference
Manual**
12.4

12.4.4

③ Enter the **TABLET** command, and then enter the Configuration
(**CFG**) option.

You should get the following on your screen.

```
Enter number of tablet menus desired (0-4):
```

④ Enter 3.

You should now have the following on your screen.

```
Digitize upper left corner of menu area 1:
```

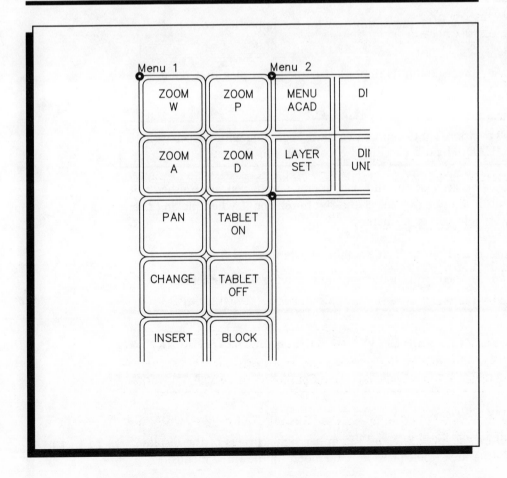

5 Locate the upper left corner of menu 1 and pick that point. (The point is indicated on the overlay by a small donut.)

NOTE:

In this particular overlay, menu 1 is comprised of the first two columns.

6 Pick the lower left corner of menu 1 (also indicated by a small donut)...

7 ... and the lower right corner of menu 1 (the small donut two cells to the right of the preceding point).

You have just defined the boundaries of menu 1.

8 Enter 2 for the number of columns in menu 1...

9 ... and 12 for the number of rows in menu 1.

Now AutoCAD knows the exact size and location of all twenty-four cells in tablet menu 1.

AutoCAD should now be prompting you for the upper left corner of menu 2.

10 Locate menu 2 and its upper left corner, and pick that point.

NOTE:

Menu 2 is comprised of the upper two rows, beginning with the cell called MENU ACAD. Menu 2 consists of 8 columns and 2 rows.

11 Proceed exactly as you did with menu 1 until you are finished with menu 2. Be sure you select the rightmost donut when picking the lower right corner of menu 2.

12 Proceed with menu 3. It contains 9 columns and 3 rows.

After you are finished, you should get the following on your screen.

Do you want to respecify the screen pointing area? <N>

13 Reply with a Yes.

14 Digitize the lower left and the upper right corners of the display pointing area (the square area bounded by the three menus).

You are now finished with the tablet configuration. All of your changes have been stored in the file named ACAD.CFG.

Note that the right portion of the overlay has been left open for selecting screen menu items.

MENU Command

3.7

Now let's load the tablet menu called FIRSTTAB.MNU.

1 Enter the **MENU** command, type **FIRSTTAB**, and press **RETURN**.

HINT:

If FIRSTTAB.MNU is stored in a subdirectory, such as USER, specify it, *e.g.*, USER\FIRSTTAB.

If you correctly completed the above steps, you should now have full access to your new tablet menu.

2 Experiment with the tablet menu by picking each of the cells on the overlay.

3 To bring back the standard ACAD.MNU, pick the tablet menu item called **MENU ACAD** (near the upper left corner) or enter the **MENU** command and then enter **ACAD**.

You no longer have access to your tablet menu.

Combining Menus

Now let's combine FIRSTTAB.MNU with our SIMPLE1.MNU screen menu and create a new file named MERGE.MNU. This will provide us with access to both a screen and a tablet menu.

NOTE:

This process will require a word processor with a "read in" or "insert" capability.

---

1 Bring up the contents of SIMPLE1.MNU with a word processor.

2 Using the capabilities of the word processor, insert (read in) the entire contents of FIRSTTAB.MNU. Place it at the end of SIMPLE1.MNU.

3 Store all in a new file called MERGE.MNU.

The contents of your file should now look very similar to the following.

***SCREEN
[A]
[SIMPLE]
[MENU]

[LINE]^C^Cline
[ERAS L]^C^CERASE L
[ZOOM W]^C^Czoom w
[TEXT]^C^Ctext
[*Cancel*]^C^C

***BUTTONS
;
^C^CREDRAW

***TABLET1
^C^Czoom w
^C^Czoom p
^C^Czoom a
^C^Czoom d
^C^Cpan
^C^Ctablet on
^C^Cchange
^C^Ctablet off
^C^Cinsert
^C^Cblock
^C^Cstretch
^C^Cellipse
^C^Cmove
^C^Ccopy
^C^Ctrim
^C^Cmirror
^C^Cextend
^C^Cbreak
^C^Cfillet
^C^Csolid
^C^Csketch
^C^Chatch
window
last

***TABLET2
^C^Cmenu acad
^C^Cdim
horizontal
aligned
leader
status
center
angular
^C^Clayer set
undo
vertical
baseline
continue
diameter
radius
^C^C

***TABLET3
^C^Cline
^C^Cline end
^C^Cerase
^C^Cerase w
^C^Cerase l
^C^Coops
^C^C
^C^Cscale
^C^Crotate
^C^Cundo
^C^Ctext
^C^Cqtext
^C^Carc
;
^C^Ccircle
^C^Ctrace
^C^Cdonut
^C^Cpolygon
^C^Cpline
^C^Cstyle simp simplex;;;;;;;
^C^Cstyle comp complex;;;;;;;
^C^Cfiles
^C^Cstatus
^C^Credraw
^C^Cregen
^C^Cexplode
^C^Coffset

364

Now let's try it out.

1 Load AutoCAD and bring up the Drawing Editor.

NOTE:

Make sure the MERGE.MNU file is accessible by AutoCAD.

2 Enter the **MENU** command and then enter MERGE.

You should now have access to the screen menu as well as all tablet menu commands and functions.

AUTOCAD® AT WORK

*Parametric Packaging**

You have probably eaten or used at least one thing that has been in contact with a Ropak container. Ropak Corporation is a leading international manufacturer of plastic packaging and handling products for foods, coatings, and manufacturing materials. As part of its service, Ropak integrates all the functions of design, engineering, tooling, production, and even decoration of the manufactured product. The company's in-house development group works directly with customers to modify existing products for specific uses and to design unique solutions to specialized packaging problems. To provide these services quickly and efficiently, Ropak uses AutoCAD and the Synthesis parametric design package (from Synthesis, Inc.).

Like many manufacturers, Ropak produces products with a large number of variations on similar parts or assembly packages. "Family of parts" products used to require extensive and repetitive redesign efforts for any variations in specifications. With Synthesis, however, an engineer can set up a spec sheet with the design parameters of a particular product. Then, when a small modification is required, a trainee can enter variables, and the program will automatically produce modified drawings that are fully documented and ready to use in the manufacturing process.

Ropak's redesign of a fish roe (eggs) container is an example of their capabilities. The container is used to transport roe from the Pacific Northwest to the Far East. For a variety of reasons, the basic container needed to be redesigned. The improved version satisfied the customer's needs by featuring a slightly domed lid and a revised bottom to accommodate the lid for secure stacking. Redesigning the three parts making up the new container took four days. According to Ropak design engineer David Bailey, this work would have taken about three weeks just a couple of years ago.

Ropak considers the AutoCAD/Synthesis design tool to be a vital part of its effort to compete and grow in the world's marketplace. AutoCAD and Synthesis have added a whole new dimension to Ropak's manufacturing process by allowing it to increase productivity and dramatically increase its ability to serve the customer.

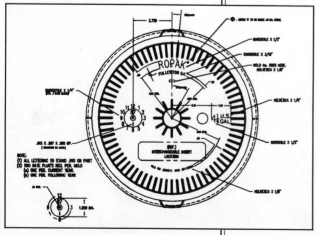

*Based on a story in *CADENCE* magazine, Vol. 3, No. 5.

Questions

1. What AutoCAD command and command option are used to configure a digitizing tablet?

_____

2. Explain the purpose of tablet configuration.

_____

_____

_____

3. What is the minimum and maximum number of tablet menus that can be included on a digitizing tablet?

_____

4. Briefly describe the process of combining the FIRSTTAB.MNU tablet menu with the SIMPLE1.MNU screen menu.

_____

_____

_____

_____

5. What command is used to load a tablet menu file?

_____

Problems

1. Develop a new tablet menu and incorporate a symbol library into one section of the menu. Use the previously created library called LIB1.DWG or create a new one. The following example should help you get started. Name the menu file LIB1.MNU.

   ***TABLET1
   ^C^Cinsert LIB1 ^C
   ^C^Cinsert TSAW drag \drag \drag
   ^C^Cinsert DRILLP drag \drag \drag
   ^C^Cinsert JOINT drag \drag \drag

   ***TABLET2
   ^C^Cline
   ^C^Cerase
   ^C^Czoom w

2. Develop a new tablet menu using the steps outlined in this unit. Make the menu as sophisticated and powerful as possible. Utilize, as much as possible, AutoCAD's macro development capability.

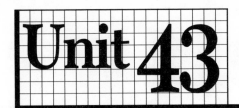

Unit 43

Customizing AutoCAD's Tablet Menu

**AutoCAD®
Reference
Manual**

A.3.4

■ OBJECTIVE:

To customize the top portion of AutoCAD's tablet menu

This unit steps you through the process of developing AutoCAD's tablet menu area number 1, located at the top of the tablet menu. Covered are techniques for positioning new AutoCAD command macros and symbol libraries on the tablet menu.

The AutoCAD tablet menu overlay is shown below. Note the empty rectangular tablet area number 1. This part of the menu, containing 200 empty cells, is set aside specifically for you to customize.

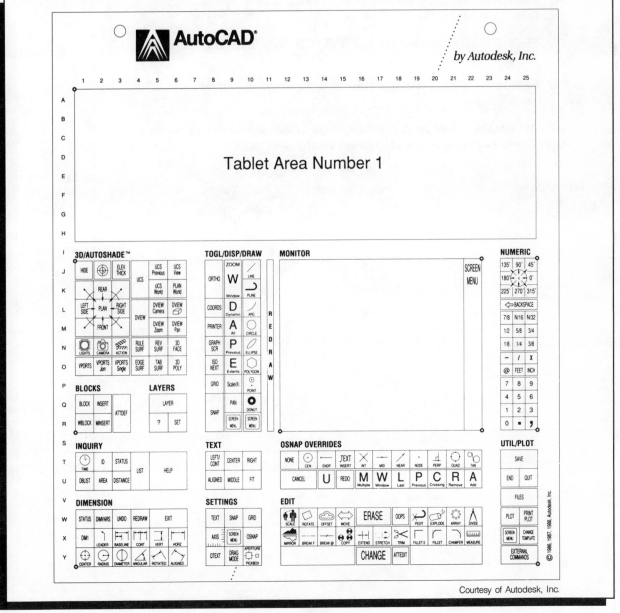

Courtesy of Autodesk, Inc.

There is more than one way to develop tablet area 1. We will use a basic method which allows you to easily follow each step of the development. This method also shows you how the other portions of the tablet menu were designed.

A word processor is required to complete the steps in the section titled "Writing the Code."

Configuring the Standard Tablet Menu _____

Be sure the tablet menu overlay is securely fastened to your digitizing tablet.

1   Load AutoCAD and bring up the Drawing Editor by entering item 1 or 2 from the Main Menu.

2   From the screen menu, select **SETTINGS**, then **TABLET:**, and then **config**.

Use of these screen menu picks simplifies and expedites the tablet configuration process.

3   As AutoCAD now requests, digitize the upper left corner of menu area 1 as shown in the illustration on the next page.

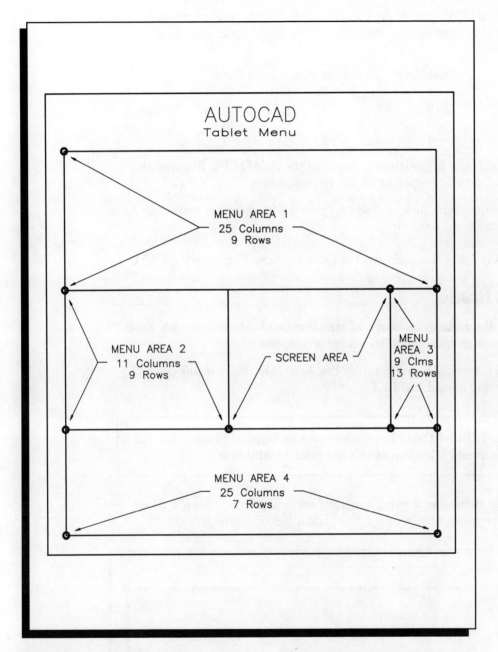

AUTOCAD
Tablet Menu

MENU AREA 1
25 Columns
9 Rows

MENU AREA 2
11 Columns
9 Rows

SCREEN AREA

MENU
AREA 3
9 Clms
13 Rows

MENU AREA 4
25 Columns
7 Rows

HINT: See section A.3.4 in Appendix A of the *AutoCAD Reference Manual* for additional information on the standard tablet menu.

4 Reply to the remaining prompts.

Notice that AutoCAD enters the following column and row numbers for you automatically. All you need to do is define the menu areas with your pointing device.

Menu area	Columns	Rows
1	25	9
2	11	9
3	9	13
4	25	7

When finished, this information is stored in the ACAD.CFG file, and the "Command:" prompt reappears on the display screen.

5 Experiment by picking items on your tablet menu to make sure it is configured properly.

6 When you're finished, exit the Drawing Editor by entering **QUIT**.

Getting Ready

Let's create the rectangular shape of area number 1. Since it already exists on file, let's use it rather than recreating a new one.

1 Load AutoCAD and bring up the AutoCAD tablet menu overlay drawing named **TABLET**.

HINT:
TABLET.DWG is contained on the AutoCAD Bonus diskette. Be sure to create a backup of this file prior to editing it.

2 After the entire drawing generates on your screen, create a Block of the tablet area number 1 as shown below. Name it **TAB1**.

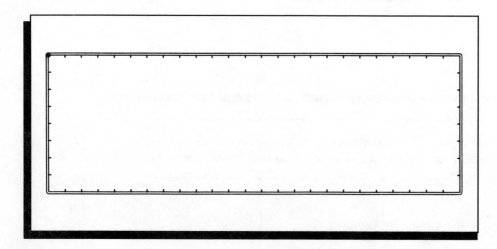

3 Immediately after it disappears from your screen, enter **OOPS** to restore it.

4 Enter the **WBLOCK** command and write TAB1 to file. Name the new file **TAB1** also.

5 When you're finished, enter **QUIT** to exit the Drawing Editor.

■ *Designing Area Number 1*

You now have a drawing file, TAB1.DWG, that matches your tablet area number 1. Let's load this file into the Drawing Editor and add a few new menu items such as command macros and symbols. When finished, you will be able to plot TAB1.DWG and slip it under the transparent area 1 on your tablet menu overlay.

1 Bring up **TAB1.DWG** into the Drawing Editor.

You should receive the rectangular menu area identical to the one in the preceding illustration.

2 Zoom in on the upper left corner and draw lines as shown here.

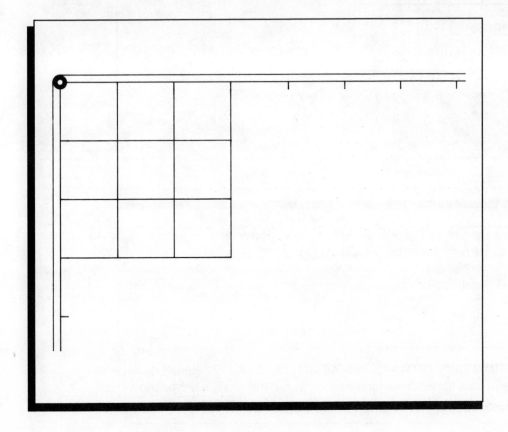

Now, let's bring in the symbol library named LIB1.DWG created in Unit 28 and place each of the tools in the above cells.

3 Insert LIB1, and be sure to cancel at the "Insertion point:" prompt.

4 Perform a Block listing to see if the tool Block definitions are now contained in your present drawing.

5 Place each of the tool symbols as shown here. You will probably have to scale down each of them; try .1 unit.

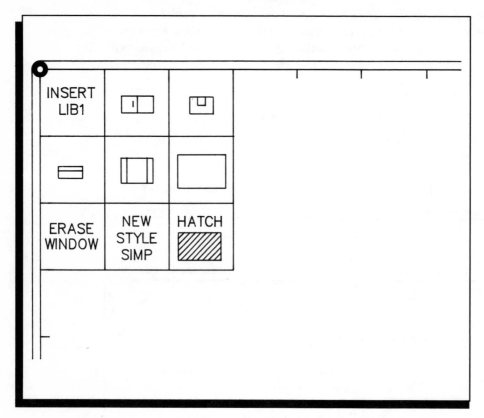

6 Place the text in the cells as shown above, and include a small hatch pattern under the word HATCH.

7 ZOOM All.

8 Enter the PLOT command.

HINT:
Use the PLOT Window option and place a window around the entire menu area (or enter coordinates such as 1,7 and 12,12 to define the window). Scale the plot at 1=1 and use B-size or larger paper.

⑨ After plotting, trim around the menu area with a knife or scissors and place the menu under your tablet menu overlay.

Writing the Code _____

This part becomes a bit more involved and requires a word processor or text editor.

① Locate the file ACAD.MNU found in your AutoCAD Source directory.

② Load your favorite word processor and bring up the ACAD.MNU text file.

③ Using your word processor's Find or Search capability, locate the item ∗∗∗TABLET1 in the ACAD.MNU file.

HINT: _____
∗∗∗TABLET1 can also be located by paging through the file until you locate it. Look for the 200 similar items that begin with [A-1], [A-2], . . .

After you locate ∗∗∗TABLET1 in the file, notice the 200 similar items (A-1 through A-25, B-1 through B-25, and so on) that follow it. The first and last portions of this section are shown below.

```
***TABLET1
[A-1]
[A-2]
[A-3]
  .
  .
  .
[H-23]
[H-24]
[H-25]
```

This is where you enter the macros which correspond with the items in menu area 1. Likewise, each of these numbers corresponds with cells in menu area 1. To illustrate this, the upper left portion of area 1 is shown on the next page.

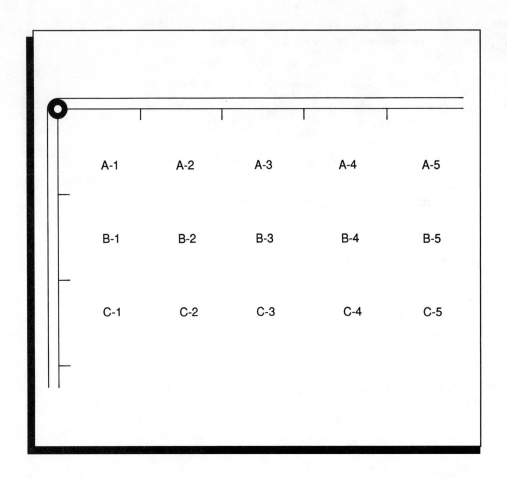

As you can see, the numbering sequence of the cells begins at the upper left corner of the tablet menu and proceeds to the right. Tablet area 1 contains 200 cells arranged into 25 columns and 8 rows.

4   Type the macros over the numbers as shown on the following page. Notice how their placement corresponds directly to the cells in the upper left portion of tablet area 1.

```
***TABLET1
^C^CINSERT LIB1;^C
^C^CINSERT TSAW DRAG \DRAG \DRAG
^C^CINSERT DRILLP DRAG \DRAG \DRAG
[A-4]
[A-5]
[A-6]
[A-7]
[A-8]
[A-9]
[A-10]
[A-11]
[A-12]
[A-13]
[A-14]
[A-15]
[A-16]
[A-17]
[A-18]
[A-19]
[A-20]
[A-21]
[A-22]
[A-23]
[A-24]
[A-25]
^C^CINSERT JOINT DRAG \DRAG \DRAG
^C^CINSERT PLANER DRAG \DRAG \DRAG
^C^CINSERT BENCH DRAG \DRAG \DRAG
[B-4]
[B-5]
[B-6]
[B-7]
[B-8]
[B-9]
[B-10]
[B-11]
[B-12]
[B-13]
[B-14]
[B-15]
[B-16]
[B-17]
[B-18]
[B-19]
[B-20]
[B-21]
[B-22]
[B-23]
[B-24]
[B-25]
^C^CERASE W
^C^CSTYLE SIMP SIMPLEX;;;;;;;
^C^CHATCH
[C-4]
[C-5]
[C-6]
[C-7]
[C-8]
```

5 Store the revised ACAD.MNU file and exit your word processor.

NOTE:

Fewer cells than 200 can be designed into menu area 1. For example, it's possible to have 30 cells made up of 10 columns and 3 rows. Then ***TABLET1 in ACAD.MNU would contain only 30 items.

6 Copy the revised ACAD.MNU to the AutoCAD directory containing your AutoCAD system files.

Using the New Menu

1 Load AutoCAD and bring up the Drawing Editor.

2 Pick the new tablet menu item called **INSERT LIB1**.

This item, as you may have noticed when you typed the macro, inserts the small symbol library, LIB1, into your current drawing.

3 Pick each of the tool symbols and place them one at a time on your screen.

4 Pick the remaining three menu items and notice what each of them does.

This should give you a taste of what can be developed with a tablet menu.

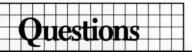

Questions

1. What is the purpose of the AutoCAD tablet menu area number 1?

   _____

   _____

2. Explain the numbering sequence of cells contained in tablet menus.

   _____

   _____

3. Could AutoCAD's tablet area 1 be designed with fewer than 200 cells? Explain.

   _____

   _____

4. Explain why a word processor is required to modify the file ACAD.MNU.

   _____

   _____

Problems

1. Experiment with different portions of the AutoCAD tablet menu areas 2, 3, and 4 to discover how these menus were designed.

2. Place additional menu items in menu area 1. Categorize the items in area 1 so that related items are grouped together. You may wish to add headings above each group of related items.

Unit 44 Exploring AutoLISP® *

■ OBJECTIVE:

To explore AutoLISP applications and capabilities by loading and invoking several AutoLISP programs

AutoLISP is AutoCAD's version of the LISP programming language. AutoLISP is embedded into AutoCAD so that AutoLISP functions can be applied in the Drawing Editor at any time. LISP, short for LISt Processing, is a powerful programming language often associated with artificial intelligence (AI) applications.

AutoLISP provides programmers with a powerful, high level language well suited to graphic applications. For instance, AutoLISP can be used to write a program for expediting the creation of a staircase in a building. If properly written, the program would prompt you for the distance between the upper and lower floors, ask you for the size and/or number of steps (risers and treads), and automatically draw the detailed staircase for you.

NOTE:

AutoLISP requires a minimum of 640 K bytes of system memory (RAM) in your computer. A special version of AutoLISP, called Extended AutoLISP, is also available for 80286- and 80386-based computers with sufficient extended memory. (See the section titled "Extended AutoLISP," later in this unit, for more information.)

AutoLISP programs, also called macros and routines, can be stored and used in at least two different formats:

1) as a file containing an .LSP file extension

2) as a menu item (screen or tablet)

Lengthy and sophisticated AutoLISP programs are most often stored as AutoLISP files (with the .LSP extension), while shorter and simpler lines of AutoLISP code are typically stored as menu items called macros.

■ *AutoLISP Example*

Let's take a look at an AutoLISP program.

1 Start your computer system, but do not proceed into AutoCAD at this time.

2 Using the **DOS CD** (Change Directory) command, change to the directory containing your AutoCAD system files, if you are not already there.

＊AutoLISP is a registered trademark of Autodesk, Inc.

③ Perform the DOS **DIR**ectory command and locate the file
SETUP.LSP.

This is an AutoLISP file. Let's review its contents.

④ At the DOS prompt, enter **TYPE SETUP.LSP** and be ready to
stop the scrolling of the screen with CTRL S.

Below is the first portion of the SETUP.LSP file.

```
;
;+----------------------------------------------------------------+
;| SETUP.LSP                                                      |
;| Ver.  1.0  Feb. 25, 1986                                       |
;|                                                                |
;| J.J.K.      Feb. 25, 1986                                      |
;|                                                                |
;| C.L.H      Nov. 29, 1987   Added error routine and input checking. |
;|                                                                |
;| This program will set the Units and Limits of a new drawing, and will |
;| draw a border line around the drawing.                         |
;+----------------------------------------------------------------+
;
;
(vmon)
(defun seterr (s)                      ;define an error handler
 (if (/= s "Function cancelled")
    (princ (strcat "\nError: " s))
 )
 (menucmd "S=S")
 (setvar "cmdecho" oce)                ;restore previous cmdecho value
 (setvar "lunits" olu)                 ;restore previous linear units value
 (setq *error* oer                    ;restore previous error handler
       seterr  nil )
 (princ)
)

(apply '(lambda (/ a b d cx cy xl yl oer olu oce)
 (setq oce (getvar "cmdecho"))        ;store current cmdecho value
```

The beginning of many AutoLISP programs briefly explains the purpose
of the program. As stated here, this program sets the Units and Limits of
a new drawing and draws a border line around the drawing.

Now that you've seen the AutoLISP code of SETUP.LSP, let's apply it in
the Drawing Editor.

① Load AutoCAD and Begin a New Drawing. Name it **LISP**.

② Find the Setup menu item located near the top of the root
page of the screen menu.

③ Pick **Setup** and watch what is entered at the "Command:"
prompt.

NOTE:

If a printer is connected to your computer, echo the text to the printer
so that you can later review it.

If you receive an error message when using AutoLISP programs, go to
the section in this unit titled "AutoLISP Error Messages."

As you may recall, the section "Setup Shortcut" in Unit 20 ("Preparing for a New Drawing") covered the Setup procedure. As explained in that section, Setup is a shortcut alternative to defining your drawing's units, scale, and paper size. But until now, you probably did not know that Setup was an AutoLISP program.

This is a good example of an AutoLISP program because it fulfills a genuine need for expediting the drawing setup process.

4 Respond to each of the Setup prompts by choosing whichever options you wish.

Do you recall seeing each of these statements embedded in the SETUP.LSP program? If not, take another look at the contents of SETUP.LSP via the AutoCAD SHELL command.

When you review the contents of SETUP.LSP using the DOS TYPE command, AutoLISP code appears. The code probably makes very little sense to you unless you're a LISP programmer. Unit 45 will cover a few AutoLISP programming techniques.

Loading/Invoking an AutoLISP File _____

Certain AutoLISP files, such as SETUP.LSP, are loaded and invoked in one step with the AutoLISP load function and are issued from the screen menu. Files like SETUP.LSP can also be loaded and invoked by typing the AutoLISP load function at the "Command:" prompt.

1 First, enter **U** to undo your last (setup) operation.

2 At the "Command:" prompt, enter exactly the following, including the parentheses. (You may use upper- or lowercase letters.) Be sure to press **RETURN** when you're finished.

(load "setup")

3 Respond to each step of the setup procedure as before.

SETUP.LSP was designed to be loaded and invoked in one step from the standard screen menu with the AutoLISP load function. Other AutoLISP files are brought into the Drawing Editor using the load function, as in Step 2 above, but they require a second step to be invoked. This is covered in the next section, "Other AutoLISP Programs."

AutoLISP code stored as macros (and not as .LSP files) and contained in menus is loaded/invoked by picking that item from the screen or tablet menu like any other menu item. This is covered in the next unit.

Other AutoLISP Programs

If you (or your school or business) returned the AutoCAD license agreement registration card, Autodesk, Inc. should have sent a Bonus diskette. Contained on the diskette are several good examples which illustrate the power and capability of AutoLISP.

1 Locate the Bonus diskette or, if these files have been copied to a directory, locate the directory containing the Bonus diskette files.

2 Review the files using the AutoCAD FILES command. (Select File Utility option **2** and enter ***.LSP** or, if the files are in a directory named BONUS, enter **BONUS*.LSP** instead.)

The following AutoLISP files are from the Bonus diskette.

```
AXROT.LSP      CHFACE.LSP      CL.LSP      DRAWMAN.LSP      FCOPY.LSP
FACT.LSP       FPRINT.LSP      SLOT.LSP    FPLOT.LSP        PROJECT.LSP
RPOLY.LSP      SPIRAL.LSP      SQR.LSP     TABLES.LSP
```

Brief descriptions of several of these files are presented in the following unit.

In addition to these examples, AutoCAD provides several useful AutoLISP utilities. They are contained on the Support diskette. Since your AutoCAD system is already installed, these LSP files are most likely contained in your main AutoCAD directory.

3 Using the AutoCAD File Utility or the DOS **DIR** command, locate and review these LSP files. They are listed here.

```
EDGE.LSP       3DARRAY.LSP     3D.LSP          CHGTEXT.LSP      DELLAYER.LSP
SETUP.LSP      SSX.LSP         LEXPLODE.LSP    ASCTEXT.LSP      ATTREDEF.LSP
REF.LSP        AFKINET.LSP     AFLIX.LSP       AFWALK.LSP       ASHADE.LSP
```

Brief descriptions of these files are provided in the following unit. Let's try two of them now.

DELLAYER.LSP Utility

DELLAYER.LSP lets you erase all entities on a specified layer.

1. In preparation for applying the DELLAYER.LSP utility, create a new layer named **OBJ** and place a couple of entities on it.

2. Set layer **0** and place a couple of entities on it, too.

3. At the "Command:" prompt, enter the following in upper- or lowercase letters—including the parentheses—and press **RETURN**.

(load "dellayer")

HINT:

If you receive the message "error: LOAD failed," the DELLAYER.LSP file may not be contained in the default directory. Instead, the file may be contained in a subdirectory named LSP or SUPPORT, or it may be contained in the main ACAD directory. If so, refer to the following examples.

(load "lsp/dellayer")
or
(load "/acad/support/dellayer")
or
(load "/acad/dellayer")

If you receive a different error message, review the section "AutoLISP Error Messages," later in this unit.

If the file loaded properly, you will receive the message "C:DELLAYER."

4. To invoke this AutoLISP program, enter **DELLAYER** at the "Command:" prompt.

5. In reply to "Layer to delete:" enter **OBJ**.

All entities contained on OBJ should be automatically erased. As stated earlier, this is the purpose of the DELLAYER.LSP utility.

ASCTEXT.LSP Utility

Another useful AutoLISP routine supplied with AutoCAD is ASCTEXT.LSP. It enables you to insert any ASCII text file into a drawing file. Therefore lengthy notes and specifications can be created and edited with a word processor, then later inserted into AutoCAD.

1   Enter (**load "asctext"**) as you see it here.

If the file does not load, refer to the previous hint.

You will receive the message "C:ASCTEXT" when the file loads properly.

2   Enter **ASCTEXT** to invoke the file.

3   In reply to "File to read (including extension):" enter the path and name of any ASCII text file currently on disk.

HINT:

You may create a new ASCII text file for use with ASCTEXT.LSP. Use a word processor, text editor, or the "COPY CON:" method described near the beginning of Unit 41. Additionally, the AutoCAD file ACAD.MSG and batch files, such as AUTOEXEC.BAT, are ASCII text files and can be used here. Menu files, such as SIMPLE.MNU, are also ASCII text files. However, avoid using large files such as ACAD.MNU, README.DOC, and ACAD.HLP because of the time they will require to generate on the screen.

The file you specify will generate on the screen in the current text style. As with normal AutoCAD text, each line of text is treated as a single entity and can be altered using the CHANGE command.

As you can see, AutoLISP programs, such as the two utilities explained here, provide additional power and capability for users of AutoCAD. Hundreds of AutoLISP routines have been developed—and some sold commercially—to fulfill a wide range of drafting, design, and engineering needs.

4   Using either the **SHELL** or **SH** command, display the contents of the ASCTEXT.LSP and DELLAYER.LSP files using the DOS **TYPE** command.

AutoLISP Error Messages

At one time or another, you may receive one of the following error messages:

Insufficient memory - AutoLISP disabled

error: insufficient node space

error: insufficient string space

NOTE:

Appendix B of the *AutoLISP Programmer's Reference* provides a complete list of AutoLISP-related error messages.

The message "Insufficient memory - AutoLISP disabled" will appear if there is not enough memory for AutoLISP to load. AutoLISP requires a minimum of 640 K bytes of RAM. If your computer contains at least 640 K bytes and you receive this error message, reboot your system and reload AutoCAD.

The "error: insufficient node space" or "error: insufficient string space" message appears when your computer runs out of "heap" space. The heap is an area of memory set aside for storage of all AutoLISP functions and variables (also called nodes). Elaborate AutoLISP programs require greater amounts of heap and stack space.

The stack is also an area of memory set aside by AutoLISP. Stack holds function arguments and partial results; the deeper you "nest" functions, the more stack space is used. The heap and stack space can be increased using the DOS SET command contained in an AUTOEXEC.BAT file. The default size for heap is 40,000; for stack, 3,000. As a starting point, recommended settings are:

C>SET LISPHEAP=39000

C>SET LISPSTACK=5000

The total of heap and stack cannot exceed 45,000. A full explanation on placing the above in a batch file is provided in Appendix H.

NOTE:

Chapter 6 of the *AutoLISP Programmer's Reference* also provides details on the use of heap and stack.

Recovering Node Space

If you are in need of additional node space, you can undefine a previously loaded AutoLISP program. For example, once you have loaded and used the function named SETUP, you can enter the following at the "Command:" prompt.

(setq setup nil)

This will recover the node space taken by SETUP.LSP and will make it available to other AutoLISP programs and routines.

If you anticipate a need to recover node space regularly, store the following function in a file named ACAD.LSP.

```
(defun C:CLEAN (/ i item)
    (setq i 0)
    (while (not (equal (setq item (nth i atomlist)) 'C:CLEAN))
      (if (= (type (eval item)) 'FILE)    ; ensure files closed
        (close (eval item)))
      (setq i (1+ i))
    )
    (setq atomlist (member 'C:CLEAN atomlist))
    'DONE
)
```

Each time an AutoCAD Drawing Editor session begins, AutoLISP loads the file ACAD.LSP (if it exists). If the preceding function is contained in ACAD.LSP, it will also be loaded automatically. Then, when you need to recover node space, enter CLEAN at the "Command:" prompt. This function will trim all functions and variables contained in the "ATOMLIST." AutoLISP uses the ATOMLIST to hold the names of all the system-defined functions and variables. To review its contents, enter !ATOMLIST at the "Command:" prompt.

NOTE:

You can also place other commonly used functions in the ACAD.LSP file to be loaded automatically at the beginning of each Drawing Editor session.

Extended AutoLISP

The enhanced version of AutoLISP, Extended AutoLISP, is available for 80286- and 80386-based computers with at least 512 K bytes of extended memory. As its name implies, Extended AutoLISP runs in extended memory. It provides access to 14 megabytes of node (memory) space. This equates to 1,470,000 nodes compared to just 3072 nodes possible in the standard implementation of AutoLISP. Extended AutoLISP, therefore, eliminates "Out of Node Space" and other memory-related error messages.

Extended AutoLISP also enables AutoCAD to run more efficiently since it does not rob AutoCAD of precious I/O page space imposed by DOS's 640 K byte memory limitation. Yet the function definitions of Extended AutoLISP and standard AutoLISP are identical.

Running Extended AutoLISP _____

Extended AutoLISP is implemented as a separate program called
EXTLISP.EXE. You must run this program prior to starting AutoCAD.
EXTLISP.EXE is a terminate-and-stay-resident (TSR) program that resides
partially in extended memory. It communicates with AutoCAD by means
of the ACADLX.OVL overlay file.

If your computer contains at least 512 K bytes of extended memory and
you want to run Extended AutoLISP, execute the following steps.

1 Start your computer system.

The DOS Prompt (*e.g.*, C:\\>) should be present.

2 Change to the main AutoCAD directory using the **CD DOS**
command.

3 Enter **EXTLISP**.

A message will appear to confirm that Extended AutoLISP is loaded
properly. If it does not load, the EXTLISP.EXE file is not present in your
current directory or your computer does not contain sufficient extended
memory.

4 Start AutoCAD.

The AutoCAD Main Menu should be present.

5 Select Main Menu item 5, "Configure AutoCAD."

6 Select Configuration Menu item 8, "Configure Operating
Parameters."

7 Select Operating Parameters Menu item 7, "AutoLISP Feature."

8 Enter Yes in reply to "Do you want AutoLISP enabled?".

9 Enter Yes in reply to "Do you want to use Extended AutoLISP?".

10 Exit to the Configuration Menu and then exit the Configuration
Menu.

Extended AutoLISP is now operational.

NOTE: _____

If you want to remove EXTLISP.EXE and free the space taken by it,
enter REMLISP at the DOS prompt. (You must be in the main AutoCAD
directory when entering REMLISP.)

Questions

1. What is AutoLISP?

2. Name two applications for AutoLISP.

3. What file extension do AutoLISP programs use?

4. What effect does the heap and stack space have on running AutoLISP programs?

5. What specific purpose does the SETUP.LSP program serve?

6. How would you load the file SPIRAL.LSP?

Problem

Load and invoke the remaining AutoLISP programs contained on the Bonus diskette.

Unit 45 — Easing into AutoLISP® Programming*

■ OBJECTIVE:

To practice simple AutoLISP programming techniques and to create new AutoLISP files and AutoCAD commands

The significance of LISP embedded into AutoCAD has captured the interest of many. This unit will introduce AutoLISP programming so that you can decide whether or not it's for you. Like many others, you may remain satisfied with applying the power of already-developed AutoLISP programs. On the other hand, you may find AutoLISP programming very intriguing and challenging.

If you enjoy programming, you should continue with the unit following this one and, after that, explore and learn other AutoLISP commands and functions on your own. Someday, you may even be in a position to serve the AutoLISP programming needs of the AutoCAD user community.

■ *AutoLISP Arithmetic*

11.4.3

As illustrated in the previous unit, AutoLISP functions, such as (load " "), can be entered directly at the "Command:" prompt. Let's enter an AutoLISP arithmetic expression.

1 Load AutoCAD and Begin a New Drawing. Name it **LISP2**.

2 At the "Command:" prompt, type (*** 5 6**) and press **RETURN**.

The number 30 should appear at the bottom of the screen because $5 \times 6 = 30$.

3 Enter (**/ 15 3**).

You should receive 5 because $15 \div 3 = 5$.

4 Try (**+ 25 4**).

Did 29 appear?

■ *SETQ Function*

11.4.2

The SETQ function is used to assign values to a variable.

1 Type (**setq A 10**) and press **RETURN**. ("A" can be typed in upper- or lowercase.)

The value of variable A is now 10.

2 Enter (**setq B (− 20 4**)).

*ACKNOWLEDGEMENT: Some of the basic principles presented here are from the *CADalyst Journal* AutoLISP tutorial series printed in Vol. 3, No. 2 and Vol. 3, No. 3.

The variable B now holds the value of 16. Notice the parentheses.

③ To restore the value of A, enter **!A**.

Did 10 appear?

④ Enter **!B**.

Let's try something a bit more complex.

⑤ Enter **(setq CAT (− B A))**.

Now CAT is equal to the value of B minus the value of A.

Let's try one more.

⑥ Enter **(setq DOG (* (* 2 CAT)(/ A 5)))**.

The variable DOG is now equal to 24.

NOTE:

The number of left parentheses must equal the number of right parentheses. If they are not equal, you will receive a message such as **1>**. This means you lack one right parenthesis. Add one by typing another right parenthesis and pressing RETURN.

⑦ Enter **QUIT** to exit the Drawing Editor.

Storing AutoLISP Programs as a File

AutoLISP code can be stored in an .LSP file and subsequently loaded and invoked at any time while in the Drawing Editor. Let's store the above functions to illustrate this capability.

① Create a new file with a word processor or text editor and store the following exactly as you see it. Or, you may use the "COPY CON" method outlined at the beginning of Unit 41. Name the file FIRST.LSP.

```
(defun c:FIRST ()
(setq a 10)
(setq b (− 20 4))
(setq cat (− b a))
(setq dog (* (* 2 cat)(/ a 5)))
)
```

Notice the AutoLISP function DEFUN. The DEFUN function allows you to define a new function or AutoCAD command and use it to invoke the AutoLISP file. Once loaded, the above program can be invoked by entering FIRST at the "Command:" prompt.

② Load AutoCAD and bring up the Drawing Editor by entering option 1 or 2 from the Main Menu.

③ At the "Command:" prompt, enter (**load "first"**).

After you press RETURN, "C:FIRST" should appear.

HINT:

If the FIRST.LSP file is contained in a DOS directory under the main AutoCAD directory, then specify the path when entering the load function. For example, enter (load "user/first") where USER is the name of the directory. Notice the slash mark (not a backslash).

④ Enter **FIRST**, now a new AutoCAD command, to invoke the program.

The number 24 should appear

NOTE:

The preceding code could also be stored without the DEFUN function. It would look like this:

```
(setq a 10)
(setq b (− 20 4))
(setq cat (− b a))
(setq dog (* (* 2 cat)(/ a 5)))
```

Then (load "first") would load and invoke in one step.

⑤ Enter **QUIT** to exit the Drawing Editor.

Storing AutoLISP Programs as a Menu Item ____

AutoLISP programs can also be stored and invoked as menu items. As a standard screen menu item, the above program would look like this:

```
[FIRST] ^ C ^ C+
(setq a 10)+
(setq b (− 20 4))+
(setq cat (− b a))+
(setq dog (* (* 2 cat)(/ a 5)))
```

FIRST would appear in the screen menu. Notice that menu items such as ^C can be mixed with AutoLISP functions. Also note the + (plus) signs at the end of each line of code. This connects the code so that AutoCAD treats it all as a single line.

1 Using a word processor, add the preceding macro to your SIMPLE1.MNU screen menu (created in Unit 41). Store everything in a new file named SIMPLE2.MNU and try it out.

The first portion of SIMPLE2.MNU should now look like this:

```
***SCREEN
[  A]
[SIMPLE]
[ MENU]


[LINE]^C^Cline
[ERAS L]^C^CERASE L
[ZOOM W]^C^Czoom W
[TEXT]^C^Ctext
[*Cancel*]^C^C

[FIRST]^C^C+
(setq a 10)+
(setq b (- 20 4))+
(setq cat (- b a))+
(setq dog (* (* 2 cat)(/ a 5)))

***BUTTONS
;
^C^CREDRAW

***TABLET1
^C^Czoom w
^C^Czoom p
```

As a tablet menu item, the macro would look like this:

```
^C^C+
(setq a 10)+
(setq b (- 20 4))+
(setq cat (- b a))+
(setq dog (* (* 2 cat)(/ a 5)))
```

■ *LIST Function*

11.4.2

SETQ by itself can hold only one value. The LIST function can hold a list of two elements, such as coordinates. SETQ used with list can then hold the list of coordinates as a single value. Let's step through an example.

1 Type (setq fish (list 7 6)) and press **RETURN**.

Did (7 6) appear on your screen? This is now the value of fish.

2 Enter !fish.

(7 6) should appear again.

3 Enter the **LINE** command and pick a point near the lower left corner of your screen.

4 In reply to "To point:", enter !fish.

A line should appear.

HINT:

This function is especially valuable when you need to reach a point off the screen. For instance, if the upper right corner of your screen is 15,10 and the LINE command has been issued, you can reach point 25,20 (or any point for that matter) if a variable is assigned to that point. You just enter the variable preceded by the ! as you did in the fish example. Let's try it.

1 Enter (setq trout (list 35 28)).

2 Enter the **LINE** command and pick a point anywhere on your screen.

3 In reply to "To point:", enter !trout.

Did a line appear? Does it look as though it runs off the screen?

4 Enter **ZOOM** Extents.

You should now see the endpoint 35,28 of the line.

CAR Function _____

The CAR function is used to obtain the first item in a list, such as the X-coordinate. So, what would be the CAR of fish? Let's enter it.

1 Type (**car fish**) and press **RETURN**.

The value 7 should appear.

11.4.2

CADR Function

CADR is like CAR, only CADR gives you everything *except* the first item of a list—the Y-coordinate, in this case.

1 Enter **(cadr fish).**

The value 6 should appear.

So now you see we can obtain either the X- or Y-coordinate from a LIST.

Combining Several Functions

We can also assign a new variable to a set of coordinates that contains the CADR of fish (the Y-coordinate) and 0 as the X-coordinate.

First, we must create a new LIST containing 0 and the CADR of fish. Then we need to use SETQ to assign a variable (we'll call it bird) to the new LIST. Therefore...

1 ... enter **(setq bird (list 0 (cadr fish))).**

You should receive (0 6).

2 Try a similar function using CAR and 0 (for the Y-coordinate). Use bug for the variable name.

You should receive (7 0).

Did you enter **(setq bug (list (car fish) 0))?**

3 Enter **!bird** and then enter **!bug.**

The values (0 6) and (7 0) should return.

4 Enter **QUIT** to exit the Drawing Editor.

The preceding steps gave you a taste of basic AutoLISP programming. The next unit will pick up from here and will apply most of the preceding AutoLISP programming techniques.

Few AutoCAD users will write sophisticated AutoLISP programs. Typically, drafting, design, and engineering professionals do not have the time or the interest to learn AutoLISP fully. They are likely to seek ready-made AutoLISP programs, such as those presented in the following sections.

AutoLISP and 3D

The file 3D.LSP, distributed on the AutoCAD Support diskette, creates several 3D objects including a box, cone, dish, dome, mesh, pyramid, sphere, torus, wedge, and a basic 3D mesh.

1 Enter (**load "3d"**) at the "Command:" prompt.

"C:3D" should appear.

NOTE:

If 3D.LSP does not load, the file may be contained in a user-defined subdirectory such as SUPPORT or LSP. If so, you must enter the path as illustrated by the following examples.

(load "support/3d")
or
(load "/acad/lsp/3d")

---

2 Enter **3D**.

The following should appear.

```
Box/Cone/DIsh/DOme/Mesh/Pyramid/Sphere/Torus/Wedge:
```

---

3 Enter the **B**ox option.

4 Pick any convenient point in reply to "Corner of box:".

5 Enter **3** for the length, **2** for the width, **4** for the height, and **0** for the rotation angle.

6 Using **VPOINT** and the **A**xes option, pick a point in front, to the right, and above the box.

7 Each of the remaining AutoLISP 3D command options is self-explanatory; so experiment with each of them on your own, but remain at the current viewpoint.

> **HINT:**
> You can enter 3D at the "Command:" prompt the same as any AutoCAD command and then reenter it by pressing either the space bar or RETURN. Unit 39 contains the 3D Construction dialogue box that provides an illustration of each option.

AutoLISP Programming Examples

Several additional AutoLISP programs are supplied with AutoCAD. They are good examples of AutoLISP programming techniques, so you are encouraged to review them. The following provides a brief description of those distributed on the AutoCAD Support diskette.

3DARRAY.LSP creates 3D rectangular arrays (by specifying rows, columns, and levels) and polar arrays around a desired axis.

ASCTEXT.LSP (covered fully in Unit 44) inserts ASCII text files into AutoCAD drawings.

ATTREDEF.LSP lets you redefine a Block and update the Attributes associated with any previous insertions of that Block.

CHGTEXT.LSP provides basic editing of Text entities.

DELLAYER.LSP (covered fully in Unit 44) erases all entities on a specified layer.

EDGE.LSP lets you interactively change the visibility of the edges of a 3D Face.

LEXPLODE.LSP places the components of Hatch and Dimension entities on Layer 0.

REF.LSP obtains a relative point whenever AutoCAD requests a point.

SETUP.LSP (covered fully in Units 20 and 44) sets the drawing units and limits of a new drawing based on the paper size and drawing scale.

SSX.LSP provides a convenient way of selecting entities based on entity type, color, layer, linetype, Block name, text style, and thickness.

The following provides brief descriptions of the AutoLISP files distributed on the Bonus diskette. They are intended to illustrate AutoLISP programming capabilities and techniques.

AXROT.LSP rotates one or more entities by a specified amount around the X, Y, or Z axis.

CHFACE.LSP provides a method of moving the vertices of a 3D Face.

CL.LSP constructs a pair of center lines through the center of a circle.

DRAWMAN.LSP implements a crude drawing revision control system in conjunction with the REVINFO.DWG sample drawing; it illustrates what can be done using entity handles.

FACT.LSP illustrates the use of recursion to compute the factorial of an integer.

FCOPY.LSP takes the names of two ASCII text files and copies the first into the second.

FPLOT.LSP generates a 3D polygon mesh.

FPRINT.LSP lists an ASCII text file on the screen.

PROJECT.LSP implements a limited, flat projection of 3D wireframe models onto the current UCS.

RPOLY.LSP refines a random polygon by replacing its vertices with the midpoints of its edges.

SLOT.LSP uses 3D Faces to construct slots and holes.

SPIRAL.LSP constructs a 2D spiral.

SQR.LSP implements a square root function.

TABLES.LSP contains a number of functions that exercise AutoLISP's TBLNEXT and TBLSEARCH features.

Refer to the *AutoLISP Programmer's Reference* for more information on these programs.

Questions

1. What will be returned if (* 4 5) is entered at the "Command:" prompt?

_____

2. Explain the purpose of the SETQ function.

_____

_____

3. If the value of variable XYZ is 129.5, what will return when !XYZ is entered?

_____

4. How do you load and invoke an AutoLISP file that contains (defun C:RED ()?

_____

5. What purpose do the CAR and CADR functions serve?

_____

_____

6. What is the purpose of the LIST function?

_____

_____

7. The plus sign (+) is often used in screen and tablet macros. What is its purpose?

_____

_____

_____

Problems

Using the SETQ, LIST, CAR, CADR, and DEFUN functions, create new AutoLISP files and commands. Load and invoke them while in the Drawing Editor. Use the steps outlined in this unit as a model.

AUTOCAD® AT WORK

*Designing Cams with AutoCAD**

Commercial Cam Machine (Camco) Division of Emerson Electric Company manufactures mechanical intermittent motion devices that use cam technology as their basis for operation. A cam is a mechanical device which typically operates in a rotary fashion and contains information on displacement, velocity, and acceleration for transmission to a secondary mechanical member. A cam can be thought of as a read-only memory (ROM) mechanical device.

Camco has long been involved in computer-aided design and manufacturing for its products. It began using mainframe systems in the mid-1960s. In 1984 the company added AutoCAD, primarily as a learning tool for moving data from one system to another.

Soon, however, a new application was discovered. "We recognized that the DXF file closely matched the numeric data we transmitted to machine tools for the production of cams," says Josef Mang, vice president of engineering. "Suddenly all the pieces fell into place."

By passing machine data through a postprocessor and transmitting it to AutoCAD via the DXF format, Camco could edit machine data graphically. It was a simple project to reverse the process and turn graphics data into machine instructions. So AutoCAD moved from the status of a learning tool to that of a production tool.

How is Camco using AutoCAD as a production tool? "We have written LISP routines that are general in nature and of potential value to other AutoCAD users," notes Mang. "Since Camco's primary product is the mechanical cam, a routine to draw a simple straight line cam was one of the first routines we wrote.

"Camco customers are a diverse group, from automotive giants with large CAD/CAM installations to small machine shops with only one or two engineers and no CAD. All of these customers need accurate engineering drawings for their work, but their format requirements are quite different. AutoCAD can satisfy their requirements without much additional work.

"In design work, the ability to explore various options without redrawing the items you don't plan to change is a major time saver. Most design work consists of 80 percent redraw and 20 percent original work."

While the full impact of all savings has not yet been realized, Camco is already seeing some major savings, and the company is pleased with AutoCAD. As Mang notes, "While there are a number of low cost microCAD systems on the market, none offers us as much flexibility as AutoCAD."

*Based on a story in *CADENCE* magazine, Vol 2, No. 1.

Unit 46 — Applying AutoLISP® Programming Techniques

■ OBJECTIVE:

To introduce and combine several AutoLISP functions and apply them to the development of a new program and to apply parametric programming techniques

This unit continues the lesson begun in the preceding one. The techniques you have learned so far, as well as a few new ones, will be applied.

Applying Our Knowledge _____

Let's apply several AutoLISP functions to the creation of a border line for a drawing. At this point, we'll step through the process. Later, we'll store the function as a macro and add the macro to the screen menu called SIMPLE2.MNU.

We'll use the SETQ, LIST, CAR, and CADR functions to define a rectangular border for a 36″ × 24″ paper size. In order to place the border 1″ from the outer edge of the paper, we'll use an upper left corner of 34″,22″.

1 Load AutoCAD and Begin a New Drawing called **LISP2**.

Let's begin by assigning a variable to each corner of the border. We'll call the lower left corner variable LL, the lower right variable LR, and so on.

2 Enter (setq LL (list 0 0)).

That takes care of the lower left corner. Now, for the upper right corner...

3 ... enter (setq UR (list 34 22)).

Now let's utilize car and cadr for the remaining two corners.

4 Enter (setq LR (list (car UR)(cadr LL))).

5 Enter (setq UL (list (car LL)(cadr UR))).

Let's try out the new variables.

6 One at a time enter !LL, then enter !UR, then !LR, and lastly !UL.

The correct coordinates for each corner should appear.

Using the LIMITS and LINE commands, and the above variables, let's establish the new border format.

7 Enter the **LIMITS** command.

8 In reply to "Lower left corner" enter !LL.

9 In reply to "Upper right corner" enter !UR.

10 ZOOM All.

11 Set the grid to 1 unit.

12 Enter the LINE command and enter !LL for the first point.

13 For the second point, enter !LR; for the third point, !UR; for the fourth point, !UL; and then close by entering C.

This is all very neat, but it took a lot of steps. Let's combine all the steps into one macro and store it.

Creating a New Macro

1 Using a text editor, load the SIMPLE2.MNU file.

2 Enter the following just above the buttons menu (✳✳✳BUTTONS).

```
[34×22]^C^C+
(setq LL (list 0 0))+
(setq UR (list 34 22))+
(setq LR (list (car UR)(cadr LL)))+
(setq UL (list (car LL)(cadr UR)));+
limits !LL !UR zoom a grid 1;+
line !LL !LR !UR !UL c
```

Notice the [34×22] followed by two cancels and a plus sign. 34×22 will appear as a menu item in the screen menu. The two cancels will cancel any command that may be entered. The plus signs connect the macro elements so that they are treated as one line of code. The two semicolons are present to issue RETURN at the appropriate times.

The first portion of your file should now look like the list on the following page.

```
***SCREEN
[  A]
[SIMPLE]
[ MENU]


[LINE]^C^Cline
[ERAS L]^C^CERASE L
[ZOOM W]^C^Czoom w
[TEXT]^C^Ctext
[*Cancel*]^C^C

[FIRST]^C^C+
(setq a 10)+
(setq b (- 20 4))+
(setq cat (- b a))+
(setq dog (* (* 2 cat)(/ a 5)))

[34x22]^C^C+
(setq LL (list 0 0))+
(setq UR (list 34 22))+
(setq LR (list (car UR)(cadr LL)))+
(setq UL (list (car LL)(cadr UR)));+
limits !LL !UR zoom a grid 1;+
line !LL !LR !UR !UL c

***BUTTONS
;
^C^CREDRAW

***TABLET1
^C^Czoom w
^C^Czoom p
```

③ Store the contents in a new file named SIMPLE3.MNU and copy it to the directory containing the AutoCAD system files.

④ Load AutoCAD and bring up the Drawing Editor.

⑤ Enter the **MENU** command, and then enter **SIMPLE3**.

⑥ Pick the **34×22** menu item.

The following should automatically appear on your screen. If it doesn't, then your macro probably contains a bug. If so,...

⑦ ... edit SIMPLE3.MNU so that it is identical to the one above and reissue the 34×22 item.

403

```
Command: (setq LL (list 0 0))(setq UR (list 34 22))(setq LR (list (car UR)
(cadr LL)))(setq UL (list (car LL)(cadr UR)))
(0 22)

Command: limits
ON/OFF/<Lower left corner> <0.0000,0.0000>: !LL
Upper right corner <34.0000,22.0000>: !UR
Command: zoom
All/Center/Dynamic/Extents/Left/Previous/Window/<Scale(X)>: a Regenerating
drawing.

Command: grid
Grid spacing (X) or ON/OFF/Snap/Aspect <1.0000>: 1

Command: line From point: !LL
To point: !LR
To point: !UR
To point: !UL
To point: c
```

If your macro issues properly, congratulations!

 ## *AutoLISP COMMAND Function*_____

The AutoLISP COMMAND function executes AutoCAD commands from
within AutoLISP. In the [34×22] macro, let's change the LIMITS,
ZOOM, GRID, and LINE commands to the format below using the
AutoLISP COMMAND function.

1 Enter the code exactly as you see it here.

```
[34×22]^C^C+
(setq LL (list 0 0))+
(setq UR (list 34 22))+
(setq LR (list (car UR)(cadr LL)))+
(setq UL (list (car LL)(cadr UR)))+
(command "LIMITS" LL UR)+
(command "ZOOM" "A")+
(command "GRID" "1")+
(command "LINE" LL LR UR UL LL "")
```

Notice how the AutoCAD commands and command options are
enclosed by double quotes ("). The two consecutive double
quotes ("") are equivalent to pressing the space bar.

2 Store your changes in a new file named SIMPLE4.MNU.

3 Try the file in the Drawing Editor.

A Macro in a File Format _____

Let's convert our macro to an AutoLISP file and add explanatory remarks at the beginning of the file.

1 With a word processor, create a new file and enter the following. Type it exactly as you see it here, and name the file 34×22.LSP.

```
;     This program establishes drawing limits
;     for a 34" × 22" format (36" × 24" paper size)
;     and draws a border line.
;

(defun C:34×22 ()
        (setq LL (list 0 0))
        (setq UR (list 34 22))
        (setq LR (list (car UR)(cadr LL)))
        (setq UL (list (car LL)(cadr UR)))

(command "LIMITS" LL UR)
(command "ZOOM" "A")
(command "GRID" "1")
(command "LINE" LL LR UR UL LL "")
)
```

HINT: If your word processor has the capability to write a portion of a file to disk, then write to disk the [34×22] macro from the SIMPLE4.MNU file. Name the new file 34×22.LSP. This will save you some retyping.

Notice the semicolons (;) in the above program. These allow you to include explanatory remarks about your program. This documentation can be extremely important to other users of the program.

As you can see, the first line of the macro, [32×22] C C+, has been removed. All of the plus signs have also been taken out since they are no longer needed. The lines containing the SETQ function have been indented for better readability.

Also notice the inclusion of the AutoLISP DEFUN function and the right parenthesis at the program's last line. This right parenthesis evens the number of left and right parentheses.

Other AutoLISP Functions _____

Here is a list of other commonly used AutoLISP functions. Experiment with them and discover ways of incorporating them into the 34×22.LSP file and others.

SETVAR — sets an AutoCAD system variable to a given value and returns that value. The variable name must be enclosed in double quotes.

Example: (setvar "CHAMFERA" 1.5)

This would set the first chamfer distance at 1.5.

GETVAR — retrieves the value of an AutoCAD system variable. The variable name must be enclosed in double quotes.

Example: (getvar "CHAMFERA")

This would return 1.5 assuming the first chamfer distance specified most recently was 1.5.

GETPOINT — pauses for user input of a point. You may specify a point by pointing or by typing a coordinate in the current units format.

Example: (setq xyz (getpoint "Where? "))

GETREAL — pauses for user input of a real number.

Example: (setq sf (getreal "Scale factor: "))

GETDIST — pauses for user input of a distance. You may specify a distance by typing a number in AutoCAD's current units format, or you may enter the distance by pointing to two locations on the screen.

Example: (setq dist (getdist "How far "))

GETSTRING — pauses for user input of a string.

Example: (setq str (getstring "Your name? "))

DISTANCE — returns the distance between two points.

Example: (distance '(1 1) '(1 3))

This would return 2.

You are encouraged to further explore AutoLISP's potential. Review the *AutoLISP Programmer Reference* supplied with your AutoCAD package and experiment with the AutoLISP functions outlined in the manual.

Parametric Programming

The AutoCAD INSERT command lets you insert Blocks at any height and width. An architectural window symbol, for example, may be inserted into an elevation drawing at .6 on the X axis and .9 on the Y axis. *Parametrics* function in a very similar fashion, but with far more flexibility and sophistication.

Unlike Blocks, interior and exterior dimensions of parametrics-based objects remain variable. This enables you to specify not only the height and width of an object, but also different sizes of geometry inside the object.

Consider a bicycle design. With parametrics, all elements that make up the frame are adjusted to user-specified sizes. The wheels and tires are adjusted to another size, the sprockets to yet another, and so on. This reduces the potentially large number of variations of a design to just one because each variation shares the same basic geometry. Hence, parametrics reduces the number of files and disk storage space, while increasing flexibility and speed.

The following door and window variations were created using a custom parametric program called DWELEV.LSP, written by Bruce Chase of Chase Systems (Westerville, OH).

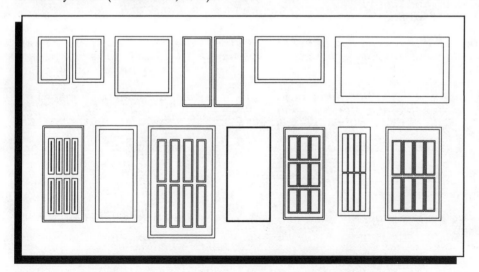

The DWELEV.LSP program code is printed on the following pages.

```
;Simple parametric DOOR/WINDOW ELEVATION drawing program

; Copywritten by Bruce R Chase, Chase Systems.
; May be copied for non-commercial use.


(setq hpi (* pi 0.5))
(defun d_wel (pl x y off / tp)      ;draws the rectang & offsets
   (command "pline" pl "w" 0.0 0.0
       (setq tp (polar pl angl x))
       (setq tp (polar tp (+ angl hpi) y))
               (polar tp (- angl pi)  x)
       "cl"
   )
   (setq e (entlast))
   (if off (command "offset" "t"
           (cons (entlast)(list pl))
           (polar (polar pl angl off)(+ angl hpi) off) ""))
   (setq ee (entlast))
)


(defun d_we2 (spt offbase offside offtop x y numx numy sx sy offin trim /
              pl p2 p3 p4 xx yy e ee)
   (d_wel spt x y (if trim (* -1 trim) nil))        ; base d/w w\trim
   (if (and numx numy)(progn                        ; set base of panels
       (setq pl (polar
                   (if offside (polar spt angl offside) spt)
                   (+ angl hpi)
                   (if offbase offbase 0.0)))
     (d_wel pl                                      ; build panels
         (setq xx (if numy (/ (- x offside offside (* (- numy 1) sy)) numy) x))
         (setq yy (if numy (/ (- y offtop  offbase (* (- numx 1) sx)) numx) y))
         (if offin offin nil)                       ; raised panel or glass trim
     )
   (command "array" e ee "" "R" numx numy  pl       ; array the base panel
        (polar (polar pl angl (+ sy xx))
                       (+ angl hpi)(+ sx yy))))
))
)




(defun drwdr2 (spt xx x / tp)                        ; getdist or default program
  (terpri)(terpri)
  (prompt (strcat xx " <"))
  (princ (rtos x (getvar "lunits")(getvar "luprec")))
  (if (Null (setq tp (if spt (getdist spt ">: ")(getdist ">: ")))) x tp)
)
(defun d_we3 ()
    (while (null (setq spt (getpoint "\n \nLower left corner of door/window: "
))))
    (setq angl (if (null
          (setq tp (getorient spt "\nBase angle of door/window <0.0>: ")))
          0.0 tp))
)
```

(continued next page)

```
(defun c:dwelev ( / spt offbase offside offtop          ; gather all the info
                   x y numx numy sx sy offin trim tp angl)
     (d_we3)
     (setq x (drwdr2 spt "Width of door/window" 36.0))
     (setq y (drwdr2 spt "Height of door/window" 80.0))
     (setq trim (if (zerop (setq tp (drwdr2 spt "Trim width" 0.0))) nil tp))

     (if (setq numy (getint "\nNumber of panels rows <none>: "))(progn
         (setq numx (if (null (setq numx
                 (getint "\nNumber of panel columns <1>: "))) 1 numx))
         (setq offbase (drwdr2 spt "Bottom rail width" 10.0))
         (setq offtop  (drwdr2 spt "Top rail width"     6.0))
         (setq offside (drwdr2 spt "Side rail width"    4.0))
         (if (> numx 1)(setq sx
                 (drwdr2 nil "Spacing between panel rows" 1.0)))
         (if (> numy 1)(setq sy
                 (drwdr2 nil "Spacing between panel columns"   1.0)))
         (setq offin    (if (zerop
                             (setq tp (drwdr2 nil "Offset distance for raised pa
nel"  0)))
                             nil tp))
     ))
     (d_we2 spt offbase offside offtop x y numx numy sx sy offin trim)
(princ)
)
(prompt "\nCommand: DWELEV \n")


(c:dwelev)             ;call up program with this command
                       ;or use within another procedure with actual sizes:

;(progn (d_we3)
;  ----------- spt offbase offside offtop  x    y   numx numy sx  sy  offin tri
m----
;          (d_we2 spt 10.0    4.0     6.0   40.0 84.0 2    4   2.0 3.0 1.5    4
.0)
;)
```

Let's create and use the DWELEV.LSP program.

1 Using a word processor or text editor, accurately enter this AutoLISP program and store it using the name **DWELEV.LSP**.

This program is also available on the optional *Applying AutoCAD Diskette*, available from Glencoe.

2 Copy the file to your AutoCAD directory, if it is not already there.

3 Start AutoCAD and Begin a New Drawing. Name it **PARAMET**.

Let's establish an architectural working environment using the Setup facility found in the root page of the standard screen menu.

4 Select **Setup, archtect, 1/4″=1′,** and **B−11×17.**

5 At the "Command:" prompt, enter (load "DWELEV").

This loads the program and automatically enters the new DWELEV command created by the program.

NOTE:

> If the program does not appear to load, compare your program code to the DWELEV.LSP code printed in this unit. They *must* be identical. Also, be sure the program is contained in the directory you specify. For instance, if it is contained in a subdirectory named CHAD, enter (load "CHAD/DWELEV").

The rest is mostly self-explanatory because the program employs easy-to-understand prompts. However, . . .

6 . . . use the following as a guide as you enter your responses.

Lower left corner of door/window: (*Pick a point at any convenient location.*)
Base angle of door/window <0.0>: (*Press RETURN.*)
Width of door/window <3'>: **4'**
Height of door/window <6'-8">: **6'8"**

Trim width <0">: **1.5"**
Number of panels rows <none>: **4**
Number of panel columns <1>: **2**

Bottom rail width <10">: **8"**
Top rail width <6">: **6"**
Side rail width <4">: **5"**
Spacing between panel rows <1">: **2"**
Spacing between panel columns <1">: **3"**
Offset distance for raised panel <0">: **1"**

Notice the commands that automatically enter as the door develops on the screen. You may want to print this information (using CTRL Q) and compare it with the AutoLISP program code.

7 Zoom in on the door and examine it.

Your door should look identical to the following.

410

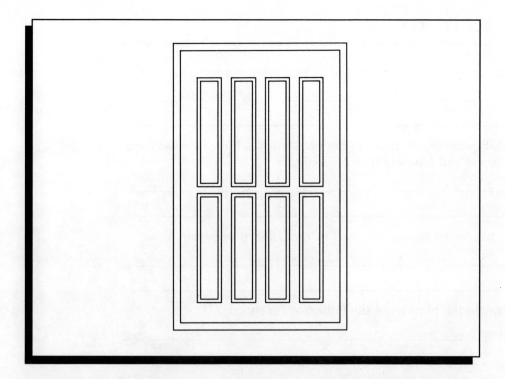

Windows are also created using DWELEV.LSP. Just specify 0 in reply to the "number of panel rows and columns." Two or more windows can be linked together (using COPY or ARRAY) to create casement style windows (shown earlier).

⑧ Create additional doors and windows by entering **DWELEV** at the "Command:" prompt, and enter **END** when you are finished.

The DWELEV.LSP program is intentionally basic so that it is easier for you to understand its internal operation. If you are an accomplished programmer, you may choose to embellish the program by including doorknobs, window molding, and other details normally included on door and window symbology.

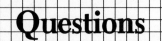

Questions

1. Explain the purpose of the AutoLISP "COMMAND" function.

   _____

   _____

2. If AutoLISP programs or routines are not stored as files, in what form
   are they stored and how are they invoked?

   _____

   _____

3. For what reason are semicolons used in AutoLISP programs?

   _____

   _____

4. Briefly explain the purpose of the following functions:

   GETVAR _____

   _____

   GETPOINT _____

   _____

   DISTANCE _____

   _____

5. Explain the benefits of applying parametric programming techniques.

   _____

   _____

   _____

Problems

1. Combine several AutoCAD commands and AutoLISP functions to create powerful and useful macros.

2. On your own, learn other AutoLISP functions and develop them into new AutoLISP programs.

3. Using the DWELEV.LSP program and AutoCAD commands, create an architectural elevation drawing similar to the one here.

PRB46-1

AUTOCAD® AT WORK

Making the Deserts Bloom with Micro-Based CAD

The problem is basic: central and southern Arizona need water, for agriculture and industry as well as people. The water in the rivers of Arizona's deserts has all been spoken for, and rainfall barely makes a dent in the area's hot, dry climate. One of Arizona's largest cities, Tucson, has pumped out so much of its groundwater for agriculture and municipal use that the land on which Tucson sits is literally sinking.

To help resolve the water imbalance the Bureau of Reclamation, a branch of the United States Department of the Interior, is building the long-planned Central Arizona Project (CAP). Administered by the Bureau's Arizona Projects Office (APO), CAP's goal is a major one—to bring water from the Colorado River (whose water supply is renewed yearly by rainfall and melted snow) to the Arizona desert. The project involves creating a 335-mile network of open canals, tunnels, pipe siphons, and pumping plants to form a water conveyance system. Two new dams and two renovated dams will serve as facilities for water conservation and flood control.

To increase efficiency and productivity on this huge project, the APO's engineers, technicians, and drafters are using microcomputers and AutoCAD software. Drawings can be created faster and changed more easily with AutoCAD than with manual methods. Furthermore, because the system can be easily customized, APO was able to create menus specific to Bureau tasks as well as build libraries of commonly used shapes and title blocks. Such customization has helped users become productive more quickly and has ensured that drawings met or exceeded all Bureau of Reclamation standards.

APO staffers aren't just automating drafting tasks, however; they're also integrating the micro-based CAD system into all parts of their project. A good example is the tract map. This map shows the land through which a canal, pipeline, or other structure is going to pass and indicates which land needs to be acquired. The land must be fully surveyed and described, and precision is crucial. The information collected in the field is processed on the Bureau's Cyber mainframe computer in Denver, Colorado, and then turned into a drawing.

Previously, it took 1 1/2 to 2 weeks just for a person to draft the location of the canal or the roadway and determine how much land would have to be bought. Now this information is fed from the host Cyber system in Denver straight into AutoCAD through the AutoLISP programming language to create the tract map. Total turnaround time is 3 1/2 minutes.

Rob Toy, Chief of the Engineering and Microcomputer Support Branch, says micro-based CAD's capabilities were substantially greater than had been expected. "With AutoCAD," he says, "we're achieving 90% of what we had anticipated from a mainframe CAD system, at 10% of the price. The system is really putting data processing at the fingertips of the people that should be using it, not ADP Support Services, not my branch, but the users—the engineers and technicians."

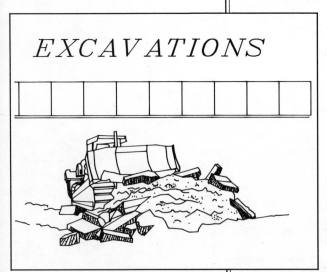

EXCAVATIONS

Courtesy of U.S. Dept. of Interior and Autodesk, Inc.

Unit 47 Digitizing Hardcopy Drawings

AutoCAD®
Reference
Manual

12.3

■ OBJECTIVE:

To input a hardcopy drawing into AutoCAD using the TABLET command

The intent of this unit is to step through the process of digitizing. Note that you must have a digitizing tablet connected to your CAD system in order to complete this unit.

There will be times, especially in a business environment, when you'll wish your hand-completed drawings were stored in AutoCAD. Suppose your firm has recently implemented CAD. All of your previous drawings were completed by hand and you need to revise one or more of them. As you know, it's very time-consuming to redraw them by hand.

Fortunately, most CAD systems, including AutoCAD, offer a method of transferring those drawings onto disk. It is not always practical to digitize drawings, but usually it is much faster than starting the drawings from scratch.

■ *Setting Up*

Since you may not have easy access to a simple drawing not yet in AutoCAD, let's digitize the previously created drawing DIMEN2. This drawing was completed during the dimensioning exercise (Unit 23) and is shown on the next page.

NOTE:

> If you do not have a hard copy of DIMEN2, plot the drawing now or make a photocopy of the drawing on the next page.

1 Load AutoCAD and select task 1, "Begin a New Drawing."

To save time in establishing the drawing settings, you can use DIMEN2 as the prototype drawing. Therefore . . .

2 . . . enter **DIGIT=DIMEN2**.

If you choose not to use DIMEN2 as the prototype drawing, you will need to set each of the drawing parameters, such as the units, limits, etc., to correspond with the DIMEN2 drawing in Unit 23.

3 When the drawing comes up, erase all of it.

NOTE:

> Be sure the snap resolution is set at 6″ and is turned on. Also be sure the limits are ZOOMed All.

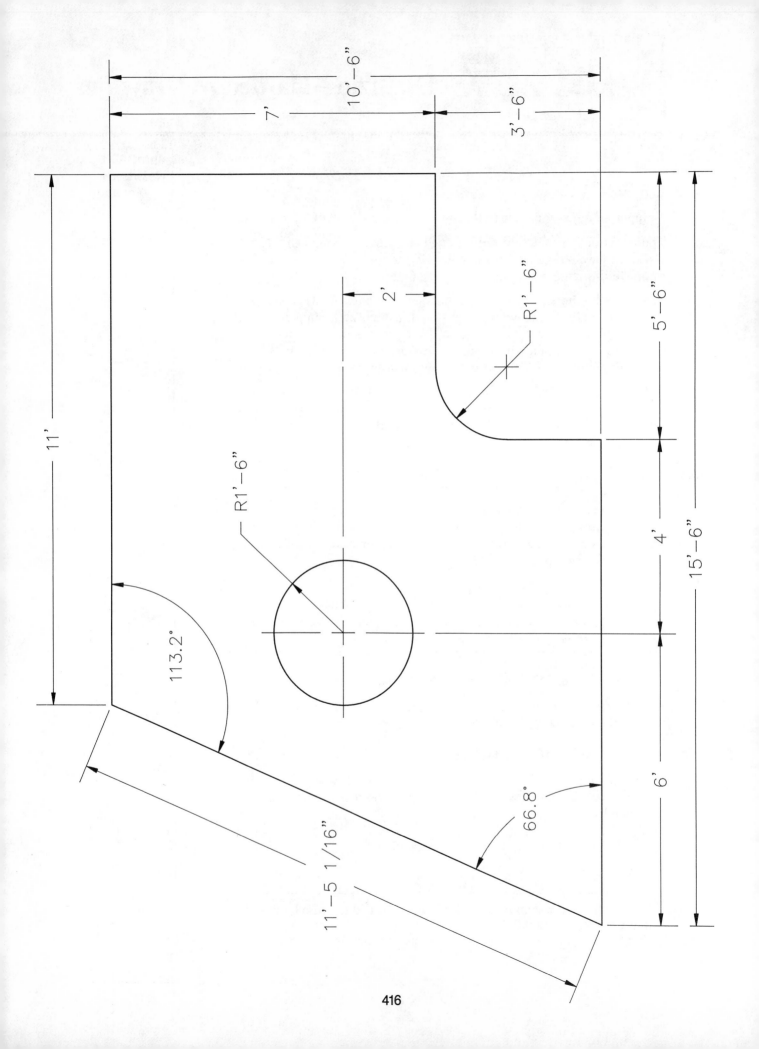

4 Set the layer called **OBJ**, if it is not already set.

5 Using drafting tape, fasten the drawing called DIMEN2 onto the center of your digitizing tablet.

Calibrating the Drawing ——————————

Now, let's calibrate your drawing using the TABLET command.

1 Enter the **TABLET** command and select the **CAL**ibrate option.

12.4.1

We need to identify two known (absolute) points on the drawing. Let's call the lower left corner of the object absolute point 6',6'.

2 In reply to "Digitize first known point:" pick this point (be precise) and enter the coordinates **6',6'**.

—————— NOTE: ——————

You will not have crosshairs on your screen when you pick the point.

Now we need to pick a second known point. Let's choose the corner located 10' to the right of the first point.

3 Pick this point and enter **16',6'** for the coordinates.

You have just calibrated your drawing and AutoCAD can now size the drawing according to this calibration.

Note that the word "Tablet" now appears in the status line. This means the Tablet mode is on. The Tablet mode can be toggled on and off with a function key, usually F10.

4 Toggle Tablet mode on and off and notice the difference in the position of the crosshairs.

5 Toggle Tablet mode off.

Digitizing the Drawing ——————————

Let's begin to trace (digitize) the drawing by doing the object outline. Let's start at the lower left corner of the object, point 6',6'.

1 Enter the **LINE** command.

2 Turn on the Tablet mode with the function key and digitize (pick) point 6',6'.

Whenever you digitize points from your drawing, the Tablet mode *must be on*. Whenever you select commands from the standard screen or pull-down menus, the Tablet mode must be turned *off*.

HINT:

If you are encountering difficulty reaching absolute point 6',6' or any other portion of your screen with your pointing device, it may be that your screen pointing area is too small. If this is the case, enter the TABLET command, CFG option, and enlarge the screen pointing area. Also, when drawing the first five line segments, have the Ortho mode turned on.

3 With the Tablet mode on, digitize the next corner point, working counterclockwise.

This should complete the first line segment.

4 When digitizing the third point, ignore the fillet and pick the approximate location of the corner. With Snap on, your selection of the corner will be accurate. The fillet will be inserted later.

5 Continue around the object until you close the polygon.

6 Using the **FILLET** command, specify a fillet radius of 1'6" and place the fillet at the appropriate location. Remember to turn Tablet off if you want to use the screen menu.

7 Using the **CIRCLE** command, place the circle.

HINT:

When picking the circle's center and radius, be sure Tablet is on and digitize the center and radius from the hardcopy drawing.

8 Set the layer called DIM.

9 Using AutoCAD's dimensioning commands, fully dimension the object with Tablet mode off.

You're finished.

10 Enter **END** to save your work and to exit the Drawing Editor.

Questions

1. What command and command option are used to calibrate a drawing to be digitized?

2. Why is the calibration process necessary?

3. Briefly explain the process of calibrating a drawing to be digitized.

4. Why is the snap resolution important when digitizing?

5. Describe when the Tablet mode should be turned on and when it should be turned off.

6. If you have a mouse, explain whether or not you can digitize a drawing using only a conventional mouse.

Problems

Obtain two hand-completed drawings and digitize each.

NOTE:

It is possible to digitize drawings that are larger than your digitizing tablet. Simply move the drawing into the active area on your tablet and recalibrate.

AUTOCAD® AT WORK

*Digitizing 50 Years of Data**

Highland Park, Texas, is located slightly north of bustling downtown Dallas and is known for its lovely homes and affluent population. The town has a geographic area of 2.5 square miles and a population of about 9,000.

The town's public work infrastructure was built primarily during the 1920s and 1930s. The original mapping system consisted of five sets of maps dating back to 1931. Each set was made up of 97 section maps for water, sanitary sewer, storm sewer, street lights, and paving detail. Town engineer James B. Dower was faced with the task of bringing these maps, which had not been changed since 1951, up to date.

He determined that computer-based mapping would be the best solution, and AutoCAD was chosen as the software. A local company, Laser Data-Images, manually digitized the old maps for use in AutoCAD. Laser Data-Images provided a composite map made up of each of the five sets of 97 detail maps. "The resulting map was very clean and accurate and is now a complete working copy," says Dower. "We have since made one thorough update of the electronic maps to include changes and fixtures not clearly shown on the originals and have now placed these maps in service."

Dower is very pleased with the new system. Updating the maps is easy, and new maps can be created from the base map files. "Given the success we've had with our new electronic mapping system, I'd strongly recommend that other municipalities consider implementing such a system."

*Based on a story in *CADENCE* magazine, Vol. 3, No. 4.

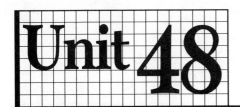

Unit 48 — Translating Via DXF and IGES

■ OBJECTIVE:

To practice DXF and IGES translations with AutoCAD

Standard file formats are important for moving CAD drawings from one system to another. This unit steps through the entire translation process using two industry standard formats: DXF and IGES.

NOTE:

Drawing files created by AutoCAD are totally compatible with AutoCAD running on different operating systems, such as Unix, and different computers, such as Apollo and Sun workstations running their version of Unix.

■ *DXF*

C.1

The DXF file format is the de facto standard for translating files from one microCAD system, such as AutoCAD, to another, such as VersaCAD. Autodesk, Inc., makers of AutoCAD, created the DXF format, also referred to as a drawing interchange file format. DXF files can be translated to other DXF compatible CAD systems or submitted to programs for specialized analysis. Certain numerical control (NC) post-processing software uses DXF files to generate code for tool paths for numerically controlled machines such as NC mills and lathes.

■ *DXFOUT Command*

C.1.1

You can generate a drawing interchange (DXF) file from an existing drawing (DWG) by means of the DXFOUT command.

1. Load AutoCAD and select option **2**, "Edit an EXISTING drawing," from the Main Menu. (Choose any simple drawing to translate.)

2. In the Drawing Editor, select **UTILITY** from the root page of the standard screen menu.

3. Select **DXF/DXB** from the screen menu.

NOTE:

DXB, short for "drawing interchange binary," is a much more compact file format used by programs such as Autodesk's AutoShade rendering software.

4. Select **DXFOUT**.

5. If you want to use the same directory and file name, press **RETURN**. Your file will have a DXF file extension.

6 Press **RETURN** in reply to "Decimal places of accuracy."

The translation may take a while, especially with complex drawings. When the "Command:" prompt returns, the translation is complete.

7 Enter the **SH** command.

8 Perform a **DIR**ectory listing of the directory containing the new DXF file.

How much larger than the DWG file is the DXF file?

9 Using the DOS **TYPE** command, review the contents of your new ASCII DXF file. (See Appendix F for instructions on using the TYPE command.)

NOTE:

Press CTRL S to stop the scrolling of the screen. Press CTRL C to cancel.

The format and contents of the beginning of your ASCII text file should look similar to the following.

```
      0
SECTION
      2
HEADER
      9
$ACADVER
      1
AC1006
      9
$INSBASE
     10
0.0
     20
0.0
     30
0.0
      9
$EXTMIN
     10
0.191002
     20
    -1.0
      9
$EXTMAX
     10
9.88388
     20
```

422

10 If you do not already have the "Command:" prompt, enter **EXIT** to return to AutoCAD.

Binary DXF Files

C.2.1

The DXFOUT command provides a "Binary" option that creates binary DXF files instead of ASCII text files. Binary DXF files contain all of the information in an ASCII DXF file, but are much more compact. Their file size is approximately 25 percent smaller and they can be written and read by AutoCAD about five times faster.

1 Enter **DXFOUT**

2 Slightly modify the name of the new file so it does not overwrite the DXF file you created earlier.

3 At the next prompt, enter **Binary**.

Notice that the file is created much faster than the ASCII DXF file.

4 Using the DOS **DIR** command, compare the size of the ASCII DXF file with the binary DXF file.

The binary DXF file should be at least 25 percent smaller. Also, all of the floating-point accuracy in the data base is preserved. ASCII DXF files, instead, increase in size as you increase the decimal places of accuracy.

DXFIN Command

C.1.2

Both ASCII and binary DXF files can be converted to an AutoCAD (DWG) drawing by means of the DXFIN command.

1 Begin a New Drawing. Name it **FRESH**.

2 Enter the **DXFIN** command.

3 In reply to "DXFIN File name:" enter the name of a DXF file currently on disk. If you do not have one you want to convert to a DWG format, enter the name of one of the DXF files you just created. Omit the DXF extension.

The DXF file will generate on the screen as it is translated into a DWG format. When complete, FRESH.DWG (your current drawing) will be the new DWG file created from the DXF file.

4 Enter **END** to save the new drawing and to exit.

IGES

IGES stands for the Initial Graphics Exchange Specification. IGES is the industry standard approved by the American National Standards Institute (ANSI) for interchange of graphic files between small and large-scale CAD systems.

Files translated via IGES from one CAD system to another are useful. However, each CAD system has its uniquenesses. Consequently, certain characteristics such as layers, Blocks, linetypes, colors, and text are potential problem areas after the translated file is brought into the CAD system.

For example, some CAD systems use numbers for layer names and do not accept names such as OBJ or DIM. If an AutoCAD drawing file is translated to a system using only layer numbers, all of the AutoCAD layers' names will be changed to numbers. These types of potential problems are also present when translating files using the DXF file format.

IGESOUT Command

You can generate an IGES interchange file from an existing AutoCAD drawing file by means of the IGESOUT command.

1 Call up any drawing you have on disk, but avoid using a complex drawing.

2 Select the **UTILITY** menu.

3 Select **IGES** from the screen menu.

4 Select **IGESOUT**.

5 In reply to "IGESOUT File name" press **RETURN** because you want to use your current drawing.

The translation may take a while (maybe even several minutes) depending upon the size and complexity of your drawing. Be patient.

The IGES file will have the same file name as your current drawing, but with an IGS file extension.

When the "Command:" prompt returns, the IGES translation is complete.

6 Enter the **SH** command and then **RETURN**.

7 With the **DIR** command, review the directory containing the new IGES file.

Do you see it? Its size will be larger than a corresponding DXF file.

⑧ With the DOS **TYPE** command, display the contents of your new IGES file.

The format and contents of the beginning of your IGES file should look similar to the following.

```
IGES file generated from an AutoCAD drawing by the IGES            S0000001

translator from Autodesk, Inc., translator version IGESOUT-2.0.     S0000002

,,3HART,7HART.IGS,13HAutoCAD-10 c2,11HIGESOUT-2.0,16,38,6,99,15,3HART,  G0000001

1.0,1,4HINCH,32767,3.2767D1,13H890123.004207,1.0D-8,1.244121936422D1,6HTG0000002

hroop,14HAutodesk, Inc.,4,0;                                        G0000003

    124        1        1                               00010000D0000001

    124                          1        0                     D0000002

    110        2        1        1                     00010200D0000003

    110                          2                             D0000004

    110        4        1        1                     00010200D0000005

    110                          2                             D0000006

    110        6        1        1                     00010200D0000007

    110                          2
```

⑨ Enter **EXIT** to return to the AutoCAD Drawing Editor.

⑩ Enter **QUIT** to exit AutoCAD.

IGESIN Command

C.4.2

An IGES interchange file can be converted into an AutoCAD drawing by means of the IGESIN command.

① Begin a New Drawing. Name it **NEW**.

② Enter the **IGESIN** command.

③ In reply to "IGESIN File name" enter the name of an IGES file currently on disk. If you do not have one you want translated into a DWG format, enter the name of the IGES file you just created. Omit the IGS extension.

The translation can take a while, so be patient. Eventually, it will generate on the screen. When complete, the "Command:" prompt will return. NEW.DWG (your current drawing) is the new DWG file created from the IGES file.

Questions

1. What is a DXF file and what is its purpose?

_____

_____

2. For what does IGES stand? What is the purpose of an IGES file?

_____

_____

3. Explain the purpose of the DXFOUT command.

_____

_____

4. Explain the advantages of using binary DXF files instead of ASCII DXF files.

_____

_____

_____

5. Explain the purpose of the DXFIN command.

_____

_____

6. Explain the purpose of the IGESOUT command.

_____

_____

7. Explain the purpose of the IGESIN command.

_____

_____

8. What are the potential problem areas associated with translating DXF and IGES files from one CAD system to another?

_____

_____

Problems

1. With AutoCAD drawings, create DXF and IGES files using the facilities provided by AutoCAD. After the translations are complete, review the contents of the DXF and IGES files.

2. If you have access to another CAD system, load the above DXF or IGES files into that system. (Note: The CAD system must have a facility similar to AutoCAD's DXFIN or IGESIN to bring in the files.) If you are successful, review characteristics of the drawings, such as layers, Blocks, and text, and note the differences between the CAD systems.

3. Create DXF and IGES files from another CAD system. Bring those files into AutoCAD using the DXFIN and IGESIN commands. Note the differences between characteristics of AutoCAD and the files brought into AutoCAD.

Unit 49 Lights, Camera, ...

**AutoCAD®
Reference
Manual**

■ OBJECTIVE:

To apply MSLIDE, VSLIDE, SCRIPT, RSCRIPT, DELAY, and RESUME in developing a slide show in a script file and to create a slide library

The purpose of this unit is to develop a slide show by making slides and including them in a script file. Though it may sound complicated, it is really very simple. A word processor or text editor is recommended for creation of sophisticated slide shows or script files.

The following is an example of a script file. It's nothing more than a text file stored with an .SCR file extension. It can be executed while you begin a new drawing or when you are in the Drawing Editor.

11.1

```
UNITS 4 4 1 0 0 N
LIMITS 0,0 15',10'
ZOOM A
GRID 1'
SNAP ON
```

With earlier versions of AutoCAD, users often used script files such as the one above to store drawing parameters and settings, expediting the setup process. The use of prototype drawings has largely replaced this practice.

Script files can be used for other purposes too. A common application is for showing a continuous sequence of drawings, a sort of electronic flipchart. AutoCAD calls this a slide show.

11.2

MSLIDE Command _____

11.2.1

Before the script file can be created, we must first have slides to include in the script. Slides are created with existing drawings, using the MSLIDE command (short for Make Slide). Let's load a couple of drawings and create slides from each. Use the previously created drawings named THREE-D and DIMEN. Or, if you prefer, choose two others.

1 Load AutoCAD and Begin a New Drawing. Name it **SLIDE**.

2 Using the **INSERT** command, insert your drawing called THREE-D. Enter **0,0** for the insertion point.

3 With **VPOINT**, create a 3D view.

4 Enter the **MSLIDE** command and give the slide file the same name as the drawing file (**THREE-D**). Do not specify the extension, .SLD. AutoCAD does that for you.

NOTE: _____

The new slide file has a file extension of .SLD (THREE-D.SLD). This type of file cannot be edited. Drawing files used to create slides remain untouched and can be edited.

5 Erase the THREE-D drawing so that your screen is again blank.

6 Insert the second drawing (DIMEN) and create another slide using MSLIDE command.

VSLIDE Command

Let's apply the VSLIDE (View Slide) command to look at the first slide we created.

1 Enter **VSLIDE** and **THREE-D** (the .SLD extension is assumed).

The THREE-D slide should appear on your screen.

2 To restore your original screen, enter **REGEN**.

3 If you'd like to make additional slides from other drawings, create them now.

4 When you're finished, return to the Main Menu by entering **QUIT**.

5 Exit AutoCAD.

Creating the Script File

Now let's create the script file (slide show). It's going to be a short one!

1 If you have not done so yet, obtain your DOS prompt (*e.g.,* C:\ACAD>).

2 Begin a new file using the COPY CON method as shown below. Name the file SHOW.SCR, and be sure to specify the appropriate drive if necessary.

C:\ACAD> **COPY CON:SHOW.SCR** (press **RETURN**)

3 Now type the following. Be sure to specify the appropriate drive if the slides reside on a drive or directory other than the default drive or directory. If you make a mistake, backspace or start over.

VSLIDE THREE-D (press **RETURN**)
DELAY 1000 (press **RETURN**)
VSLIDE DIMEN (press **RETURN**)
DELAY 500 (press **RETURN**)
REDRAW (press **RETURN**)
(press **F6** function key and **RETURN**)

NOTE:

If you've chosen different drawings for slides, you must of course enter their names instead of "THREE-D" and "DIMEN."

You have just created a simple slide show stored in a script file.

NOTE:

The DELAY command tells AutoCAD to hold the slide on the screen for X number of milliseconds. Some computers run faster than others; nevertheless, 1000 milliseconds is approximately a one-second delay.

11.1.3

Showtime

Now let's try the slide show.

1 Load AutoCAD and bring up the Drawing Editor.

2 Enter the **SCRIPT** command, and type **SHOW**.

11.1.2

Each slide should be displayed on the screen.

3 To repeat the slide show, enter the **RSCRIPT** command.

11.1.6

This command could be included at the end of your script file to automatically repeat the slide show.

NOTE:

CTRL C or the back space key will interrupt a running script. This allows you to issue other AutoCAD commands. If you wish to return to the script, enter the RESUME command.

11.1.4

4 Enter **QUIT** to exit the Drawing Editor.

5 Create new slides from other drawings and include them in your SHOW.SCR file. Include the RSCRIPT command at the end of your script.

6 Run your revised slide show in the Drawing Editor.

7 When you're finished, enter **QUIT** to exit the Drawing Editor.

Creating Slide Libraries

The slide library facility lets you collect slide files into a single file similar to filling a carousel tray of 35-mm slides.

Once the slide library is created, it can be used in conjunction with a slide show. The individual slide files need not be present.

NOTE:

Icon menus require the use of slide libraries. See Unit 50 for details.

1 Identify slide files you would like to group in a slide library. Choose or create 3 or 4 for now.

2 If you have not already, **QUIT** or **END** AutoCAD, but remain in the main ACAD directory.

3 At the DOS prompt, enter the following to create a slide library file named FIRST.SLB.

C:\ACAD>**SLIDELIB FIRST** (press **RETURN**)

This will start the SLIDELIB.EXE program (which must be present in your current directory), and a copyright statement should appear on the screen.

4 At the flashing cursor, type the first slide file name (with or without the .SLD file extension), in upper or lowercase letters, and then press **RETURN**.

HINT:

If your slide files reside in a directory under the main ACAD directory, then specify the name of that directory, such as USER\DIMEN. Here, the file DIMEN.SLD resides in the directory named USER. The USER directory resides in the main ACAD directory.

5 Enter each of the remaining slide file names.

6 When you are finished, press the **F6** function key and then press **RETURN**.

The new slide library file will be stored on your hard disk. It contains images of the slide files you entered. The slide library resides in the main ACAD directory.

Viewing Slides from the Slide Library _____

1 Start AutoCAD and proceed into the Drawing Editor by beginning or editing a drawing.

2 Enter the **VSLIDE** command.

3 In reply to "Slide file:" type the slide library name followed by one of the slide file names (enclosed in parentheses) and press **RETURN**. Here is an example:

FIRST(DIMEN) and press **RETURN**

The slide image should appear. Try another.

4 Enter **QUIT** to exit the Drawing Editor.

If you are interested in taking further advantage of the slide library facility, combine a slide library with a script file to create a slide show.

Unit 50 applies slide libraries to the creation of icon menus.

Questions

1. Briefly describe the purpose of each of the following commands.

   MSLIDE _____

   VSLIDE _____

   SCRIPT _____

   RSCRIPT _____

   DELAY _____

   RESUME _____

2. Describe the purpose of an AutoCAD script file.

   _____

   _____

3. What is the file extension of a script file?

   _____

4. What does the number following the DELAY command indicate?

   _____

   _____

5. Is it more practical to store a drawing setup in a script file or in a prototype drawing? Explain why.

   _____

   _____

   _____

   _____

Problems

1. Create a dozen or so slides of previously created drawings. Include them in a slide show stored in a script file. Run the show.

2. Develop a script file that includes several AutoCAD commands. Make it as sophisticated as possible. When you're finished, print the file so that you can work out the bugs as you run it.

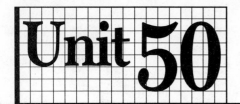

Unit 50 Icon Menus

■ OBJECTIVE:

To develop an icon menu using the slide library facility in connection with the icon menu creation procedures.

Icons are small pictures, and they can be used to create menus. For example, icon menus make it easier for you to use Blocks you've created. Instead of having to remember Block names or referring to hard copy, you can call up icon menus (that represent your Blocks) on the screen. This enables you to easily review and choose the Blocks, and it eliminates the need to repeatedly enter the INSERT command and the Block name.

NOTE:

This unit requires knowledge of AutoCAD's ACAD.MNU menu, presented in Units 40-42. It also requires the use of a text editor or word processor.

Sampling an Icon Menu

Below is an icon menu for choosing a hatch pattern. Let's experiment with the Hatch icon menu.

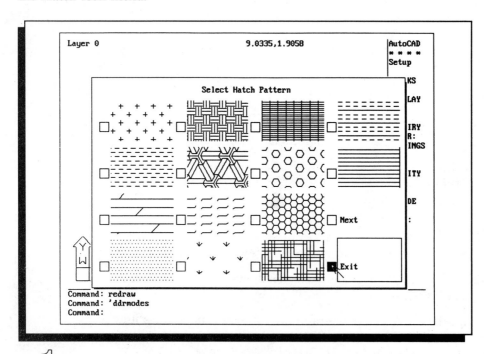

1 Load AutoCAD and Begin a New Drawing, or edit an existing one.

2 Select the **Draw** pull-down menu.

434

3 Choose the "**Hatch** . . ." item found in the Draw pull-down menu.

The hatch icon menu should appear.

4 Select the **Next** item from the icon menu.

A second Hatch icon menu should appear.

5 Choose the **Next** item once more.

6 Pick one of the hatch pattern icons.

You should now understand the benefits of using icon menus.

7 Press **CTRL C** to cancel the hatch operation.

Let's step through the process of creating an icon menu using Blocks instead of hatch patterns.

Creating the Slide Library _____

First we must create a slide library. Before we can do this, however, we must identify (or create) several Blocks to be included in the slide library. As an example, let's use the small symbol library of Blocks from Unit 28. They are printed here for your reference.

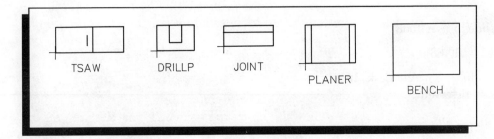

These five blocks will later become your icons.

1 If these Blocks exist on disk, load the drawing that contains them; then skip to Step 5. If they do not exist or you cannot find them, continue with Step 2.

2 Begin a New Drawing and name it **TOOLS**.

3 Create each of the five items shown in the preceding illustration at any convenient size and store each of them as a Block using the names shown. (Refer to Unit 27 if you don't remember how to create Blocks.)

4 Insert each of the five Blocks in any convenient location on the screen.

5 Using the **MSLIDE** command, produce a slide of each Block. Use the Block name for the slide name.

6 After you are confident you have five slide files that correspond with the five Blocks, enter **END** to save your work and to exit the Drawing Editor.

7 Create a slide library named **TOOLS** using the procedures outlined in the previous unit.

If you are using a subdirectory (such as USER) for storing your slide files and library file, the information on your screen may look similar to the following.

C:\ACAD> slidelib user\tools

SLIDELIB 1.1 (2/10/88)

(C) Copyright 1987, 88, Autodesk, Inc.
      All Rights Reserved
user\tsaw
user\drillp
user\joint
user\planer
user\bench
^Z

C:\ACAD>

If you are not storing in a subdirectory, your screen information will look the same but without the subdirectory names.

Creating the Icon Menu_____

The steps in creating an icon menu involve the alteration of AutoCAD's source menu ACAD.MNU. This requires the use of a text editor such as EDLIN or a word processor.

1 Locate the ACAD.MNU file found on the AutoCAD "Source" diskette.

2 Copy ACAD.MNU to the main ACAD directory unless it is already present.

_____ NOTE: _____

Be sure you have at least one backup copy of this file before you proceed further.

3 Display the contents of ACAD.MNU with a text editor or word processor.

4 Place the following (exactly as you see it here) just prior to the information that describes the root page of the screen menu, or at any convenient location in ACAD.MNU.

```
***icon
**tools
[Select Component]
[tools(tsaw)]^cinsert tsaw \\\\$i=tools $i=*
[tools(drillp)]^cinsert drillp \\\\$i=tools $i=*
[tools(joint)]^cinsert joint \\\\$i=tools $i=*
[tools(planer)]^cinsert planer \\\\$i=tools $i=*
[tools(bench)]^cinsert bench \\\\$i=tools $i=*
[ Exit] ^ c
```

Each of the five consistently structured menu items will do the following: (1) display the slide image as an icon on the screen, (2) allow you to choose it, (3) if chosen, insert the corresponding Block, and (4) redisplay the icon menu on the screen so that you may choose others.

If you want to learn more about the specific components within these menu items, review Unit 40.

Making the Icon Menu Accessible_____

In the Drawing Editor, the icon menu is accessed and invoked using the screen menu and/or the pull-down menu and/or the tablet menu. In any case, a new menu item must be added in ACAD.MNU.

1 Near the beginning of the ACAD.MNU file, locate the Options pull-down menu indicated by the ✳✳✳POP6 menu item.

2 Enter the following as the last line in ✳✳✳POP6.

[Tools]^c^cinsert tools ^c$i=tools $i=✳

This will display the word Tools in the Options pull-down menu. In addition, it will insert the five block definitions contained in TOOLS.DWG. Any graphics that may be contained in TOOLS.DWG will not insert because a "Cancel" is automatically issued at the "Insertion point:" step of the INSERT command. The last part of the macro addresses the tools icon menu and displays it on the screen.

NOTE:

You have the freedom to include this menu item elsewhere in the pull-down menus, or in a screen or tablet menu.

3 Store your revised ACAD.MNU.

4 Make a backup copy of your revised ACAD.MNU.

Make sure your revised ACAD.MNU is resident in your main AutoCAD directory (ACAD).

5 Copy TOOLS.SLB and TOOLS.DWG to the main AutoCAD directory.

Using the Icon Menu

1 Load AutoCAD and Begin a New Drawing or edit an existing one.

2 Select the **Options** pull-down menu.

The new Tools item should be present.

3 Choose the **Tools** item.

The new icon menu should appear. If it did not appear, there may be a typing error in the new information entered in ACAD.MNU. Review the additions you made and correct any mistakes.

Making Additional Slides for Use in Icon Menus

When preparing slides for use in icon menus, keep them simple. Complex icons take longer to display on the screen and their complexity may confuse more than communicate.

Also, do not create solid-filled images because icon menus will not display them. Therefore, you may want to turn off FILL before preparing the slides.

Hierarchical Icon Menus _____

An icon menu can accommodate only 16 selections: 15 Blocks (icons) and one Exit item. However, it is not unusual to want to include more than 15 Blocks.

It is possible to construct hierarchical icon menus in which a selection displays another icon menu, a selection in that menu displays another icon menu, and so on. Thus a series of similar icon menus can be connected to one another.

The Hatch item contained in the Draw pull-down menu is a good example of this. Notice the Next selection contained in the Hatch icon menu. This feature is implemented by adding the following to the icon menu:

[Next]$i=hatch2 $i=*

The $i=hatch2 item addresses the hatch2 icon menu, which in this case is the second set of hatch patterns. The $i=* item displays the icon menu.

Questions

1. Why are icon menus beneficial?

   _____

   _____

2. Name at least two rules you should consider before creating slides for use in an icon menu.

   _____

   _____

3. From what type of files does the slide library facility create a slide library file?

   _____

4. In what AutoCAD file should you enter the icon menu information necessary for displaying the icon menu on the screen?

   _____

5. The ✱✱✱icon menu item specifies what?

   _____

6. Explain the following: [Tools]^c^cinsert tools ^c$i=tools $i= ✱.

   _____

   _____

7. Suppose you want to include more than 50 selections in your icon menu. How do you go about it when icon menus are limited to 16 selections?

   _____

   _____

Problem

First, group several Blocks and create a slide of each. Second, create a slide library using the slide files. Third, use the slide library to create an icon menu. Use the steps outlined in this unit to complete this problem.

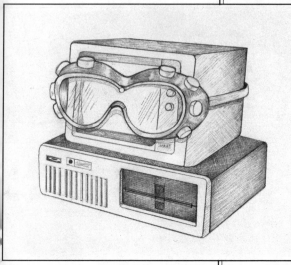

AUTOCAD® AT WORK

CAD/CAM with AutoCAD

Cutting plastic parts is time-consuming and sometimes dangerous work. Working with a table saw and a hand-held router, a parts manufacturer spends hours on a single job. And a slip of the hand may result in a serious cut or dismemberment.

A company which manufactures plastic parts for small household conveniences, such as paper towel holders, recently computerized its manufacturing division in order to increase production and reduce injuries. Using AutoCAD, the company's designers draw the path a router should follow. The drawing is then sent electronically to a numerical control (NC) router, which includes a 5′ × 10′ table with a blade whose movements can be programmed. The router operator mounts the uncut plastic on the table and starts the programmed router, which cuts out a perfectly tooled part.

Both safety and product quality have increased at the plant since the introduction of AutoCAD. The company's president notes, "When I use AutoCAD to draw, I don't reach for a French curve—I choose from nine different ways to create an arc in AutoCAD. I pick whatever suits my needs and let the computer draw it for me."

AutoCAD's three-dimensional visualization feature offers another advantage for parts manufacturers. Having a three-dimensional drawing of the tool path geometry allows the designer to see what a shape will look like before it is created.

According to the president, CAD is responsible for dramatic increases in production in the last year: "Before acquiring AutoCAD, we were just cutting by hand. With one man operating a machine interfaced with AutoCAD, we can cut 1,000 paper towel holder blanks in a day. By hand there's no way to get that kind of output or product consistency."

Optional Problems

INTRODUCTION

The following problems are provided to give you additional practice with AutoCAD. These problems will help you to expand your knowledge and ability, and they will offer you new and exciting experiences with the system.

The problems range from simple to advanced, and they encompass a variety of disciplines. They have been sequenced from simple to advanced, but your instructor may ask you to complete the problems in a different order.

Regardless of the type of problem, the key to successful completion is: **plan before beginning**. Review previously learned commands and techniques and ask yourself how they can best be applied to your problem. For example, when laying out rectangular objects, plan to utilize the Grid, Snap, and Ortho features. When drawing lines of specific lengths and angles, consider using relative and polar methods of specifying endpoints. Plan how to use COPY, MIRROR, and ARRAY to simplify and speed your work.

As you discover new and easier methods of creating drawings, apply these methods when solving the problems. Since there is usually more than one way to complete a drawing, experiment with alternative methods. Discuss these alternatives with other users and create strategies for efficient completion of the problems.

Remember, there is no substitute for practice. The expertise you gain will equate with the time you spend on the system. Set aside blocks of time to work with AutoCAD, think through your approach, and enjoy!

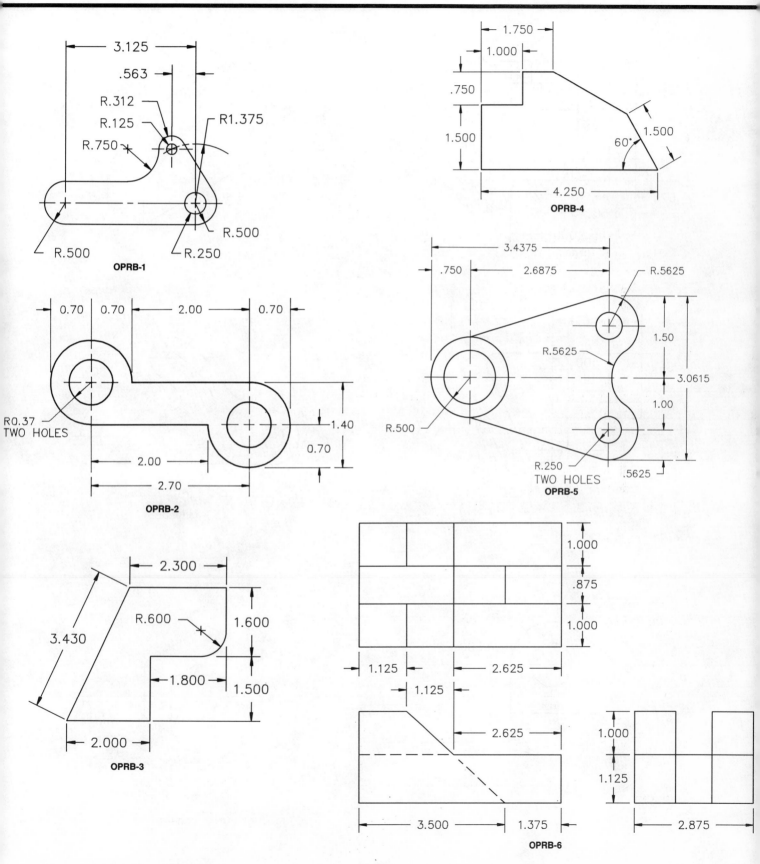

OPRB-1

OPRB-2

OPRB-3

OPRB-4

OPRB-5

OPRB-6

443

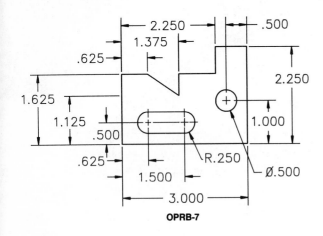

OPRB-7

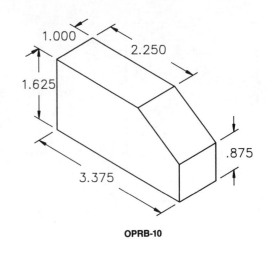

OPRB-10

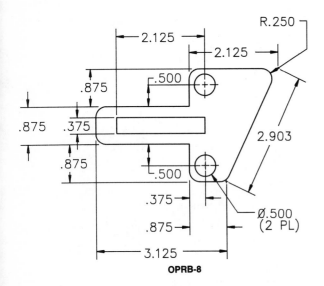

OPRB-8

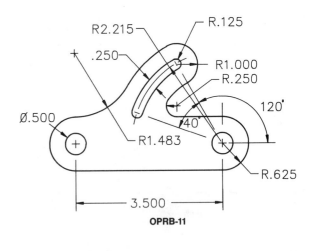

OPRB-11

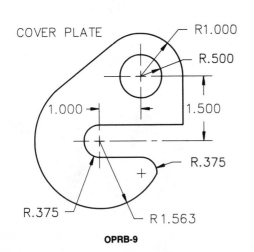

COVER PLATE

OPRB-9

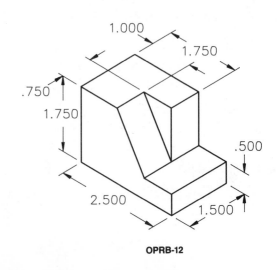

OPRB-12

Note: Consider drawing orthographic views of the
isometric drawings on this and the following pages.

444

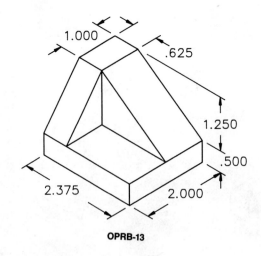

OPRB-13

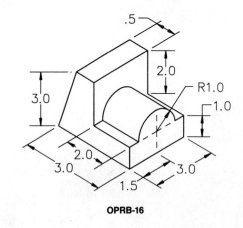

OPRB-16

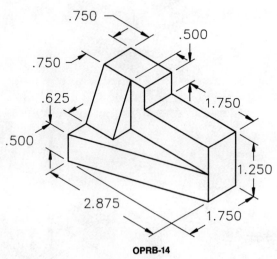

OPRB-14

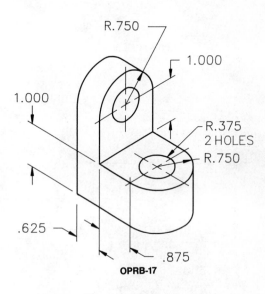

OPRB-17

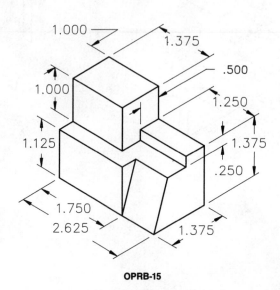

OPRB-15

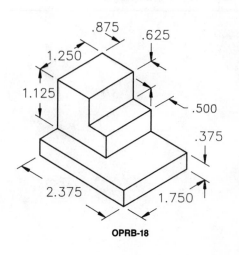

OPRB-18

445

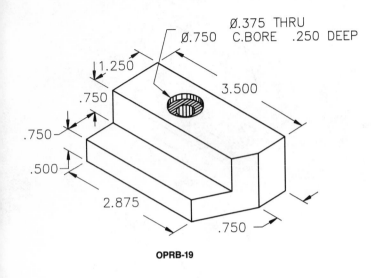

Ø.375 THRU
Ø.750 C.BORE .250 DEEP

1.250
.750
.750
.500
3.500
2.875
.750

OPRB-19

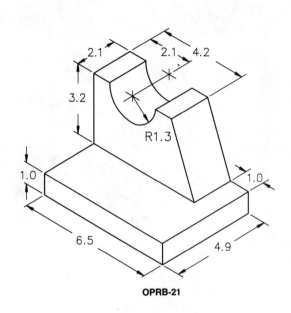

2.1
3.2
2.1
4.2
R1.3
1.0
1.0
6.5
4.9

OPRB-21

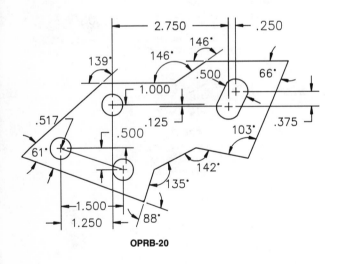

2.750
.250
139°
146°
146°
1.000
.500
66°
.517
.125
.500
103°
.375
61°
142°
.500
135°
1.500
88°
1.250

OPRB-20

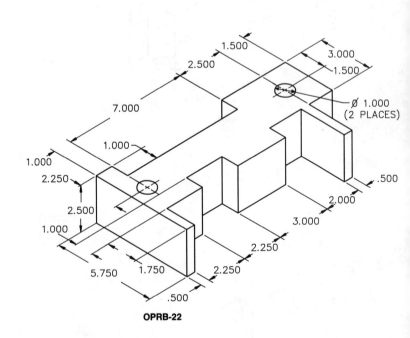

1.500
2.500
3.000
1.500
7.000
1.000
Ø 1.000
(2 PLACES)
1.000
2.250
.500
2.500
2.000
1.000
3.000
5.750
1.750
2.250
2.250
.500

OPRB-22

446

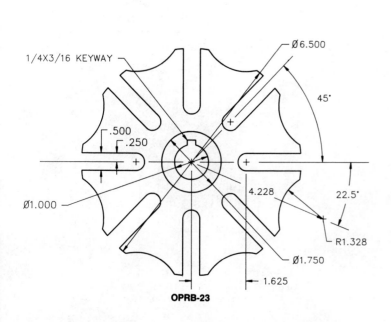

1/4X3/16 KEYWAY

Ø6.500

45°

.500
.250

Ø1.000

4.228

22.5°

R1.328

Ø1.750

1.625

OPRB-23

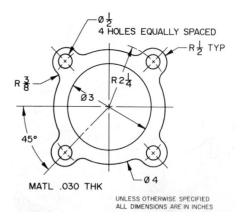

Ø$\frac{1}{2}$
4 HOLES EQUALLY SPACED

R$\frac{1}{2}$ TYP

R$\frac{3}{8}$

R2$\frac{1}{4}$

Ø3

45°

Ø4

MATL .030 THK

UNLESS OTHERWISE SPECIFIED
ALL DIMENSIONS ARE IN INCHES

OPRB-25 (from the textbook *Drafting Fundamentals* by Scott, Foy, and Schwendau)

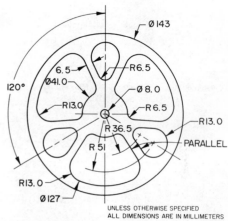

Ø143

6.5
R6.5
Ø41.0
R13.0
Ø8.0
R6.5
120°
R13.0
R 36.5
R 51
PARALLEL
R13.0
Ø127

UNLESS OTHERWISE SPECIFIED
ALL DIMENSIONS ARE IN MILLIMETERS

OPRB-26 (from the textbook *Drafting Fundamentals* by Scott, Foy, and Schwendau)

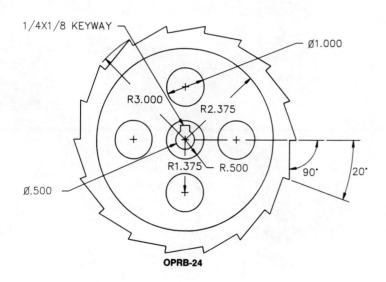

1/4X1/8 KEYWAY

Ø1.000

R3.000

R2.375

R1.375   R.500

Ø.500

90°   20°

OPRB-24

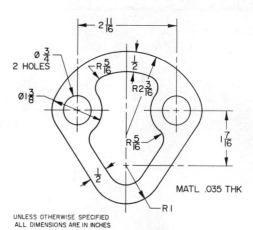

2$\frac{11}{16}$

Ø$\frac{3}{4}$
2 HOLES

R$\frac{5}{16}$
$\frac{1}{2}$
R2$\frac{3}{16}$

Ø1$\frac{3}{8}$

R$\frac{5}{16}$

$\frac{1}{2}$

1$\frac{7}{16}$

MATL .035 THK

R1

UNLESS OTHERWISE SPECIFIED
ALL DIMENSIONS ARE IN INCHES

OPRB-27 (from the textbook *Drafting Fundamentals* by Scott, Foy, and Schwendau)

447

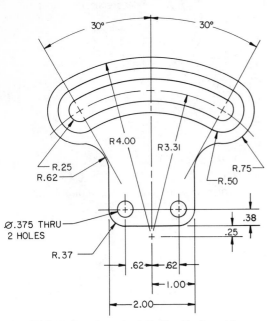

OPRB-28 (from the textbook *Drafting Fundamentals* by Scott, Foy, and Schwendau)

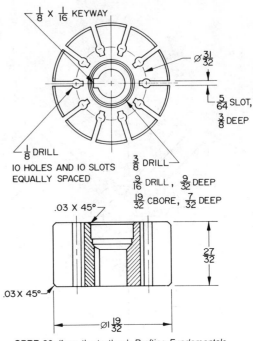

OPRB-30 (from the textbook *Drafting Fundamentals* by Scott, Foy, and Schwendau)

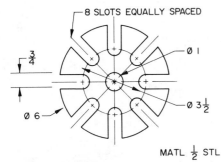

MATL $\frac{1}{2}$ STL

UNLESS OTHERWISE SPECIFIED
ALL DIMENSIONS ARE IN INCHES   REF. ANSI Y14.5M–1982

OPRB-29 (from the textbook *Drafting Fundamentals* by Scott, Foy, and Schwendau)

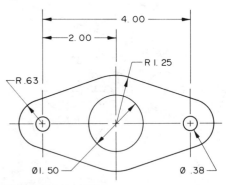

MATL .06 ASBESTOS

UNLESS OTHERWISE SPECIFIED
REF. ANSI Y14.5M–1982   ALL DIMENSIONS ARE IN INCHES

OPRB-31 (from the textbook *Drafting Fundamentals* by Scott, Foy, and Schwendau)

448

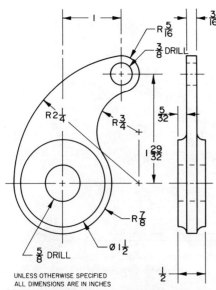

UNLESS OTHERWISE SPECIFIED
ALL DIMENSIONS ARE IN INCHES

OPRB-32 (from the textbook *Drafting Fundamentals* by Scott, Foy, and Schwendau)

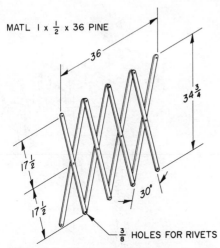

MATL 1 x ½ x 36 PINE

$\frac{3}{8}$ HOLES FOR RIVETS

OPRB-33 (from the textbook *Drafting Fundamentals* by Scott, Foy, and Schwendau)

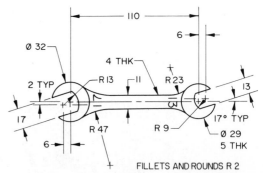

FILLETS AND ROUNDS R 2

MATL FORGED STL

UNLESS OTHERWISE SPECIFIED
ALL DIMENSIONS ARE IN MILLIMETERS   REF. ANSI Y14.5M – 1982

OPRB-34 (from the textbook *Drafting Fundamentals* by Scott, Foy, and Schwendau)

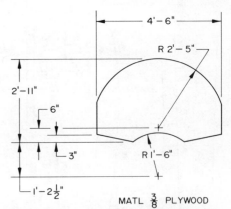

MATL $\frac{3}{8}$ PLYWOOD

OPRB-35 (from the textbook *Drafting Fundamentals* by Scott, Foy, and Schwendau)

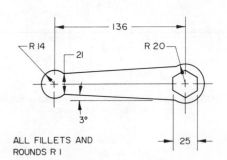

ALL FILLETS AND
ROUNDS R 1

MATL 4 MM GALVANIZED STL

REF. ANSI Y14.5M-1982   UNLESS OTHERWISE SPECIFIED
ALL DIMENSIONS ARE IN MILLIMETERS

OPRB-36 (from the textbook *Drafting Fundamentals* by Scott, Foy, and Schwendau)

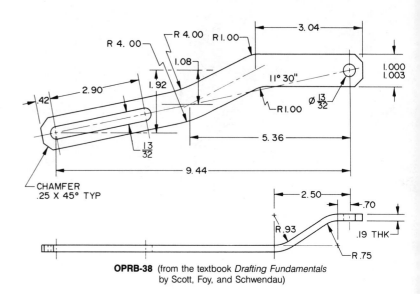

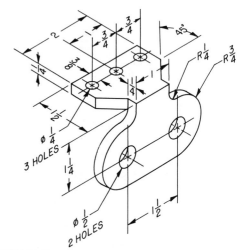

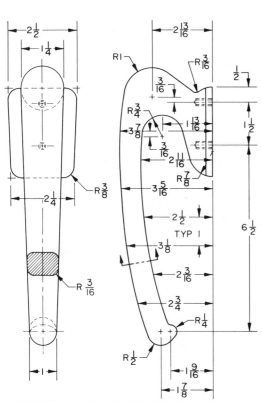

OPRB-38 (from the textbook *Drafting Fundamentals*
by Scott, Foy, and Schwendau)

OPRB-37 (from the textbook *Drafting Fundamentals*
by Scott, Foy, and Schwendau)

OPRB-39 (from the textbook *Drafting Fundamentals*
by Scott, Foy, and Schwendau)

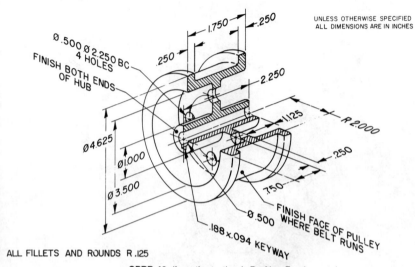

UNLESS OTHERWISE SPECIFIED
ALL DIMENSIONS ARE IN INCHES

Ø .500 Ø 2.250 BC
4 HOLES

FINISH BOTH ENDS
OF HUB

Ø4.625

Ø1.000

Ø 3.500

1.750   .250

.250

2.250

1.125

R 2.000

.250

.750

FINISH FACE OF PULLEY
WHERE BELT RUNS

Ø .500

.188 x .094 KEYWAY

ALL FILLETS AND ROUNDS R .125

OPRB-40 (from the textbook *Drafting Fundamentals*
by Scott, Foy, and Schwendau)

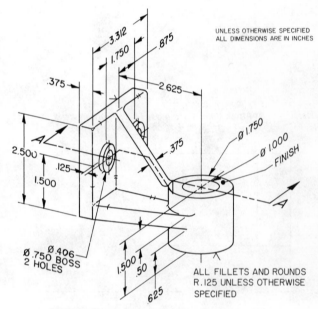

UNLESS OTHERWISE SPECIFIED
ALL DIMENSIONS ARE IN INCHES

3.312

1.750   .875

.375

2.625

A

2.500

.125

1.500

.375

Ø 1.750

Ø 1.000

FINISH

Ø .750 BOSS
2 HOLES

Ø .406

1.500   .50

.625

A

ALL FILLETS AND ROUNDS
R .125 UNLESS OTHERWISE
SPECIFIED

OPRB-42 (from the textbook *Drafting Fundamentals*
by Scott, Foy, and Schwendau)

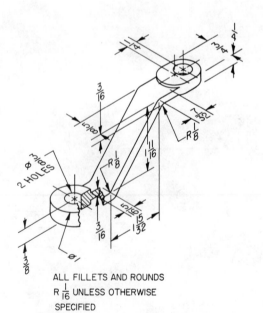

ALL FILLETS AND ROUNDS
R $\frac{1}{16}$ UNLESS OTHERWISE
SPECIFIED

OPRB-41 (from the textbook *Drafting Fundamentals*
by Scott, Foy, and Schwendau)

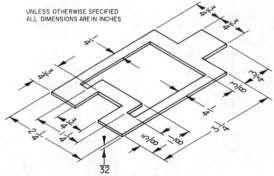

UNLESS OTHERWISE SPECIFIED
ALL DIMENSIONS ARE IN INCHES

OPRB-43 (from the textbook *Drafting Fundamentals*
by Scott, Foy, and Schwendau)

451

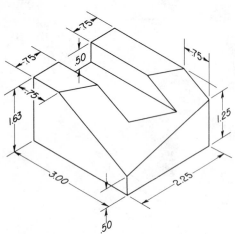

OPRB-44 (from the textbook *Drafting Fundamentals* by Scott, Foy, and Schwendau)

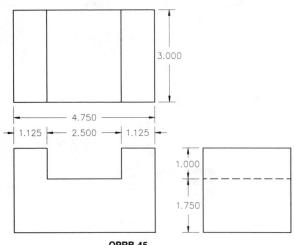

OPRB-45

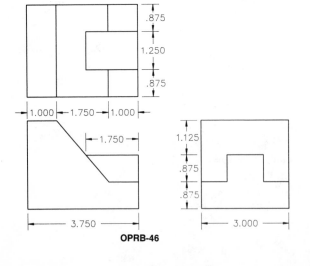

OPRB-46

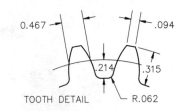

TOOTH DETAIL

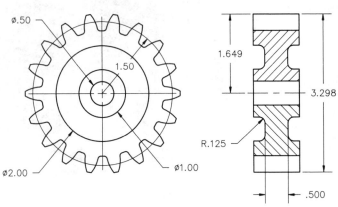

OPRB-47

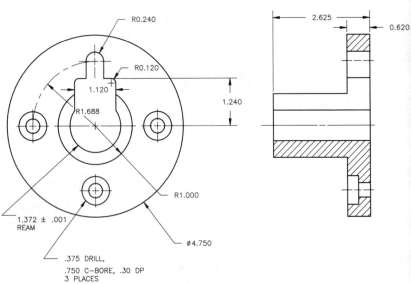

OPRB-48 (courtesy of Steve Huycke, Lake Michigan College)

NOTE: Consider making isometric drawings of these orthographic views.

452

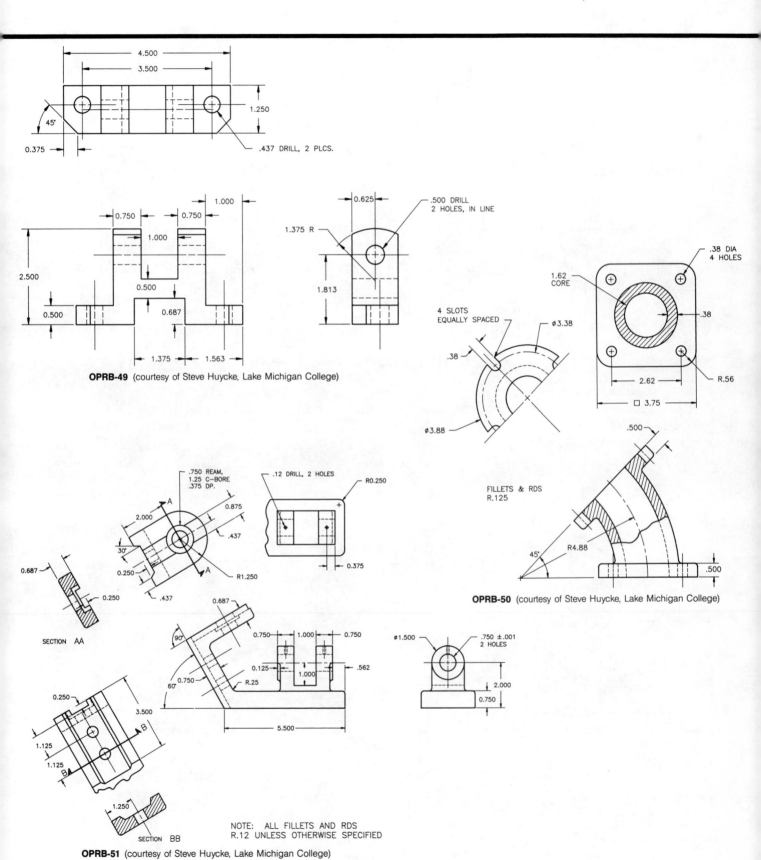

OPRB-49 (courtesy of Steve Huycke, Lake Michigan College)

.500 DRILL
2 HOLES, IN LINE

1.375 R

4 SLOTS
EQUALLY SPACED

.38 DIA
4 HOLES

1.62
CORE

ø3.38

ø3.88

.38

.38

2.62

R.56

□ 3.75

FILLETS & RDS
R.125

R4.88

45°

.500

.500

OPRB-50 (courtesy of Steve Huycke, Lake Michigan College)

.750 REAM,
1.25 C-BORE
.375 DP.

.12 DRILL, 2 HOLES

R0.250

SECTION AA

SECTION BB

NOTE: ALL FILLETS AND RDS
R.12 UNLESS OTHERWISE SPECIFIED

ø1.500

.750 ±.001
2 HOLES

OPRB-51 (courtesy of Steve Huycke, Lake Michigan College)

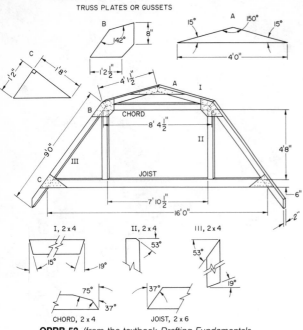

TRUSS PLATES OR GUSSETS

OPRB-52 (from the textbook *Drafting Fundamentals* by Scott, Foy, and Schwendau)

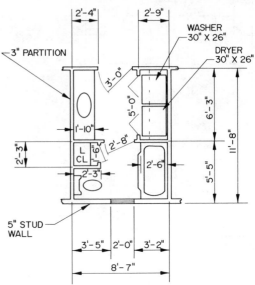

OPRB-54 (from the textbook *Drafting Fundamentals* by Scott, Foy, and Schwendau)

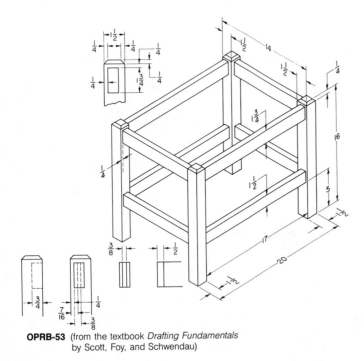

OPRB-53 (from the textbook *Drafting Fundamentals* by Scott, Foy, and Schwendau)

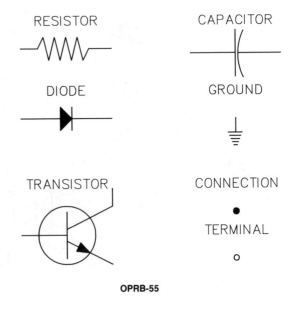

RESISTOR

DIODE

TRANSISTOR

CAPACITOR

GROUND

CONNECTION

TERMINAL

OPRB-55

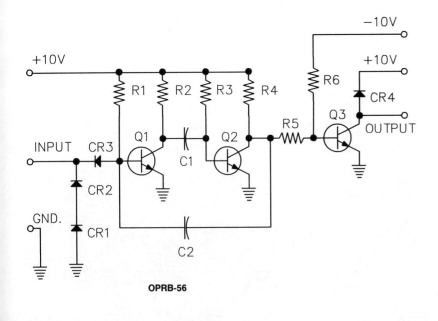

OPRB-56

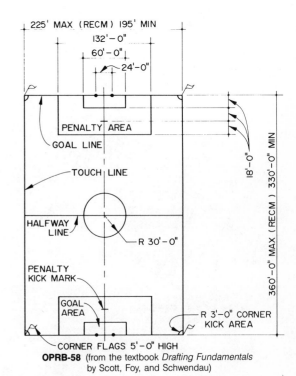

OPRB-58 (from the textbook *Drafting Fundamentals* by Scott, Foy, and Schwendau)

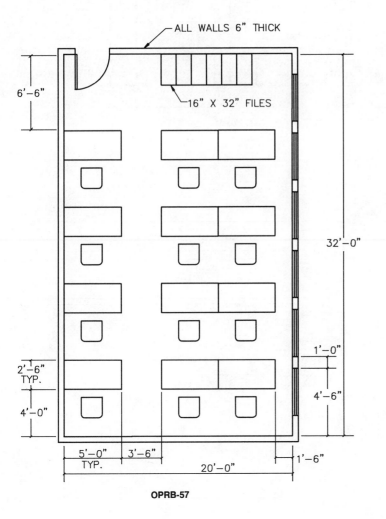

OPRB-57

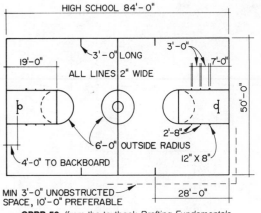

OPRB-59 (from the textbook *Drafting Fundamentals* by Scott, Foy, and Schwendau)

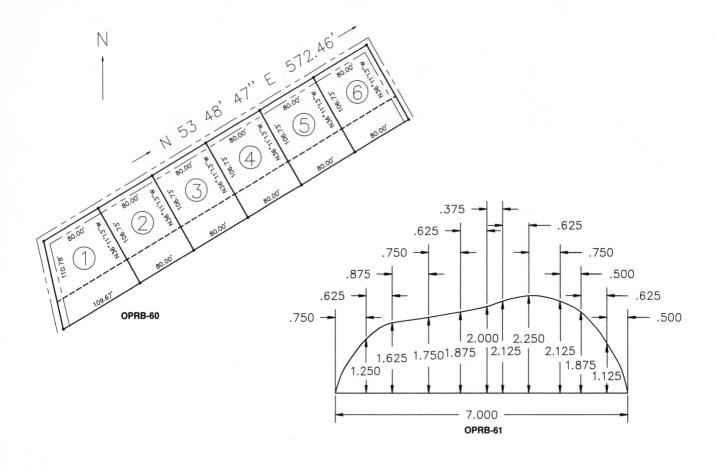

OPRB-60

OPRB-61

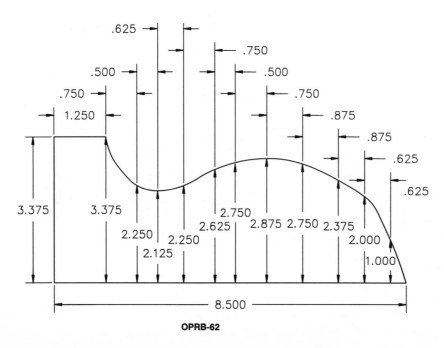

OPRB-62

OPRB-63 (courtesy of Mill Brothers Landscape and Nursery, Inc. Created using LANDCADD software with AutoCAD.)

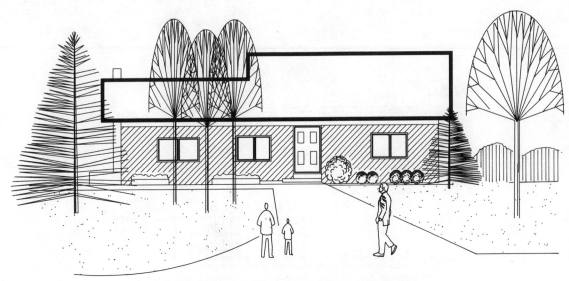

OPRB-64 (courtesy of Mill Brothers Landscape and Nursery, Inc. Created using LANDCADD software with AutoCAD.)

457

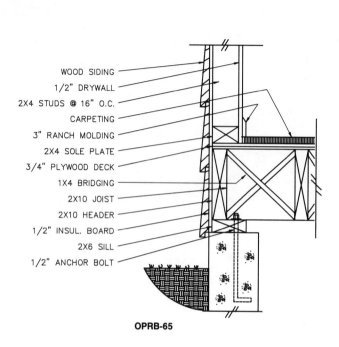

WOOD SIDING
1/2" DRYWALL
2X4 STUDS @ 16" O.C.
CARPETING
3" RANCH MOLDING
2X4 SOLE PLATE
3/4" PLYWOOD DECK
1X4 BRIDGING
2X10 JOIST
2X10 HEADER
1/2" INSUL. BOARD
2X6 SILL
1/2" ANCHOR BOLT

OPRB-65

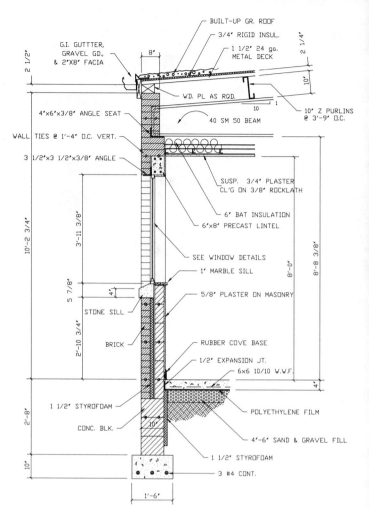

BUILT-UP GR. ROOF
3/4" RIGID INSUL.
1 1/2" 24 ga. METAL DECK
G.I. GUTTTER, GRAVEL GD., & 2"X8" FACIA
WD. PL AS RQD.
10" Z PURLINS @ 3'-9" O.C.
4"x6"x3/8" ANGLE SEAT
40 SM 50 BEAM
WALL TIES @ 1'-4" O.C. VERT.
3 1/2"x3 1/2"x3/8" ANGLE
SUSP. 3/4" PLASTER CL'G ON 3/8" ROCKLATH
6" BAT INSULATION
6"x8" PRECAST LINTEL
SEE WINDOW DETAILS
1" MARBLE SILL
5/8" PLASTER ON MASONRY
STONE SILL
BRICK
RUBBER COVE BASE
1/2" EXPANSION JT.
6x6 10/10 W.W.F.
1 1/2" STYROFOAM
CONC. BLK.
POLYETHYLENE FILM
4'-6" SAND & GRAVEL FILL
1 1/2" STYROFOAM
3 #4 CONT.

OPRB-66 (courtesy of Paul Driscoll)

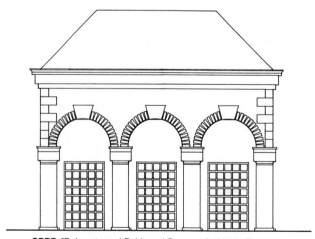

OPRB-67 (courtesy of Robb and Brenner, Architects/Planners

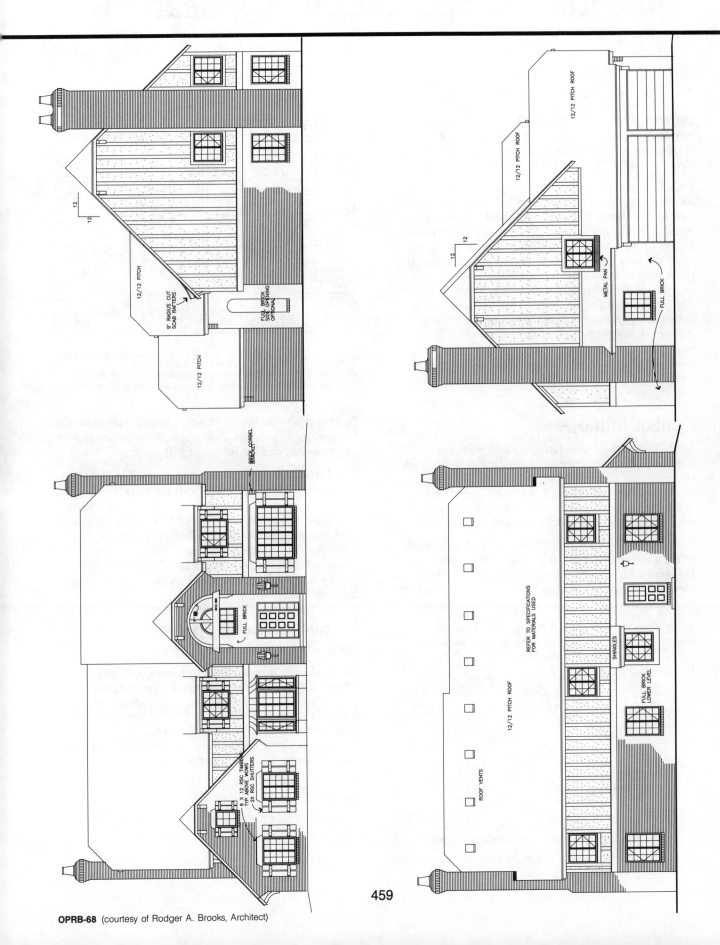

459

OPRB-68 (courtesy of Rodger A. Brooks, Architect)

Appendix A: Specialized Applications

AutoCAD and its applications have matured in recent years. Today there is a variety of peripheral hardware and software that functions with AutoCAD to solve advanced design and drafting problems. These components allow experienced users to more fully tap the potential of the AutoCAD software.

For example, application-specific symbol libraries are available to speed electrical drafting, office layout, and tool fixture design. Spreadsheet programs work with AutoCAD to generate bills of materials. Finite element analysis programs perform sophisticated engineering stress analysis on building structures and mechanical parts such as automobile components. Numerical control (NC) machines, coupled with AutoCAD and postprocessing software, provide for computer-aided design/computer-aided manufacturing (CAD/CAM). Advanced programming techniques, using artificial intelligence, are making CAD systems smarter and easier to use. These add-on components have raised AutoCAD to a sophisticated level of drafting, design, and engineering.

Symbol Libraries

Symbol libraries, also referred to as component libraries, speed the design and drafting process. Once a component is stored on disk, it is a simple matter to insert the component into a drawing. In addition to creating your own, you can purchase ready-made symbol libraries. A few examples are described here.

Carr Lane Manufacturing Company (St. Louis, MO) offers a comprehensive library called the Tool Designer's Assistant™. It includes over 6000 individual view drawings, representing 2600 industry-standard tooling components.

Every drawing component is full-scale. Examples include such parts as toggle clamps, plug gages, SWIFTSURE Power Workholding, and Modular Fixturing.

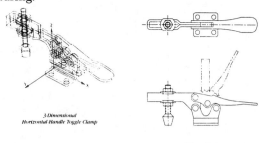

*3-Dimensional
Horizontal-Handle Toggle Clamp*

*2-Dimensional
Horizontal-Handle Toggle Clamp*

Courtesy of Carr Lane Manufacturing Company

These toggle clamp symbols are from the Tool Designer's Assistant library of jigs and fixtures.

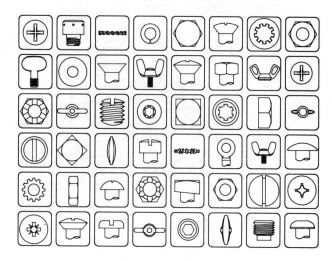

Courtesy of SPOCAD

SPOCAD (Spokane, WA) offers an extensive library of fastener symbols called AutoFasteners. A small sample is provided here.

Jergens (Cleveland, OH) offers a similar package called FixturePro. It provides 1800 standard work-holding components stored as 47 symbol libraries.

The LANDCADD software offers symbol libraries for landscape architecture. With this software, landscape architects insert plant symbols such as shrubs, trees, and other site amenities. The LANDCADD software package, produced by LANDCADD (Franktown, CO), also provides a host of other capabilities. Drawings produced with AutoCAD and LANDCADD software can be found on page 457 and on the front cover of this book.

Word Processing, Spreadsheet, and Data Base Programs

AutoCAD can be connected to general business software for developing notes and specifications, preparing bills of materials, and generating reports. AutoCAD attribute extract files (.DXX) can be read into word processors such as Volkswriter or WordPerfect, spreadsheets such as Lotus 1-2-3, and data base programs such as dBase and Reflex.

Courtesy of Rodger A. Brooks, Architect

Door and window schedules and bills of materials can be produced from attribute information extracted from AutoCAD drawings.

Just as AutoCAD is strong in editing graphics, word processors are strong in editing text. Since AutoCAD attributes are text information, word processors are useful for formatting reports and correcting mistakes.

With a spreadsheet, you have even more power at your fingertips. Without needing to learn a programming language (such as BASIC or LISP), you can perform powerful operations on your drawing's attributes. Spreadsheets display information in cells made up of rows and columns. Formulas, such as those for calculating costs of building materials, are assigned to values in the spreadsheet. As new values are input by the user, the program makes the calculations that show how the changes affect overall costs. Using a spreadsheet program can greatly improve the speed and accuracy of estimates.

COST	MODEL	DESCRIPTION
160	Five-drawer	File Cabinet
375	Oak/Standard	Desk Chair
1250	Deluxe	Desk
235	Tan/Cloth	Office Chair
325	Deluxe Oak	Coffee Table
1575	Cloth/Oak Trim	Sofa
235	Tan Cloth	Office Chair
75	Fern	Plant
4230	TOTAL COST	

Lotus 1-2-3 was used to create this table from information in an AutoCAD attribute extract file.

The strength of a data base program is its ability to handle large amounts of data, sort the data, and provide specialized reports. For example, a large commercial building, such as a hospital, contains hundreds of electrical fixtures. Attributes from these fixtures, extracted and stored as individual records, can be filtered and sorted according to a field specification in the data base program. The field specification may be fluorescent lighting, for instance, and a report on all fluorescent lighting fixtures could then be generated.

Before an AutoCAD extract file can be read by a word processing, spreadsheet, or data base program, the file must be translated into the required format. With a third-party program called LADS, you can convert an attribute extract file into a standard ASCII (text) file. The LADS program, produced by Birmingham Computer Consulting (Birmingham, AL), is fast and easy to use. Within a couple of minutes, a new file is created which can be manipulated by a word processor.

The LADS program also converts an attribute extract file to a DIF file format. The DIF format can be read by most spreadsheet programs, such as Lotus 1-2-3, and some data base programs. Once the file is converted to a DIF format, the Lotus Utility is used to convert the DIF file to a WKS (work sheet) file. This is the file type that Lotus accepts.

Parametrics

Parametrics is a fascinating concept for the efficient design, storage, and retrieval of drawings and symbols. (A parametric application is practiced in Unit 46.) With parametrics, drawing information is stored on disk, but the dimensions of the object remain variable. When the object, such as a door symbol, is inserted on the screen, you are prompted to enter design parameters such as the door type, height, width, trim, panels, etc. Hence, you can produce unlimited variations of the same basic door design. Storage of the object is very efficient too because only one file is stored on disk as opposed to hundreds.

Two popular software packages use parametric programming techniques. ACAD Partner, produced by Chase Systems (Westerville, OH), is a selection of symbol libraries for a variety of applications such as office layout, architecture, process piping, welding, and electrical design. Symbols and specialized commands are contained on tablet menu overlays (templates) for easy retrieval.

Synthesis, produced by Synthesis, Inc. (Bellingham, WA), is a preprocessor for AutoCAD. An AutoCAD drawing, such as an automobile, is entered into

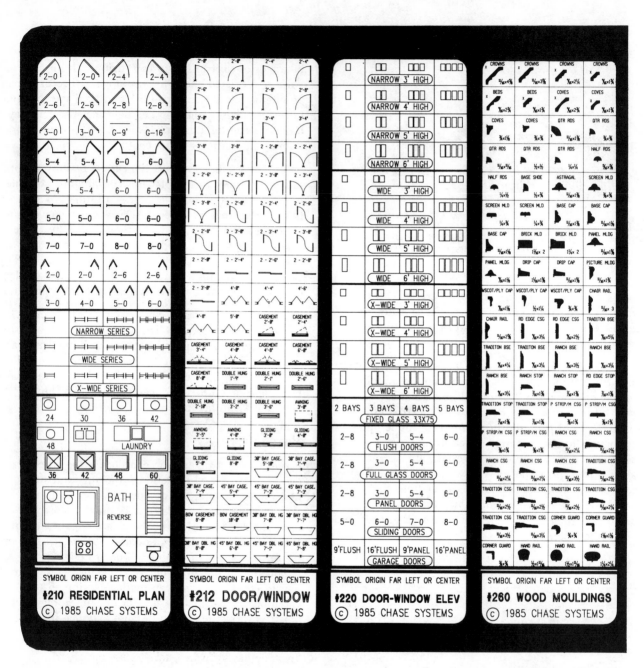

Courtesy of Chase Systems

The ACAD Partner tablet menu template series uses parametrics for very efficient storage and versatile insertion of symbols. Shown here are a few sample templates.

Synthesis and variables are assigned to its dimensions. These variables are later replaced by dimension values to produce a specific design. As with ACAD Partner, unlimited variations of the basic design can be produced.

AutoCAD AEC® Architectural

AutoCAD AEC Architectural is an extension to AutoCAD. It is a powerful and useful option for professionals in architecture, engineering, and construction (AEC).

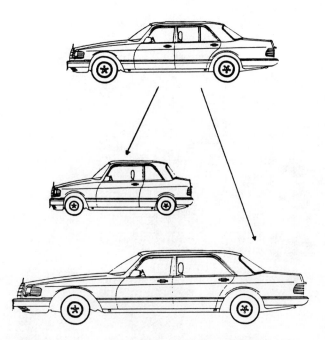

Courtesy of Synthesis, Inc.

Synthesis software speeds the design process and allows you to experiment with numerous variations of the same basic design.

AutoCAD AEC Architectural comes with a tablet menu template very similar to the standard AutoCAD tablet menu. (See p. 464.) However, the AEC menu contains numerous symbols and details, including doors, windows, appliances, electrical fixtures, plumbing, landscaping, and furniture. With AutoCAD AEC Architectural, the creation of stairs is automated too.

Door and window schedules are created from attributes stored in the architectural symbols. For instance, a door symbol may contain information about the size of the door, style, material, swing, manufacturer, etc. These items of information (attributes) are extracted to form a door schedule. The same is true with windows, appliances, building materials, and plumbing fixtures.

AutoCAD AEC Architectural has a double line capability for creating walls in floor plans. Specific thicknesses for the walls are entered by typing a value on the keyboard. The double line capability also offers a facility for proper joining of wall intersections and corners.

Space Diagrams

AutoCAD AEC Architectural enables you to create space diagrams. This facility assists you with the floor plan design process. The space diagrams are then converted to standard floor plan drawings.

The first step in using this feature is to define individual spaces such as a kitchen, living room, bath, and bedrooms. These spaces are simple rectangular diagrams made up of single lines produced with AutoCAD. Next, with AutoCAD, you place the spaces in any desired relationship to one another. You then enter the desired interior and exterior wall thicknesses. The system automatically converts the schematics to walls and properly connects them. AutoCAD even allows you to view the floor plan in 3D so that you can evaluate the spaces in terms of volume.

AutoShade™

AutoShade is a color rendering software package (available through Autodesk, Inc.) that converts 3D wireframe models produced by AutoCAD into lifelike shaded images showing perspective, lighting, and specular (mirror-like) reflection.

AutoShade uses a technique called faceted shading (instead of smooth shading), which generates renderings in 16 shades of gray or 256 colors, depending on your graphics display system.

AutoShade's operation is based on a photographer's studio metaphor. Preliminary work is done in the AutoCAD Drawing Editor, where you place special symbols that represent the lights and cameras.

When the preliminary work is done, you exit AutoCAD and load AutoShade. AutoShade, therefore, is considered a postprocessor.

AutoShade uses pull-down menus and dialogue boxes, similar to those in AutoCAD, that allow the specification of rendering parameters, such as viewpoint and light source selection, and different camera lenses in millimeters.

Courtesy of Autodesk, Inc.

Shaded image created with AutoShade.

463

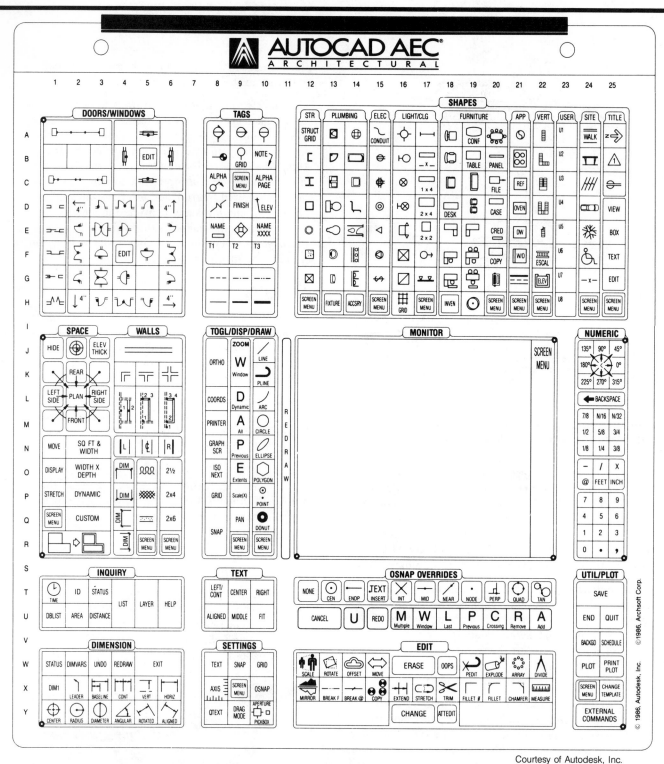

Courtesy of Autodesk, Inc.

The AutoCAD AEC Architectural tablet menu template contains numerous architectural symbols and functions.

Optical Scanners

Scanners provide a means for automatic conversion of paper drawings to an AutoCAD format. Houston Instrument's SCAN-CAD is an example of a low-cost scanning device. This accessory attaches to Houston Instrument's DMP-60 series pen plotters and automatically inputs A-size (8 1/2″ × 11″) through E-size (36″ × 48″) drawings from paper, vellum, acetate film, and blueline.

The time it takes to scan a drawing varies according to the computer speed, disk access time, drawing size and complexity, and scan velocity. For instance, when using an IBM PC/AT with a drawing of medium complexity and a scan velocity of two inches per second, SCAN-CAD inputs a D-size (24″ × 36″) drawing in 12 minutes and an E-size drawing in 24 minutes.

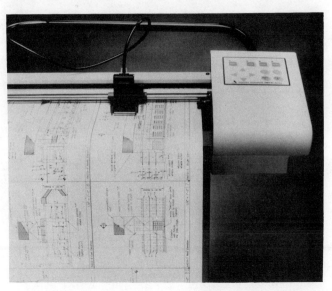

Courtesy of Houston Instrument

Houston Instrument's SCAN-CAD accessory turns any DMP-60 series pen plotter into an optical scanner.

After a drawing is scanned with an optical scanner, such as SCAN-CAD or Datacopy's (Mountain View, CA) flatbed scanning camera, it is stored in the computer's memory as a raster image file. Special raster-to-vector conversion software then converts the scanned image into the vector format required by AutoCAD and other CAD systems. As a vector file, the drawing can be revised, scaled, combined with other drawings, and plotted as the user chooses.

Raster-to-vector conversion software uses artificial intelligence techniques similar to those employed in robotic vision technology. It is especially useful for converting contour maps to AutoCAD. These maps usually contain hundreds of curved lines, which are especially difficult to input by hand with a digitizer. Also, maps typically have few symbols. Symbols are potential problem areas for scanners in general. Recognition of text and dimensions is also a weak area in current scanner technology, but future developments should largely overcome this problem.

Structural Engineering

Finite element analysis is the measurement of physical and/or thermal stress within a mechanical member. Software is available to determine the amount of stress that a mechanical member can withstand before it deforms or breaks.

Supersap software, produced by Algor Interactive Systems (Pittsburgh, PA), is an example of such a program. It is available for AutoCAD and runs on IBM PC/AT compatible computers and the DEC MicroVAX II computer. Supersap analyzes static and dynamic loads, pressure, thermal stress, constant acceleration and centrifugal loads, weight and center of gravity, and steady state heat transfer.

MSC/pal 2, produced by MacNeal-Schwendler Corporation (Los Angeles, CA), is a finite element program for stress and vibration analysis of structures.

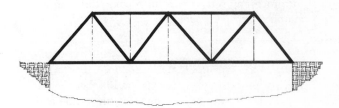

Algor's Supersap finite element analysis software performs sophisticated structural engineering tasks on truss elements of a bridge.

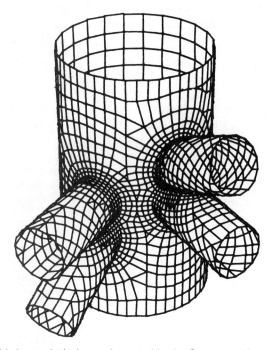

This is a typical wire mesh created by the Supersap software.

AutoCAD-Based CAD/CAM

AutoCAD-based CAD/CAM is AutoCAD linked to computer-aided manufacturing. AutoCAD-based CAD/CAM is simpler than mainframe-based CAD/CAM, and it can provide satisfactory performance at a low cost.

This level of CAD/CAM is still in its infancy. At present, the process is more easily understood when described as separate components rather than a complete system. These components include the AutoCAD software, NC (numerical control) postprocessing software, a microcomputer, and a computerized NC machine.

Postprocessing Software

The postprocessing software is the link between AutoCAD and the NC machine. It saves time and increases accuracy by eliminating the recreation of tool path geometry. The postprocessor generates the tool path from the AutoCAD drawing, creating the path in numerical control code. (See next page.)

The NC Programmer was one of the first IBM PC-based postprocessing packages available. NC Programmer, produced by NC Microproducts (Plano, TX), works with AutoCAD. The Complete Postprocessor package, also by NC Microproducts, configures the generic NC code produced by the NC Programmer and makes it compatible with your specific machine tool controller. (See p. 468.)

Another popular choice is SmartCAM, produced by Point Control Company (Eugene, OR). Both SmartCAM and the NC Programmer are 2 1/2-axis programs. For more complex 3-axis machining, NICAM by Numeridex (Wheeling, IL) is available. It uses APT programming and requires knowledge of this language.

Another 3-axis package is NC-Auto-Code by Kramer Consulting (Hilliard, OH). This package uses AutoCAD's user programming language, AutoLISP. Like the NC Programmer and SmartCAM, NC-Auto-Code also supports punching, drilling, lathing, and profiling.

Low-Cost NC Machines

The NC machine is usually the most expensive component of the AutoCAD-based CAD/CAM system. However, for developing plastic prototypes or for training, there are several low-cost options. One of them is the CAMM-3, a 3-axis vertical mill manufactured by Roland DG (Los Angeles, CA). Unlike large industrial mills, the CAMM-3 is a lightweight tabletop machine well suited for prototyping. It cuts a variety of materials, such as aluminum, brass, wood, plastics, and wax, and is accurate to .01 mm. (See p. 468.)

The Trainer CNC Bridgeport Retrofit is a kit for converting a manual Bridgeport industrial mill to an NC mill. All machine capabilities, including accuracy to .0005 inch, are the same as before the retrofit. The manufacturer, Cardinal Engineering (Cameron, IL), offers unlimited factory training as part of the retrofit package.

```
#SEQNO#PB#CIRCUL/CLW;CIRCUL/CCLW#Y#X#YCI#XCI#PA=$ARC1.1        G97;C=SPD-RPM
#SEQNO#PB#LINEAR;RAPID#Y#X#Z#PA=$LINE1.1                       H#3#3;A=H
#SEQNO#PB#LINEAR;RAPID#Y#X#Z#PA=$POINT1.1                      L#3#3;A=L
#SEQNO#PB#PC#PA=$TEXT1.1                                       M#2#2;A=AUX
#OPSEQNO#PB#LINEAR;RAPID#Y#X#Z#PA=$LINE2.1                     M00;A=PSTOP
LINEAR=$HEADER.1                                               M01;A=OPSTOP
%=BEGIN                                                        M02;C=ENDP
%=END                                                         M03;C=SPINDL/CLW
^13^10=EOB                                                     M04;C=SPINDL/CCLW
ASCII=FORMAT                                                   M05;C=SPINDL/OFF
F#3.3#3.3;A=FEDRAT                                             M06;C=TURRET/SHORTST
G00;D#LINEAR;E#RAPID;M#0#CIRCUL/CLW#CIRCUL/CCLW=RAPID          M08;C=COOLNT/ON
G01;D#RAPID;E#LINEAR;M#0#CIRCUL/CLW#CIRCUL/CCLW=LINEAR         M09;C=COOLNT/OFF
G02;D#CIRCUL/CCLW;E#CIRCUL/CLW;M#0#LINEAR#RAPID=CIRCUL/CLW     M10;A=CHUCK/CLAMP
G03;D#CIRCUL/CLW;E#CIRCUL/CCLW;M#0#LINEAR#RAPID=CIRCUL/CCLW    M11;A=CHUCK/UNCLAMP
G04;C=DWELL                                                   M15;A=TURRET/CLW
G21;A=EMPTY                                                    M16;A=TURRET/CCLW
G25;A=SUBCALL                                                  M17;A=TAILSTK/EXTEND
G27;A=JUMP                                                     M18;A=TAILSTK/RETRCT
G33;C=THREAD                                                   M21;A=CATCHER/RETRCT
G40;A=CUTCOM/OFF                                               M22;A=CATCHER/EXTEND
G45;A=CUTCOM/ADD                                               M27;A=CORNRNG/ONEBLK
G46;A=CUTCOM/SUB                                               M28;A=CONPATH/ON
G47;A=TOOLRAD/2ADD                                             M29;A=CONPATH/OFF
G48;A=TOOLRAD/2SUB                                             M31;A=REPEAT/CYCL
G64;A=FEEDWO/CURRNT                                            M50;A=OPTION1/ON
G65;A=MAGTAPE                                                  M51;A=OPTION1/OFF
G66;A=RS232                                                    M52;A=OPTION2/ON
G72;A=CYCLE/MPCKET                                             M54;A=OPTION2/OFF
G74;A=CYCLE/THREADL                                            N#4#4;I#1=SEQNO
G81;A=CYCLE/BORE                                               \N#4#4;V#SEQNO=OPSEQNO
G82;A=CYCLE/DBORE                                              K#2.4#4.2;A=QWORD
G83;A=CYCLE/CRBORE                                             R#2.4#4.2;A=RWORD
G84;A=CYCLE/THREAD                                             S#4#4;C=SPEED
G85;A=CYCLE/REAM                                               T#2#2;B=TOOLNO
G89;A=CYCLE/DREAM                                              Z#2.4#4.2;M#1=X
G90;C=ABS                                                      X#2.4#4.2;M#1=Y
G91;C=INCR                                                     Y#2.4#4.2;M#1=Z
G92;B=COORD/SET                                                Z#2.4#4.2;M#1=ZAXIS
G93;C=COORD/CLR                                                K#2.4;M#1=XCI
G94;C=FEED/PER-MIN                                             I#2.4;M#1=YCI
G95;C=FEED/PER-REV                                             J#2.4;M#1=ZC
G96;B=SPD-CSS                                                  =ZA
                                                              =ZI
```

Courtesy of NC Microproducts

This numerical control code was produced by the NC Programmer postprocessor software package.

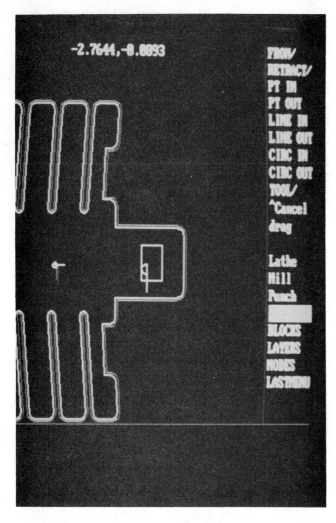

This machine tool path was created from an AutoCAD drawing with the NC Programmer.

When considering any of these machines, be sure to confirm their compatibility with your specific software and hardware. Also, be selective when considering converter or retrofit kits.

Fortunately, expensive and sophisticated controllers are not necessary for these machines because AutoCAD handles the front-end geometry creation.

New Developments in CAD/CAM

A very expensive design and manufacturing stage, known as *prototype building*, occurs prior to the mass production of automobile and airplane parts, electronic

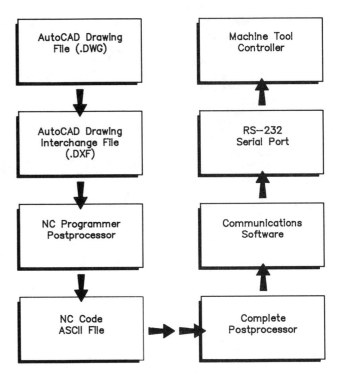

This chart illustrates the route AutoCAD geometry takes when sent to a numerical control machine tool using NC Programmer.

The CAMM-3 NC vertical mill is a small, lightweight machine used for developing prototypes and for training NC operators.

equipment, and toys. The prototype, usually hand-built, goes beyond the CAD-generated model. It lets the engineer further examine the part for design flaws and for style. And, the physical prototype is portable. Only after the proposed design passes this very important stage will it go to manufacturing.

The time it takes to create conventional prototypes of wax, plastic, or aluminum ranges from a week to several months depending on the complexity of the design. It is not uncommon to spend three to six months and $20,000 to $40,000 to produce the final prototype. Multiply that by the 250,000 models and prototypes created each year by General Motor's Fisher Guide Division.

Now imagine a laser beam hitting liquid plastic, solidifying the liquid as it hits and creating a real 3D model with complex internal geometry. This process, known as stereolithography, is a revolutionary method of producing models from liquid polymer.

The producer, 3D Systems, Inc. (Valencia, CA) refers to its 3D model maker as the Stereolithography Apparatus (SLA). 3D Systems is one of the few companies developing a product of this kind. The system links with popular 3D CAD systems and consists of an 80386-based computer controller, an X-Y scanner and laser, a photopolymer vat, and an elevator.

First, a part is designed using the 3D CAD system. Wall thickness and interior detail are included. The part is oriented on the computer screen in the way the designer would like to have it built.

To complete the CAD model, the operator designs a support structure at the bottom of the part. During the creation of the plastic model, the support structure will hold the model and connect it to the SLA elevator. The support structure is built as part of the model and is later cut from the finished model.

The CAD model and support structure are sent to the SLA computer for processing. The SLA interface slices the 3D model into thin horizontal cross sections at user-defined thicknesses and generates a pattern of vectors for each cross section. The bottom cross section will be the first to "print."

The printing process, known as photopolymerization, is the solidification of liquid polymer as ultraviolet light strikes the liquid. The SLA's X-Y scanner, driven by the computer-generated vectors, drives the UV laser beam to "draw" on the surface of the liquid polymer. As the laser beam touches the surface of the liquid, the

polymer solidifies. The first solidified layer becomes the bottom cross section of the model.

The SLA elevator then lowers the first cross section a fraction of an inch into the liquid. The next cross section is drawn on top of the first, and the two layers adhere to one another. Repeating this process creates a plastic model which is usually accurate to .005 inches, regardless of internal and external complexity.

When it is complete, the plastic model is removed from the SLA for post processing. This consists of heating the part in an oven to drain excess liquid. The part can either remain in the oven or be exposed to a flood of UV light to complete the hardening process. Last, the support structure is removed and the model is painted or treated with a surface finish of some sort.

Expect the automobile, aerospace, electric appliance, toy, and a range of other industries to use the SLA. Additionally, the SLA will eventually find its way into the AEC and civil engineering communities for the construction of buildings and other structural models. Medical professionals will find SLA beneficial for modeling bones from CAT scan data.

Since photocurable polymers adhere well to other materials, add-on structures can be grown on existing metal and plastic parts. Like CAD, the SLA is limited only by the creativity of the user and his/her budget.

Looking Ahead

The open architecture of AutoCAD combined with its user programming language, AutoLISP, contributes greatly to the growth and shape of the micro-based CAD industry. Literally hundreds of AutoLISP macros and routines are being developed to increase AutoCAD's drafting and design capabilities.

With an AutoLISP program, for example, stair generation is automatic. AutoCAD prompts you for the distance between floors and the maximum and minimum riser and tread sizes. The program then draws the detailed staircase for you.

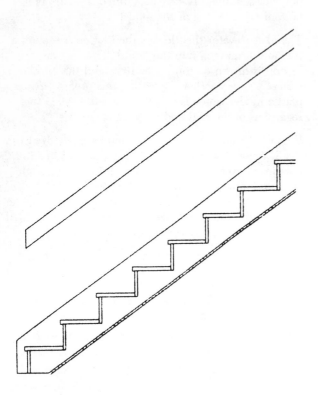

This staircase drawing was generated automatically with AutoCAD and AutoLISP.

In the future, architects, engineers, designers, and drafters will work from the same AutoCAD data base. Cost estimates will be more easily and accurately quoted because subcontractors will work from the same set of drawings and specifications. As a result, building and product designs, schedules, and costs will improve.

Last, imagine this. You're an architect designing an apartment complex. At the initial design stage, the system asks for the style of building, the approximate square footage, and the number of living units. You enter the information. It then asks you for types and sizes of rooms, halls, wall thicknesses, windows, doors, appliances, etc. Considerations such as city building codes are already in the system, providing a knowledge base upon which to make design-related decisions. Good architectural design practices such as efficient plumbing (bathrooms back-to-back, for instance) and people traffic flow considerations are in the system too.

The computer evaluates the information, and before your eyes, it draws an optimized floor plan according to your specifications. It also proposes an efficient use of floor space, suggests building materials, and calculates approximate cost per square foot.

The computer then asks whether or not you like the preliminary floor plan design and provides an opportunity for making alterations. Finally, you embellish the drawing with detail.

You can expect this level of sophistication in a CAD system of the future. This incredible system will bring fascinating power and artificial intelligence capability well beyond our present-day CAD technology. Just around the bend, a totally new dimension to the design and drafting process awaits us.

Appendix B: Hardware Overview

Hardware for CAD systems is quickly becoming more powerful and less expensive. Weekly, new product announcements appear in technical journals and newsletters. These hardware products offer outstanding performance at an affordable price. In combination with software, such as AutoCAD, they are revolutionizing the drafting field.

Among the new hardware products are lightning-fast computers, high-quality color graphics monitors, and highly functional and easy to use input devices such as digitizers and mice. Also in the new CAD hardware arena are fast and accurate pen plotters, electrostatic plotters, laser printers, and other developing output devices such as thermal and impact printers.

Computers

The computer is the heart of the CAD system. All information passes through the computer and all hardware peripherals are connected to the computer. Generally speaking, the faster the computer, the more powerful the CAD system.

Mainframe and minicomputers are large-scale computers. Examples are the IBM 4300, the DEC VAX 8600, and the Prime 9950. A Cyber 205 and a Cray are super-mainframe computers providing enormous power to hundreds of users simultaneously.

Mainframe and minicomputers are multi-user systems. This means a number of people can use the system at the same time through computer terminals connected to the

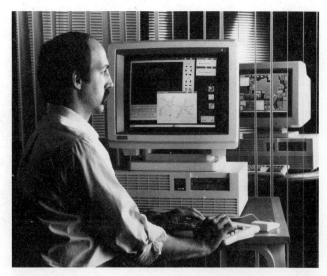

Courtesy of Apollo Computer Inc.

The Apollo is another high-performance 32-bit workstation well suited for CAD applications.

host computer. If too many people access the computer simultaneously, however, the graphics response time at the terminals may slow.

Microcomputers are small-scale desktop computers. Examples are the Compaq Deskpro series, the IBM Personal System/2 family, and the Apple Macintosh family. The VAXstation 2000 by Digital Equipment Corporation (DEC) is a super-microcomputer.

Courtesy of Sun Microsystems, Inc.

The Sun is a high-performance 32-bit workstation based on a Motorola microprocessor.

Courtesy of Digital Equipment Corp.

The DEC VAXstation 2000 uses a Motorola 68020 microprocessor like the Apollo 3000 and the Sun 3/60 workstations.

Courtesy of Compaq Computer Corp.

At the top of the Compaq line is the Deskpro 386/25 computer. It is based on the 25-megahertz Intel 80386 microprocessor.

Confusion exists in the industry as to the definitions of a microcomputer, minicomputer, and mainframe. At one time there were clear distinctions between each. Today, though, there are microcomputers which are more powerful than mainframes of the past. Examples include the Compaq Deskpro 386/25 and the IBM Personal System/2 Model 80. Microcomputers were once considered single-user units, but today many offer multi-user capabilities when linked in a network using the Unix® operating system.

One thing is certain: the price of microcomputers continues to decline as the performance continues to rise. Because of this, almost all computers will one day be based on microcomputer technology.

Microcomputer Components

CPU

The "brain" of a microcomputer is its microprocessor, a single chip which serves as the computer's CPU (central processing unit). All information passes through the CPU prior to its display on the monitor. Generally, the more powerful the CPU, the faster the computer.

A basic IBM PC contains an Intel 8088 microprocessor, and an IBM PC/AT contains an 80286 microprocessor. Newer and faster computers, such as the Compaq Deskpro 386 and the IBM Personal System/2 Model 80,

contain the Intel 80386 chip. The Apple Macintosh II contains a powerful Motorola 68020 chip, the same chip contained in the Apollo and Sun workstations. Both the 80386 chip and the 68020 chip are 32-bit microprocessors, whereas the 80286 chip is a 16-bit microprocessor.

Math Coprocessors

Also referred to as numeric coprocessors, these speed the generation of floating point graphics on the screen. Examples include the Intel 8087, 80287, and 80387 and the Motorola 68881 and 68882 coprocessors. Since graphics information is stored as coordinates (which are numbers), the math chip helps to process this information faster. A graphic image will generate on the screen three to five times faster when a math coprocessor is resident in the computer. For AutoCAD Release 9 and later versions, a math coprocessor is required.

RAM

RAM (random access memory) is also referred to as the system memory. It is the temporary storage area in the computer. Data and programs are input, manipulated, and output here. Generally, the more RAM, the better. A microcomputer-based CAD system contains RAM ranging from 512 KB (512 thousand bytes or single characters) of information to 16 MB (16 million bytes) of information. (The letters KB stand for kilobyte—1,000 bytes. The letters MB stand for megabyte—1 million bytes.)

Courtesy of Apple Computer, Inc.

The high-performance 68020-based Macintosh® II computer comes standard with either 1 or 4 MB of RAM and a 40 MB hard disk.

472

Courtesy of IBM Corporation

The IBM Personal System/2 Model 80 is a floor-standing personal computer.

Courtesy of Compaq Computer Corp.

This computer contains both a 5 1/4″ and a 3 1/2″ disk drive.

Once the computer is turned off, all the information stored in RAM is lost. For this reason, computer systems need permanent storage devices.

Permanent Storage Devices

FLOPPY DISKETTE DRIVES — The most common devices for permanent storage are floppy diskettes and hard disks. Floppy diskettes are thin, flexible disks in a protective cover. They are inserted into diskette drives, which are connected to, or contained inside, the computer. Standard floppy diskettes are currently made in three diameters: 3 1/2″, 5 1/4″, and 8″. The 5 1/4″ diskettes are the most popular, while the 8″ are the least. High-capacity 3 1/2″ diskettes are quickly becoming popular and someday may replace the 5 1/4″ diskettes.

HARD DISKS — Hard disks, also referred to as fixed disks, are many times faster than floppy diskette units and can store huge amounts of data. For instance, a 20 MB fixed disk stores over 55 times as much data as a 360 KB floppy diskette used in a standard IBM PC. Unlike floppy diskettes, fixed disks are not removable from the disk drive unit.

These are 5 1/4″ floppy diskettes. When not in use, they should be stored in a safe place away from heat, humidity, magnets, and electrical devices.

473

The AppleCD SC™ is the first CD-ROM drive from a major personal computer manufacturer to be available through retail computer stores. A single CD-ROM disk can hold 656 MB of information.

Monitors

Also referred to as displays and screens, monitors vary greatly in purpose, size, quality, and price. Single-color (monochrome) monitors are popular for applications such as word processing. Color is more desirable for CAD, though monochrome monitors are often used. Elaborate systems often contain two monitors: a large color monitor for the graphics and a small monochrome monitor for the text information.

The resolution of a graphics monitor affects the quality of the image more than anything else. *Resolution* refers to the fineness of detail observable in the images on the monitor. Monitors of low resolution display coarse images. For instance, diagonal lines may appear as a set of stairsteps. As the resolution increases, the stair-step effect diminishes.

Resolution is measured in pixels. One pixel is one lighted dot on the screen. All monitors have an x number of pixels horizontally and a y number of pixels vertically on the screen. Low-resolution monitors have approximately 200-400 pixels horizontally and 100-200 vertically. Medium-resolution monitors are in the 640 (horizontally) $\times$ 400 (vertically) range. High-resolution monitors have a resolution of 1000 $\times$ 800 pixels or higher.

The size of the monitor affects the resolution too. For instance, an image viewed on an 11″ monitor at 640 $\times$ 400 resolution will appear much better than the same image viewed on a 19″ monitor at the same resolution.

The streaming tape unit shown here is self-powered and can store up to 60 MB of hard disk data on one high performance tape cartridge.

TAPE SYSTEMS — Streaming tape backup systems are used to store backup files. Backup files are just that— they serve as a backup in case the files stored on the floppy diskette or fixed disk are lost or damaged. Some computers have built-in tape backup systems, while others do not. Another popular practice is to create backup files on standard floppy diskettes.

Standard Ports

Input and output devices connect to the ports found at the rear of a microcomputer. Most input devices, such as a digitizer (tablet), and output devices, such as a pen plotter, connect to the standard RS-232 serial port. Most matrix and daisy wheel printers connect to the standard parallel port.

Expansion Slots

Most computers are built for expansion. Inside are several empty bus slots. Printed circuit boards, also referred to as cards, are plugged into these slots. New cards may be inserted to increase RAM, add serial ports, or increase graphics speed.

Courtesy of Control Systems

This 19″ monitor and graphics board set provides 256 colors at a resolution of 1024 × 768.

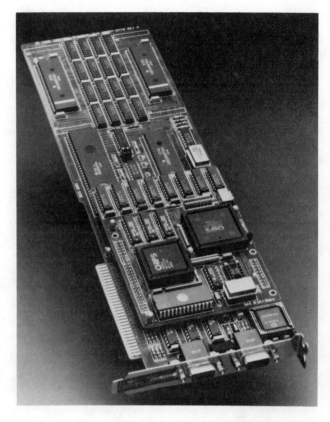

Courtesy of Control Systems

The Artist 8 controller provides 800 × 600 non-interlaced color resolution.

Graphics Adapters and Controllers

The printed circuit board connected to the graphics monitor is the graphics adapter, sometimes referred to as the graphics controller. Technically, a graphics adapter is a lower-cost and less functional device, whereas a graphics controller has more capabilities and costs more. Like monitors, adapters and controllers are specified by resolution and color. An adapter or controller must have as good a resolution and color capability as the monitor to which it is connected in order for the monitor to display its own resolution and color capabilities. In other words, the monitor displays the lesser of the capabilities offered by the two. Ideally, they both have the same capabilities.

Input and Pointing Devices

Keyboard

The keyboard offers a means for alphanumeric (letters and numbers) input. No device currently available is used more than a keyboard for enter information into a

computer. However, to use it efficiently, you must know how to type.

Courtesy of Texas Instruments

A computer keyboard. The top row contains the function keys. The hand is pointing to the keys which move the cursor.

The Artist XJ10™ graphic controller offers display list processing capabilities that permit extremely fast pans and zooms. The controller provides 1024 × 768 noninterlaced resolution in 16 colors. With the 512 KB memory module (left), the controller can be upgraded to 256 colors. The VGA module (right) provides single-screen VGA compatibility on a multi-sync monitor.

Mice

A mouse pointing device is used for picking points and objects that appear on the screen and for selecting screen menu items. A mouse is one of the least costly pointing devices. The mouse connects to the standard RS-232 serial port or into a special board mounted in one of the bus slots inside the computer.

Some mice have a small roller ball underneath. The ball turns as it moves across the table. The screen cursor tracks this motion. Other mice are optical. They contain a small light source that shines on a pad containing a metal grid. The light and grid combination controls the motion of the screen cursor.

Digitizers

Digitizers, also referred to as tablets, are larger and more expensive than mice, but they offer more capabilities. For instance, a menu overlay can be attached to the digitizer. Commands on the menu are entered into the computer by "picking" them with the digitizer's cursor control. This

This 3-button optical mouse operates on a pad.

is much faster than entering commands from the keyboard. In addition, symbol libraries can be part of the tablet menu.

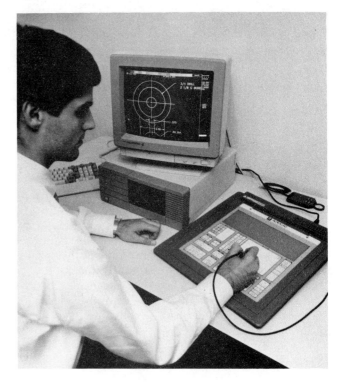

Houston Instrument's HIPAD Plus models 9012 and 9018 digitizers feature selectable resolution up to 2,000 lines per inch (100 lines/mm) and accuracy of ±0.01 inch.

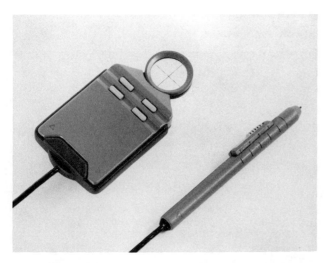

Pictured at the left is a four-button cursor control, and at the right is a stylus.

A stylus or puck-type cursor control is used with a digitizer. A stylus is a pen-like object used for such functions as drawing lines and picking items from the tablet menu. A puck performs these functions too. In addition, it contains one or more buttons. The buttons activate functions such as Snap and the RETURN key, or even commands such as LINE, ERASE, and ZOOM.

Digitizers are capable of tracing hardcopy drawings. This process is known as digitizing. A paper drawing is taped to the surface of the digitizer. In conjunction with the CAD commands and functions, coordinates are digitized from the drawing. Digitizing is often faster than recreating the drawing from scratch. Large digitizers are used to digitize large drawings such as maps of land developments.

Other Pointing Devices

A variety of other pointing devices is available, but they are less popular for CAD. They include light pens, joysticks, function boxes, track balls, dials, and optical scanners.

Digitizing a hardcopy drawing. The operator is using a puck-type cursor control.

A joystick.

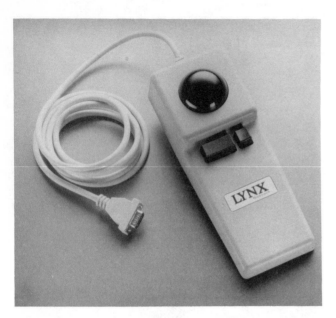

Courtesy of Honeywell, Disc Instruments Subsidiary

This trackball was designed for use with an Apple Macintosh computer.

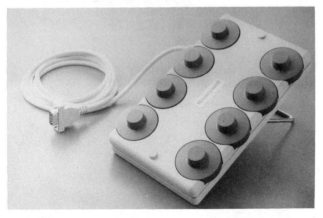

A dial set.   Courtesy of Honeywell, Disc Instruments Subsidiary

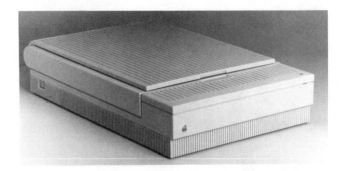

Courtesy of Apple Computer, Inc.

The Apple® Scanner features an 8.5 × 14-inch flatbed design and produces 300 dpi output. The Apple Scanner includes easy-to-use AppleScan™ software for desktop publishing or gray scale applications and HyperScan™ for graphics input into HyperCard® stacks.

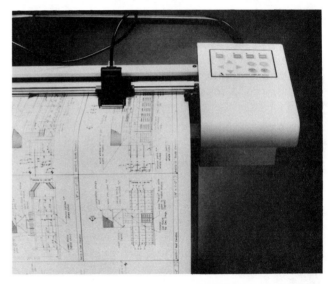

Courtesy of Houston Instrument

Houston Instrument's SCAN-CAD accessory is capable of detecting lines as fine as 0.007 inch.

Graphics Output Devices

Pen Plotters

Pen plotters are the most popular device for producing quality CAD line drawings. There is a variety of plotter styles and sizes available, and the plotter pens come in various widths and colors. A pen plotter operates by movement of a pen and a medium, such as paper. Microgrip (the most common type) and drum style plotters move the paper on one axis while the pen moves across the other axis. Simultaneous movement results in angular or curved lines. Flatbed plotters operate on a different principle. The sheet remains stationary and the pen moves across the sheet. Flatbed plotters are usually placed on tables, while microgrip and drum style plotters are mounted on floor stands.

Pen plotters run at different speeds depending on the limitations of the plotter as well as the pens and media being used. Felt and plastic tip pens usually run at a high speed (15-25 inches per second) on paper or vellum. For much better quality, liquid ink pens are used on Mylar polyester film or vellum. These liquid ink pens should move much slower, usually between 4 and 8 inches per second. Ceramic tip pens are becoming popular. They provide nearly the quality of liquid ink pens and they run much faster and are not as messy.

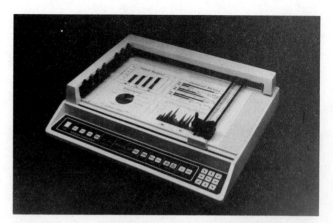

Courtesy of Houston Instrument

This 8-pen flatbed plotter has a maximum speed of 22 inches per second and a resolution of .001 inch.

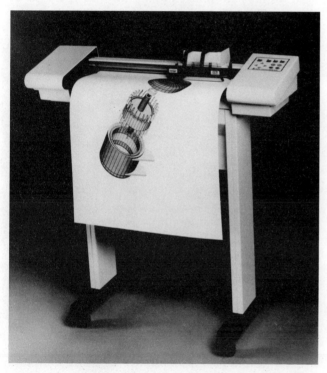

Courtesy of Houston Instrument

The precision DMP-61 drafting plotter from Houston Instrument can be upgraded with a variety of performance options, including a six-pen changer, a 1 MB plot buffer, and an optical scanner.

64F01   64F03   64F04   64F02

Felt-tip plotter pens.   Courtesy of KOH-I-NOOR

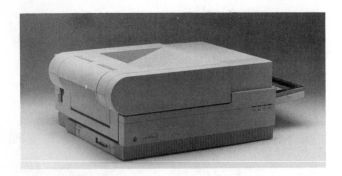

The Apple® LaserWriter® II family of modular laser printers offers computer users an easy and cost-effective method of upgrading as their printer needs grow.

Laser Printers

Laser technology offers a fast and quiet means for producing small black and white graphics and text. Laser printers are especially popular for outputting images produced by the integration of CAD graphics with computer-aided publishing systems.

Color Impact Printers

Color impact printers offer another alternative to plotters. Generally, the quality is not as good as that produced by pen plotters; but impact printers cost less, and they are fast. They are especially good for preliminary draft work.

A color impact printer/plotter.

Film Recorders

Film recorders produce 35-mm slides and color prints of the graphic image. They are an excellent means for producing graphics for presenting CAD to clients or in classrooms. The slides for the cover of this book were produced with a film recorder.

Other Graphics Output Devices

Thermal plotters, electrostatic plotters, and ink jet printers are other graphics output devices. Thermal plotters use heat to transfer lines and solid images to the media. Electrostatic plotters use an electrical charge. Ink jet printers spray a fine jet of ink onto the media.

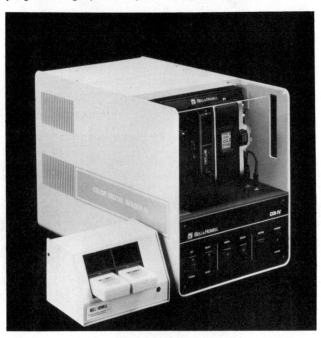

A color digital imager such as this one was used to make color slides for the front cover of *Applying AutoCAD*.

Text Output Devices

A surprising amount of text is generated from CAD systems. Examples include bills of materials, menu information, and printouts of settings such as layer information. Printers are used to produce hardcopy output of this text information.

Courtesy of CalComp

The CalComp ColorView 5912 thermal transfer plotter/printer produces fast, high-resolution color hardcopy on A- or B-size paper or transparency film for a variety of CAD/CAM/CAE, geophysical, presentation graphics, and graphic arts applications.

Matrix Impact Printers

Matrix impact printers operate on the same principle as the color impact printer mentioned earlier. Matrix impact printers are a fast and low-cost means of generating single-color text output. The characters (letters and numbers) they print are made up of small dots.

Courtesy of CalComp

This color electrostatic plotter accepts media widths of 24, 36, or 44 inches.

Courtesy of Tektronix

This color ink-jet printer, in combination with the color graphics rasterizer at the right, features a resolution of 120 dots per inch.

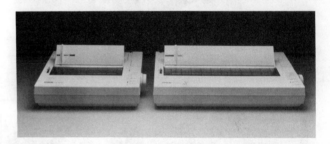

Courtesy of Epson America, Inc.

These dot-matrix printers are capable of printing 180 characters per second.

```
This text was output on a matrix
impact printer.  Note that the
characters are made up of small dots.
```

Output from a dot-matrix printer.

Daisy Wheel Printers

Daisy wheel printers, also referred to as letter-quality printers, provide print equal in quality to that of electric typewriters. However, they are slower than matrix impact printers. Daisy wheel printers print 10-50 characters per second (cps), while matrix impact printers produce 50-200 cps or even more.

481

A daisy wheel. The characters are at the end of the wheel's "spokes."

```
This text was output on a letter
quality printer. Note that the
characters are made of continuous
lines.
```

Output from a daisy wheel printer.

Networking

Small and medium-sized organizations now have as many as five, ten, or even twenty AutoCAD stations. Large corporations, such as Seattle-based Boeing, have more than 300 AutoCAD stations.

As CAD expands in organizations, two problems emerge. First, managers realize that organizing and controlling files at each individual station is nearly impossible. Hard disks become cluttered and finding files created weeks or months ago becomes an endless chore. And, no good system exists for backing up user-created files.

Second, time-consuming bottlenecks exist at the plotters and printers. Users hand-carry floppy diskettes to the computer that is connected to the output device. Known as sneakernet, this "take a number and get in line" approach lacks efficiency.

Organizations are convinced that changes are needed, such as centralizing their files, and they are seeking alternatives such as networking.

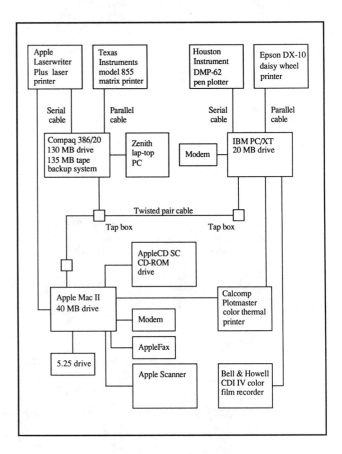

This diagram shows the local area network (LAN) at Wohlers Associates. It uses Apple's AppleTalk network to link the Apple Macintosh II to the Apple peripherals. The Compaq and IBM systems and peripherals are networked using ACS Telecom's 10CAD Plus system, a peer-to-peer network based on twisted pair cabling.

Networking is linking two or more computers so that each computer on the network can share resources from the other. In a network, a stair detail being designed on one station can be quickly transferred to another station on the network for insertion into a building section drawing. Symbol libraries, menu files, AutoLISP routines, and drawing files can be centralized. And, the station connected to the plotter enables users on the network to efficiently spool and queue their drawing files. *Spooling* means sending the plot data to an area of memory.

This frees the user's station so that he/she can continue to work. The plot data reside in memory until the plotter *queue* software instructs it to plot. Several plot files can reside in a queue at one time.

Networks with project management features let users group related drawings into projects. Each project can be described, tracked, and searched by client, company, project name, owner ID, description, recent drawing activity, and time spent on related drawings.

Appendix C: AutoCAD Management Tips

The use and maintenance of CAD systems entail considerations not found in traditional methods of drafting, design, and engineering. For example, with CAD, disk files must be stored properly for subsequent revision and plotting, and backup files must be produced regularly. If considerations such as these are overlooked or not taken seriously, the CAD system may not meet your expectations. Files will get lost, drawings will have to be redrawn, and users will become frustrated.

Whether you are an AutoCAD user or manager, the following information will help you maintain organization while creating and using AutoCAD files. For instance, if the system is properly managed, you should seldom have to create the same drawing twice.

The implementation of the system is an evolving process and does not occur quickly. Refer back to this appendix as you become more familiar with AutoCAD.

Key Management Considerations

Listed here is a sampling of the questions you should ask yourself when installing and organizing AutoCAD. They are intended to help guide your thinking, from a management perspective, as you become familiar with the various components of AutoCAD.

• What hard disk directories must I create to accommodate the AutoCAD software?

• How can I best categorize the files so that each directory does not grow to more than 75 files total?

• If I plan to install three or more AutoCAD stations, should I centralize the storage of user-created files and plotting by using a network file server?

After AutoCAD is in place and you are familiar with the system, you will create many new drawing files. The following questions address the efficiency by which these files are created and stored.

• Are there prototype drawings (or existing drawings) on file that may work well for the start of my new drawing?

• Where should my drawing file be stored, what should it be named, and how can I and others easily locate it in the future?

• Are there predefined libraries of symbols and details that I can use while I develop my drawing?

• Is there a custom screen, tablet, or icon menu that would lend itself to my drawing application?

• Are there AutoLISP routines available that help me more easily perform certain drafting operations?

• As I create the drawings, am I using time-saving techniques such as freezing layers and using the QTEXT command?

If you do not feel good about your answers to these questions, then there is probably room for improvement. The following is provided to help you organize and manage your CAD system more effectively.

NOTE:

Generally, the following applies to all AutoCAD users and files. However, there are inevitable differences among users (backgrounds/interests), drawing applications, and the specific hardware and software which make up the system.

AutoCAD System Manager

One person (possibly two, but no more) in the organization should have the responsibility for managing the system and overseeing its use. This person should be the resident AutoCAD authority and should answer questions and provide directions to other users of the system. The manager should also oversee the components of the system, including software, documentation, and hardware. The manager should work with the AutoCAD users to establish procedural standards for use of the system.

Software/Documentation

FILE MANAGEMENT — Know where files are located and the purpose of each. Understand which ones are AutoCAD system files and which are not. Create a system for backup files, and back up regularly. Emphasize this to all users. Delete "junk" files.

PROTOTYPE DRAWINGS — Create a simple system for the development, storage, and retrieval of AutoCAD prototype drawings. Allow for ongoing correction and development of each prototype drawing. Store the prototype drawings in the main AutoCAD directory or in a directory dedicated to prototype drawings so that they are more easily accessible by other users.

Document the contents of each prototype drawing by printing the drawing status information, layer listing, text styles, LTSCALE, and the status of the dimensioning variables as shown in Appendix K. On the first page of this information, write the name of the prototype drawing, its location, sheet size, and plot scale. Keep this information in a three-ring binder or similar holder for future reference by other users.

USER DRAWING FILES — Store these on separate hard disk directories. (See the hard disk structure found in Appendix G.) When creating a drawing, place drawing components on the proper layers. Assign standard colors, linetypes, and line thicknesses to standard layer names. Make a backup copy of the drawing and store it on a separate disk or tape backup system. Plot the drawings most likely to be used by others and store them in a three-ring binder or similar holder for future reference.

SYMBOL LIBRARIES — Develop a system for ongoing library development. (See Unit 28 for details on creating symbol libraries.) Make the libraries available to others and plot the symbol library drawing file. Place the library drawing on the wall near the system or in a binder. Encourage users to contribute to the libraries.

MENU FILES — Develop, set up, and make available custom screen and/or tablet menu files and tablet overlays. (See Units 41-43 for details on creating screen and tablet menus.) Store the menus in the main AutoCAD directory or in a directory dedicated to menus so they are accessible to others.

AUTOCAD UPGRADES — Handle the acquisition and installation of AutoCAD software upgrades. Inform users of the new features and changes contained in the new software.

AUTOCAD THIRD-PARTY SOFTWARE — Handle the acquisition and installation of third-party software developed for specific application and utility purposes. Inform users of its availability and use.

Hardware

Oversee the use and maintenance of all hardware components which make up the system. Consider hardware upgrades as user and software requirements change.

Procedural Standards

Develop clear and practical standards within your organization to minimize inconsistency and confusion. For example, each prototype drawing should have a standard set of drawing layers, with a specific color and linetype dedicated to each layer. A layer called DIM could be reserved for all dimensions and could always be shown in the color 2 (yellow) with a continuous linetype. Then, when plotting, color 2 could be assigned to pen 2, which could be a .3-mm black pen. That way, whenever dimensions are on a drawing, they'll be yellow on the screen and will be plotted with a .3-mm black pen. Furthermore, assign a specific pen to each stall on your pen plotter and make this information available to others. This will avoid confusion and improve consistency in all plotting within your organization. Develop similar standards for other AutoCAD-related practices.

In summary, take seriously the management of your AutoCAD system. Set up subsystems so that users can contribute to the system's ongoing development. Encourage users to experiment and to be creative by making software and hardware available to them. Make a team effort out of learning, developing, and managing the AutoCAD system so that everyone can learn and benefit from its tremendous power and capability.

Appendix D: AutoCAD Command Glossary

Brief descriptions of all AutoCAD commands are listed here. For the locations of more detailed descriptions, refer to the index.

Some commands can be used transparently (that is, used while another command is in progress) by preceding the command name with an apostrophe. Such commands are listed here with an apostrophe.

APERTURE
Purpose
Controls the size of the object snap target box.

ARC
Purpose
Draws an arc of any size.
Options
A	Included angle
C	Center point
D	Starting direction
E	End point
L	Length of chord
R	Radius
RETURN	(as reply to Start point) sets start point and direction as end of last Line or Arc

AREA
Purpose
Calculates the area and perimeter of a polygon, Polyline, or circle.
Options
A	Sets "add" mode
S	Sets "subtract" mode
E	Computes area of a selected circle or Polyline

ARRAY
Purpose
Makes multiple copies of selected objects in a rectangular or circular pattern.
Options
P	Polar (circular) array
R	Rectangular array

ATTDEF
Purpose
Creates an Attribute Definition entity for textual information to be associated with a Block Definition.
Options
I	Controls Attribute visibility
C	Controls constant/variable mode
V	Controls "verify" mode
P	Controls "preset" mode

ATTDISP
Purpose
Controls the visibility of Attribute entities on a global basis.
Options
ON	Make all Attributes visible
OFF	Make all Attributes invisible
N	Normal: visibility set individually

ATTEDIT
Purpose
Permits editing of Attributes.

ATTEXT
Purpose
Extracts Attribute data from a drawing.
Options
C	CDF comma-delimited format extract
D	DXF format extract
S	SDF format extract
E	Extract selected objects only

AXIS
Purpose
Displays a "ruler line" on the graphics display.
Options
ON	Turn axis (ruler line) on
OFF	Turn axis off
S	Lock tick spacing to Snap resolution
A	Set aspect (differing X-Y spacings)
number	Set tick spacing (0=use snap spacing)
numberX	Set spacing to multiple of snap spacing

BASE
Purpose
Specifies origin for subsequent insertion into another drawing.

BLIPMODE
Purpose
Controls display of marker blips for point selection.
Options
ON   Enable temporary marker blips
OFF   Disable temporary marker blips

BLOCK
Purpose
Forms a compound object from a group of entities.
Options
?   List names of defined Blocks

BREAK
Purpose
Erases part of an object, or splits it into two objects.
Options
F   Re-specify first point

CHAMFER
Purpose
Creates a chamfer at the intersection of two lines.
Options
D   Set chamfer distances
P   Chamfer an entire Polyline

CHANGE
Purpose
Alters the location, size, orientation or other properties of selected objects. Especially useful for Text entities.
Options
P   Change common properties of objects
C   Color
E   Elevation (to be dropped in the next major update)
LA   Layer
LT   Linetype
T   Thickness

CHPROP
Purpose
Alters properties of selected objects.
Options
C   Color
LA   Layer
LT   Linetype
T   Thickness

CIRCLE
Purpose
Draws a circle of any size.
Options
2P   Specify by 2 endpoints of diameter
3P   Specify by 3 points on circumference
D   To enter diameter instead of radius
TTR   Specify by two tangent points and radius

COLOR
Purpose
Establishes the color for subsequently drawn objects.
Options
number   Set entity color number
name   Set entity color to standard color name
BYBLOCK Set "floating" entity color
BYLAYER Use layer's color for entities

COPY
Purpose
Draws a copy of selected objects.
Options
M   Make multiple copies of the selected objects

DBLIST
Purpose
Lists data base information for every entity in the drawing.

DDATTE
Purpose
Used for dialogue-oriented Attribute editing.

'DDEMODES
Purpose
Displays a dialogue box for setting the current layer, color, linetype, elevation, and thickness.

'DDLMODES
Purpose
Displays a dialogue box that provides all of the capabilities of the LAYER command.

'DDRMODES
Purpose
Displays a dialogue box that controls on-screen drawing aids.

DDUCS

Purpose

Displays a dialogue box for control of the current User Coordinate System.

DELAY

Purpose

Delays execution of the next command for a specified time. (Used with command scripts.)

DIM

Purpose

Invokes dimensioning mode, permitting many dimension notations to be added to a drawing.

DIM1

Purpose

Allows one dimension notation to be added to a drawing, then returns to normal command mode.

DIST

Purpose

Calculates the distance between two points.

DIVIDE

Purpose

Places markers along a selected object, dividing it into a specified number of equal parts.

Options

B	Use specified Block as marker

DONUT (or DOUGHNUT)

Purpose

Draws rings with specified inside and outside diameters.

DRAGMODE

Purpose

Allows control of the dynamic specification ("dragging") feature for all appropriate commands.

Options

ON	Honor "DRAG" requests when applicable
OFF	Ignore "DRAG" requests
A	Set "Auto" mode: drag whenever possible

DTEXT

Purpose

Draws text items dynamically.

Options

See TEXT command for options

DVIEW

Purpose

Displays visual perspective views dynamically.

Options

CA	Select the camera angle relative to the target
CL	Set front and back clipping planes
D	Set camera-to-target distance, turn on perspective
H	Remove hidden lines on the selection set
OFF	Turn perspective off
PA	Pan drawing across the screen
PO	Specify the camera and target points
TA	Rotate the target point about the camera
TW	Twist the view around your line of sight
U	Undo a DVIEW subcommand
X	Exit the DVIEW command
Z	Zoom in/out, or set lens length

DXBIN

Purpose

Inserts specially-coded binary files into a drawing. Special-purpose command for programs such as AutoShade.

DXFIN

Purpose

Loads a drawing interchange (DXF) file.

DXFOUT

Purpose

Writes a drawing interchange file.

Options

B	Write binary DXF file
E	Output selected entities only

EDGESURF

Purpose

Constructs a 3D polygon mesh approximating a Coons surface patch (a bicubic surface interpolated between four adjoining edges).

ELEV
Purpose
Sets elevation and extrusion thickness for subsequently drawn entities. Used in 3-D visualizations.

ELLIPSE
Purpose
Draws ellipses using any of several specifications.
Options

C	Specify center point rather than first axis endpoint
R	Specify eccentricity via rotation rather than second axis
I	Draw isometric circle in current ISOPLANE

END
Purpose
Exits the Drawing Editor after saving the updated drawing.

ERASE
Purpose
Erases entities from the drawing.

EXPLODE
Purpose
Shatters a Block or Polyline into its constituent parts.

EXTEND
Purpose
Lengthens a Line, Arc, or Polyline to meet another object.

FILES
Purpose
Performs disk file utility tasks.

FILL
Purpose
Controls whether Solids, Traces, and wide Polylines are automatically filled on the screen and the plot output.
Options

ON	Solids, Traces, and wide Polylines filled
OFF	Solids, Traces, and wide Polylines outlined

FILLET
Purpose
Constructs a smooth arc of specified radius between two lines, arcs, or circles.
Options

P	Fillet an entire Polyline
R	Set fillet radius

FILMROLL
Purpose
Produces a file for use by the AutoShade rendering package.

'GRAPHSCR
Purpose
Flips to the graphics display on single-screen systems. Used in command scripts and menus.

GRID
Purpose
Displays a grid of dots, at desired spacing, on the screen.
Options

ON	Turn grid on
OFF	Turn grid off
S	Lock grid spacing to Snap resolution
A	Set grid aspect (differing X-Y spacings)
number	Set grid spacing (0 = use snap spacing)
numberX	Set spacing to multiple of snap spacing

HANDLES
Purpose
Assigns a unique, permanent number to each entity in a drawing.
Options

ON	Assign handles to all entities and set system variable HANDLES to 1
DESTROY	Discard all entity handles

HATCH
Purpose
Performs cross-hatching and pattern-filling.
Options

name	Use hatch pattern "name" from library file
U	Use simple user-defined hatch pattern
?	List names of available hatch patterns

"name" and "U" can be followed by a comma and a hatch style from the following list:

I	Ignore internal structure
N	Normal style: turn hatch lines off and on as internal structure is encountered
O	Hatch outermost portion only
?	List available style types

'HELP (or '?)
Purpose
Displays a list of valid commands and data entry options and obtains help for a specific command.

HIDE
Purpose
Regenerates a 3D visualization with "hidden" lines removed.

ID
Purpose
Displays the coordinates of a specified point.

IGESIN
Purpose
Loads an IGES interchange file.

IGESOUT
Purpose
Writes an IGES interchange file.

INSERT
Purpose
Inserts a copy of a previously drawn part (object) into the current drawing.
Options

name	Load file "name" as a Block
name=f	Create Block "name" from file "f"
*name	Retain individual part entities
?	List names of defined Blocks
C	(as reply to X scale prompt) specifies scale via two points (Corner specification of scale)
XYZ	(as reply to X scale prompt) readies INSERT for X, Y, and Z scales

ISOPLANE
Purpose
Selects the plane of an isometric grid to be the "current" plane for orthogonal drawing.
Options

L	Left plane
R	Right plane
T	Top plane
RETURN	Toggle to next plane

LAYER
Purpose
Creates named drawing layers and assigns color and linetype properties to those layers.
Options

C c	Set specified layers to color "c"
F a,b	Freeze layers "a" and "b"
L t	Set specified layers to linetype "t"
M a	Make "a" the current layer, creating it if necessary
N a,b	Create new layers "a" and "b"
ON a,b	Turn on layers "a" and "b"
OFF a,b	Turn off layers "a" and "b"
S a	Set current layer to existing layer "a"
T a,b	Thaw layers "a" and "b"
?	List layers and their associated colors & linetypes

LIMITS
Purpose
Changes the drawing boundaries and controls checking of those boundaries.
Options

2 points	Set lower left/upper right drawing limits
ON	Enable limits checking
OFF	Disable limits checking

LINE
Purpose
Draws straight 2D and 3D lines of any length.
Options

RETURN	(as reply to "From point:") start at end of previous Line or Arc
C	(as reply to "To point:") close polygon
U	(as reply to "To point:") undo segment

LINETYPE
Purpose
Defines linetypes (sequences of alternating line segments and spaces), loads them from libraries, and sets the linetype for subsequently drawn objects.
Options
?	List a linetype library
C	Create a linetype definition
L	Load a linetype definition
S	Set current entity linetype

"Set" suboptions:

name	Set entity linetype name
BYBLOCK	Set "floating" entity linetype
BYLAYER	Use layer's linetype for entities
?	List loaded linetypes

LIST
Purpose
Lists data base information for selected objects.

LOAD
Purpose
Loads a file of user-defined Shapes to be used with the SHAPE command.
Options
?	List the names of loaded Shape files

LTSCALE
Purpose
Specifies a scaling factor to be applied to all linetypes within the drawing.

MEASURE
Purpose
Places markers at specified intervals along a selected object.
Options
B	Use specified Block as marker

MENU
Purpose
Loads a file of Drawing Editor commands into the menu areas (screen, pull-down, tablet, and button).

MINSERT
Purpose
Inserts multiple copies of a Block in a rectangular pattern.
Options
name	Load file "name" and form a rectangular array of the resulting Block
name=f	Create Block "name" from file "f" and form a rectangular array
?	List names of defined Blocks
C	(as reply to X scale prompt) specifies scale via two points (Corner specification of scale)
XYZ	(as reply to X scale prompt) readies MINSERT for X, Y, and Z scales

MIRROR
Purpose
Reflects designated entities about a user-specified axis.

MOVE
Purpose
Moves designated entities to another location.

MSLIDE
Purpose
Makes a slide file from the current display.

MULTIPLE
Purpose
Causes AutoCAD to automatically repeat the next command until a Cancel is issued.

OFFSET
Purpose
Allows the creation of offset curves and parallel lines.
Options
number	Specifies offset distance
T	Through: allows specification of a point through which the offset curve is to pass

OOPS
Purpose
Restores erased entities.

ORTHO

Purpose

Constrains drawing so that only lines aligned with the current grid can be entered.

Options

ON	Force lines to horizontal or vertical
OFF	Do not constrain lines

OSNAP

Purpose

Enables points to be precisely located on reference points of existing objects.

Options

CEN	Center of Arc or Circle
ENDP	Closest endpoint of Arc or Line
INS	Insertion point of Text/Block/Shape
INT	Intersection of Line/Arc/Circle
MID	Midpoint of Arc or Line
NEA	Nearest point of Arc/Circle/Line/Point
NOD	Node (point)
NON	None (off)
PER	Perpendicular to Arc/Line/Circle
QUA	Quadrant point of Arc or Circle
QUI	Quick mode (first find, not closest)
TAN	Tangent to Arc or Circle

'PAN

Purpose

Moves the display window.

PEDIT (2D)

Purpose

Permits editing of 2D Polylines.

Options

C	Close an open Polyline
D	Decurve, or return a spline curve to its control frame
E	Edit vertices (see below for suboptions)
F	Fit curve to Polyline
J	Join to Polyline
O	Open a closed Polyline
S	Use the Polyline vertices as the frame for a spline curve (type set by SPLINETYPE)
U	Undo one editing operation
W	Set uniform width for Polyline
X	Exit PEDIT command

During vertex editing:

B	Set first vertex for Break
G	Go (perform Break or Straighten operation)
I	Insert new vertex after current one
M	Move current vertex
N	Make next vertex current
P	Make previous vertex current
R	Regenerate the Polyline
S	Set first vertex for Straighten
T	Set tangent direction for current vertex
W	Set new width for following segment
X	Exit vertex editing, or cancel Break/Straighten

PEDIT (3D)

Purpose

Permits editing of 3D Polylines.

Options

C	Close an open Polyline
D	Decurve, or return a spline curve to its control frame
E	Edit vertices (see below for suboptions)
O	Open a closed Polyline
S	Use the polyline vertices as the frame for a spline curve (type set by SPLINETYPE)
U	Undo one editing operation
X	Exit PEDIT command

During vertex editing:

B	Set first vertex for Break
G	Go (perform Break or Straighten operation)
I	Insert new vertex after current one
M	Move current vertex
N	Make next vertex current
P	Make previous vertex current
R	Regenerate the Polyline
S	Set first vertex for Straighten
X	Exit vertex editing, or cancel Break/Straighten

PEDIT (Mesh)
Purpose
Permits editing of 3D polygon meshes.
Options

D	Desmooth—restore original mesh
E	Edit mesh vertices (see below for suboptions)
M	Open (or close) the mesh in the M direction
N	Open (or close) the mesh in the N direction
S	Fit a smooth surface as defined by SURFTYPE
U	Undo one editing operation
X	Exit PEDIT command

During vertex editing:

D	Move "down" to previous vertex in M direction
L	Move "left" to previous vertex in N direction
M	Reposition the marked vertex
N	Move to next vertex
P	Move to previous vertex
R	Move "right" to next vertex in N direction
RE	Redisplay the polygon mesh
U	Move "up" to next vertex in M direction
X	Exit vertex editing

PLAN
Purpose
Orients the display in PLAN view (VPOINT 0,0,1) relative to either the current UCS, a specified UCS, or the WCS.
Options

C	Establishes a plan view of the current UCS
U	Establishes a plan view of the specified UCS
W	Establishes a plan view of the World Coordinate System

PLINE
Purpose
Draws 2D Polylines (connected line and arc segments, with optional width and taper).
Options

H	Set new half-width
U	Undo previous segment
W	Set new line width
RETURN	Exit PLINE command

In line mode:

A	Switch to arc mode
C	Close with straight segment
L	Segment length (continue previous segment)

In arc mode:

A	Included angle
CE	Center point
CL	Close with arc segment
D	Starting direction
L	Chord length, or switch to line mode
R	Radius
S	Second point of three-point arc

PLOT
Purpose
Plots a drawing on a pen plotter.

POINT
Purpose
Draws single points.

POLYGON
Purpose
Draws regular polygons with the specified number of sides.
Options

E	Specify polygon by showing one edge
C	Circumscribe around circle
I	Inscribe within circle

PRPLOT
Purpose
Plots a drawing on a printer.

PURGE

Purpose

Removes unused Blocks, text styles, layers, or linetypes from the drawing.

Options

A	Purge all unused named objects
B	Purge unused Blocks
LA	Purge unused layers
LT	Purge unused linetypes
SH	Purge unused shape files
ST	Purge unused text styles

QTEXT

Purpose

Enables Text entities to be identified without drawing the text detail.

Options

ON	Quick text mode on
OFF	Quick text mode off

QUIT

Purpose

Exits the Drawing Editor and returns to AutoCAD's Main Menu, discarding any changes to the drawing.

REDEFINE

Purpose

Restores the original, built-in definition of an AutoCAD command deleted by UNDEFINE.

REDO

Purpose

Reverses the previous command if it was U or UNDO.

'REDRAW

Purpose

Refreshes (cleans up) the current viewport.

'REDRAWALL

Purpose

Redraws all viewports.

REGEN

Purpose

Regenerates the current viewport.

REGENALL

Purpose

Regenerates all viewports.

REGENAUTO

Purpose

Allows control of automatic drawing regeneration performed by other commands.

Options

ON	Allow automatic regens
OFF	Prevent automatic regens

RENAME

Purpose

Changes the names associated with text styles, views, layers, linetypes, Blocks, viewport configurations, and User Coordinate Systems.

Options

B	Rename Block
LA	Rename layer
LT	Rename linetype
S	Rename text style
U	Rename UCS
VI	Rename view
VP	Rename viewport configuration

'RESUME

Purpose

Resumes an interrupted command script.

REVSURF

Purpose

Creates a 3D polygon mesh approximating a surface of revolution by rotating a curve around a selected axis.

ROTATE

Purpose

Rotates existing objects.

Options

R	Rotate with respect to reference angle

RSCRIPT

Purpose

Restarts a command script from the beginning.

RULESURF
Purpose
Creates a 3D polygon mesh approximating a ruled surface between two curves.

SAVE
Purpose
Updates the current drawing file without exiting the Drawing Editor.

SCALE
Purpose
Alters the size of existing objects.
Options
R   Resize with respect to reference size

SCRIPT
Purpose
Executes a command script.

SELECT
Purpose
Groups objects into a selection-set for use in subsequent commands.

'SETVAR
Purpose
Allows you to display and change the value of system variables.

SH
Purpose
On MS-DOS/PC-DOS systems, allows access to internal DOS commands.

SHAPE
Purpose
Draws predefined shapes.
Options
?   List available Shape names

SHELL
Purpose
Allows access to other programs while running AutoCAD.

SKETCH
Purpose
Permits freehand sketching.
Options
C   Connect: restart sketch at end point
E   Erase (back up over) temporary lines
P   Raise/lower sketching pen
Q   Discard temporary lines, exit Sketch
R   Record temporary lines, remain in Sketch
X   Record temporary lines, exit Sketch
.   Draw line to current point

SNAP
Purpose
Specifies a "round-off" interval for digitizer point entry so entities can be placed at precise locations easily.
Options
number   Set snap alignment resolution
ON   Align designated points
OFF   Do not align designated points
A   Set aspect (differing X-Y spacings)
R   Rotate snap grid
S   Select style, standard or isometric

SOLID
Purpose
Draws filled-in polygons.

STATUS
Purpose
Displays statistics about the current drawing.

STRETCH
Purpose
Allows you to move a portion of a drawing while retaining connections to other parts of the drawing.

STYLE
Purpose
Creates named text styles, with user-selected combinations of font, mirroring, obliquing, and horizontal scaling.
Options
?   List currently defined text styles

495

TABLET

Purpose

Aligns the digitizing tablet with coordinates of a paper drawing to accurately copy it with AutoCAD.

Options

ON	Turn tablet mode on
OFF	Turn tablet mode off
CAL	Calibrate tablet
CFG	Configure tablet menus, pointing area

TABSURF

Purpose

Creates a polygon mesh approximating a general tabulated surface defined by a path and a direction vector.

TEXT

Purpose

Draws text characters of any size, with selected styles.

Options

A	Align text between two points, with style-specified width factor; AutoCAD computes appropriate height
C	Center text horizontally
F	Fit text between two points, with specified height; AutoCAD computes an appropriate width factor
M	Center text horizontally and vertically
R	Right justify text
S	Select text style

'TEXTSCR

Purpose

Flips to the text display on single-screen systems. Used in command scripts and menus.

3DFACE

Purpose

Similar to the SOLID command but accepts Z coordinates for the corner points and can generate a section of a plane or a nonplanar figure.

Options

I	Make the following edge invisible.

3DMESH

Purpose

Defines a 3D polygon mesh by specifying its size (in terms of M and N) and the location of each vertex in the mesh.

3DPOLY

Purpose

Creates a 3D Polyline.

Options

C	Close the Polyline back to the first point
U	Undo (delete) the last segment entered
RETURN	Exit 3DPOLY command

TIME

Purpose

Displays drawing creation and update times and permits control of an elapsed timer.

Options

D	Display current times
ON	Start user elapsed timer
OFF	Stop user elapsed timer
R	Reset user elapsed timer

TRACE

Purpose

Draws solid lines of specified width.

TRIM

Purpose

Erases the portions of selected entities that cross a specified boundary.

U

Purpose

Reverses the effect of the previous command.

UCS

Purpose

Defines and modifies the current User Coordinate System.

Options

D	Delete one or more saved coordinate systems
E	Set a UCS with the same extrusion direction as that of the selected entity
O	Shift the origin of the current coordinate system
P	Restore the previous UCS
R	Restore a previously-saved UCS
S	Save the current UCS
V	Establish a new UCS whose Z axis is parallel to the current viewing direction
W	Set the current UCS equal to the World Coordinate System

X	Rotate the current UCS around the X axis
Y	Rotate the current UCS around the Y axis
Z	Rotate the current UCS around the Z axis.
ZA	Define a UCS using an origin point and a point on the positive portion of the Z axis
3	Define a UCS using an origin point, a point on the positive portion of the X axis, and a point on the positive Y-portion of the XY plane
?	List the saved coordinate systems

UCSICON
Purpose
Controls visibility and placement of the coordinate system icon, which indicates the origin and orientation of the current UCS.
Options

A	Change settings in all active viewports
N	Display the icon at the lower left corner of the viewport
O	Display the icon at the origin of the current UCS if possible
OFF	Disable the coordinate system icon
ON	Enable the coordinate system icon

UNDEFINE
Purpose
Deletes the built-in definition of an AutoCAD command.

UNDO
Purpose
Reverses the effect of multiple commands and provides control over the "undo" facility.
Options

number	Undoes that number of preceding commands
A	Auto: controls treatment of menu items as Undo Groups
B	Back: undoes back to previous Undo Mark
C	Control: enables/disables the Undo feature
E	End: terminates an UNDO Group
G	Group: begins sequence to be treated as one command
M	Mark: places marker in Undo file (for Back)

UNITS
Purpose
Selects coordinate and angle display formats and precision.

'VIEW
Purpose
Saves the current graphics display as a Named View and restores a saved view to the display.
Options

D	Delete named view
R	Restore named view to screen
S	Save current display as named view
W	Save specified window as named view
?	List named views

VIEWPORTS (or VPORTS)
Purpose
Divides AutoCAD's graphics display into multiple viewports, each of which may contain a different view of the current drawing.
Options

D	Delete a saved viewport configuration
J	Join (merge) two viewports
R	Restore a saved viewport configuration
S	Save the current viewport configuration
SI	Display a single viewport filling the entire graphics area
2	Divide the current viewport into 2 viewports
3	Divide the current viewport into 3 viewports
4	Divide the current viewport into 4 viewports
?	List the current and saved viewport configurations

VIEWRES
Purpose
Allows you to control the precision and speed of Circle and Arc drawing on the monitor by specifying the number of sides in a Circle.

VPOINT
Purpose
Selects the viewpoint for a 3D visualization.
Options

R	Select view point via two rotation angles
RETURN	Select view point via compass & axes tripod
x,y,z	Specifies view point

VSLIDE

Purpose

Displays a previously-created slide file.

Options

file	View slide
*file	Preload slide, next VSLIDE will view

WBLOCK

Purpose

Writes selected entities to a disk file.

Options

name	Write specified Block Definition
=	Block name same as file name
*	Write entire drawing
RETURN	Write selected objects

'ZOOM

Purpose

Enlarges or reduces the display of the drawing.

Options

number	Multiplier from original scale
numberX	Multiplier from current scale
A	All
C	Center
D	Dynamic PAN/ZOOM
E	Extents ("drawing uses")
L	Lower left corner
P	Previous
W	Window

Dimensioning Commands

ALIGNED

Purpose

Generates a linear dimension with the dimension line parallel to the specified extension line origin points. This permits you to align the dimensioning notation with the object.

ANGULAR

Purpose

Generates an arc to show the angle between two nonparallel lines.

BASELINE

Purpose

Continues a linear dimension from the baseline (first extension line) of the previous dimension.

CENTER

Purpose

Draws a Circle/Arc center mark or center lines.

CONTINUE

Purpose

Continues a linear dimension from the second extension line of the previous dimension. In effect, this breaks one long dimension into shorter segments that add up to the total measurement.

DIAMETER

Purpose

Dimensions the diameter of a circle or arc.

EXIT

Purpose

Returns to the normal Drawing Editor command mode.

HOMETEXT

Purpose

Restores the text of an associative dimension to its default ("home") location if you've moved it.

HORIZONTAL

Purpose

Generates a linear dimension with a horizontal dimension line.

LEADER

Purpose

Draws a line or sequence of lines (similar to the normal LINE command) for controlled placement of dimension text. Useful mostly for radius and diameter dimensioning.

NEWTEXT

Purpose

Changes the text of existing associative dimensions.

RADIUS

Purpose

Dimensions the radius of a circle or arc, with an optional center mark or center lines.

REDRAW

Purpose

Redraws the entire display, erasing any marker "blips" that were present (just like the normal REDRAW command).

ROTATED

Purpose

Generates a linear dimension with the dimension line drawn at a specified angle.

STATUS

Purpose

Displays all dimensioning variables and their current values.

STYLE

Purpose

Switches to a new text style.

UNDO

Purpose

Erases the annotations produced by the most recent dimensioning command.

UPDATE

Purpose

Updates exisiting associative dimension entities to use the current settings of the dimension variables, the current text style, and the current UNITS settings.

VERTICAL

Purpose

Generates a linear dimension with a vertical dimension line.

Appendix E: Formatting Diskettes

Before the computer can accept a new diskette for any type of file storage, it must first be formatted. To format a new diskette, you must locate the DOS directory (or DOS diskette) containing the file called FORMAT.COM.

1. Change to the DOS directory using the CD (Change Directory) command, or insert the DOS diskette into your computer.
(See Appendix G for instructions on the CD command.)

2. To review the contents of the DOS diskette or directory, type **DIR** (short for Directory) and press **RETURN**.

HINT:

To stop the scrolling, press CTRL S. To resume scrolling, press any key.

Your directory should look somewhat like the following. Yours may differ, depending on your specific version of DOS.

```
ANSI      SYS    1709   5-27-88   12:00p
CLOCK     SYS    1787   5-27-88   12:00p
COMMAND   COM   25332   5-27-88   12:00p
COUNTRY   SYS   11254   5-27-88   12:00p
DISKCOPY  COM    6264   5-27-88   12:00p
DISKINIT  EXE   55795   5-27-88   12:00p
DISPLAY   SYS   11651   5-27-88   12:00p
DRIVER    SYS    1385   5-27-88   12:00p
ENHDISK   SYS    3441   5-27-88   12:00p
FASTOPEN  EXE    3888   5-27-88   12:00p
FDISK     COM   54083   5-27-88   12:00p
FORMAT    COM   13691   5-27-88   12:00p
KEYB      COM   10903   5-27-88   12:00p
KEYBOARD  SYS   41144   5-27-88   12:00p
MODE      COM   15188   5-27-88   12:00p
PRINTER   SYS   13559   5-27-88   12:00p
SYS       COM    6193   5-27-88   12:00p
VDISK     SYS    3759   5-27-88   12:00p
XCOPY     EXE   11216   5-27-88   12:00p
APPEND    EXE    5794   5-27-88   12:00p
ASSIGN    COM    1530   5-27-88   12:00p
ATTRIB    EXE   10656   5-27-88   12:00p
BACKUP    COM   30048   5-27-88   12:00p
CHKDSK    COM   11939   5-27-88   12:00p
COMP      COM    4183   5-27-88   12:00p
```

You should see the FORMAT.COM file. If FORMAT.COM is resident in your computer, you can now format a new diskette.

3. Place a new diskette in an open drive (preferably drive A) in your computer.

CAUTION:

BE CAREFUL THAT YOU DO NOT ACCIDENTALLY FORMAT YOUR HARD DISK INSTEAD OF THE FLOPPY DISKETTE. Formatting hard disks will permanently erase their entire contents.

4. After the DOS prompt (*e.g.*, C:\ > or **C >**), type FORMAT in either upper- or lowercase letters. Note the example below.

C:\ > FORMAT A: (press **RETURN**)

The preceding would use the FORMAT.COM file from the C drive and would format the diskette contained in drive A. If necessary, replace "C" and "A" with the appropriate specifications.

5. Follow the instructions given by your computer until the format process is complete.

6. Remove the formatted diskette from your computer and place it in its sleeve.

7. Print your name, the date, and any other pertinent information on a self-stick label. Place the label on the newly formatted diskette.

The diskette is now ready for storing data such as AutoCAD drawing files.

Let's format another diskette, but this time let's place the DOS System on the diskette. The diskette can then be used for booting (starting) the computer system.

1. Place another new diskette in your computer.

NOTE:

As before, the FORMAT.COM file must be in your computer before you can format new diskettes.

2 This time enter the FORMAT command followed by a /S. Note the example below:

C:\>**FORMAT A:/S** (press **RETURN**)

The above will format the diskette contained in drive **A** and will also place the DOS System on the diskette.

___NOTE:___

The DOS system comprises three files: the visible COMMAND.COM file and two invisible (hidden) files. These three files allow you to start the computer system, to use the *internal* DOS commands such as DIR, COPY, DEL and REN, and to run applications programs such as AutoCAD.

3 Follow the instructions given by your computer until the format process is complete.

4 Enter **DIR** to review the contents of your newly formatted diskette. Note the example below:

C:\>**DIR A:** (press **RETURN**)

The above entry will display the contents of drive A.

The COMMAND.COM file should be contained on your newly formatted diskette.

___NOTE:___

If you plan to use your diskette only for storing data such as drawing files, then do not use the /S option because it occupies valuable storage space on your diskette.

Appendix F: Commonly Used DOS Commands

The DOS commands used most often are FORMAT, DIRectory, COPY, REName, DELete (or ERASE), TYPE, DISKCOPY, and CHKDSK (Checkdisk). FORMAT was covered in Appendix E. This appendix lets you practice the others so that you can effectively manage all AutoCAD-related files. (Additional DOS commands are discussed in other appendices. Refer to the index.)

DIR, COPY, REN, DEL, and TYPE are *internal* DOS commands. These internal commands can be entered at any time at the DOS prompt (*e.g.*, C:\>). They can also be entered at AutoCAD's "Command:" prompt.

DIR

The DIR command allows you to view the "table of contents" of your current directory. DIR also gives you the size of each file and the date and time each was created.

There are three different ways of using the DIR command. The simplest is to enter DIR. A second method is to type /P after the DIR, like this: DIR/P. The third way is to type /W after DIR, like this: DIR/W. Let's try the DIR command.

1 Start (boot) your computer system.

2 After the DOS prompt (*e.g.*, C:\>or **C>**), type **DIR** and press **RETURN**. Press **CTRL S** to stop the scrolling, and press any key to resume scrolling.

That's all there is to it.

Note each column in the directory and the information each provides. Also note the file names and their extensions. The file extension indicates the type of file. A list of file extensions and their meanings is provided here. These are the file extensions commonly used by AutoCAD users.

File extension Meaning

.BAK	AutoCAD backup file*
.BAS	DOS BASIC file (file written in the BASIC language)
.BAT	DOS batch file
.CFG	AutoCAD configuration file
.COM	DOS command file

*This file type does *not* serve as a true backup file. AutoCAD automatically creates the .BAK file each time you edit a drawing file. The .BAK file stores the drawing as it was prior to editing. Thus the .BAK file does not contain the latest version of the drawing but rather the one prior to it. Only the .DWG file contains the latest version of your work.

.DOC	Documentation update file
.DRV	AutoCAD device driver file
.DVP	AutoCAD device parameters file (required by some drivers)
.DWG	AutoCAD drawing file
.DXB	Binary drawing interchange file
.DXF	Drawing interchange file
.DXX	Attribute extract file in DXF format
.$$$	AutoCAD temporary drawing file
.$AC	AutoCAD temporary drawing file
.$RF	AutoCAD current working file
.EXE	AutoCAD execution file
.HDX	AutoCAD help index file
.HLP	AutoCAD help file
.IGS	IGES interchange file
.LIN	AutoCAD linetype library file
.LSP	AutoLISP file
.LST	Spooled printer plot file
.MID	Diskette identification file
.MNU	AutoCAD menu source file (in noncompiled ASCII form)
.MNX	AutoCAD compiled menu file
.MSG	AutoCAD sign-on message
.OLD	Old (original) version of a converted .DWG file
.OVL	AutoCAD overlays file
.PAT	AutoCAD hatch pattern file
.PGP	AutoCAD program parameters file
.PLT	Spooled plot file
.SCR	AutoCAD script file
.SHP	AutoCAD shape or font source file (in noncompiled ASCII form)
.SHX	AutoCAD compiled shape or font file
.SLB	AutoCAD slide library file
.SLD	AutoCAD slide file
.TXT	Attribute extract file (in space- or comma-delimited form)

3 Next, select a directory that contains more than one screenful of directory information.

4 Enter **DIR/P** (P is for Pause) and press **RETURN**.

As you can see, the /P option causes the computer to pause after it displays a screenful of information.

5 Enter **DIR/W** (W is for Wide) and press **RETURN**.

The /W option displays the information in wide format. However, it omits the date and time information.

502

COPY

The COPY command allows you to copy files (and produce backup copies) from one directory to another. A common use of the COPY command is to make backups of existing files such as drawing files.

1　With the COPY command, copy a file (of your choice) from a hard disk directory to a diskette as shown in the example below.

C>COPY HOUSE.DWG A: (press **RETURN**)

The above entry will copy the file named HOUSE.DWG from the current directory of C drive to drive A. When using the COPY command, be sure to specify the correct drives depending upon where the files reside and where the files are being copied.

2　Perform a **DIR**ectory to make sure the file was copied.

3　This time, copy all *drawing* files from drive A to your current hard disk directory. Note the example below.

C>COPY A:*.DWG (press **RETURN**)

This entry will copy all drawing files from drive A and place them on your current drive C directory. Be sure to specify the correct drive.

4　Copy *all* files from one directory to another. Note the example below.

C>COPY *.* A: (press **RETURN**)

This entry will copy all files from your current drive C directory and place them on your current drive A directory.

REN

Now let's focus on the REName command. The REN command allows you to change the name of any of your files. Let's try it.

1　Rename one of the files you copied by using the REN command. Note the example below.

C> REN A:HOUSE.DWG HUT.DWG
(press **RETURN**)

This entry will find the file on drive A named HOUSE.DWG and rename it HUT.DWG.

2　Perform a **DIR**ectory to make sure the file name was changed.

That's all there is to the REN command.

DEL (ERASE)

The DEL (ERASE) command allows you to do exactly that: delete or erase a file. Before using this command, be sure you don't need the file you are about to erase. Once you've erased a file, it's almost impossible to get it back.

1　DELete the file you renamed. Note the examples below.

C>DEL A:HUT.DWG (press **RETURN**)
C>DEL \ACAD\ACAD.MSG (press **RETURN**)

The first entry would delete the file located on drive A and named HUT.DWG. The second entry would delete the file ACAD.MSG contained in the \ACAD directory.

2　Enter **DIR** to see whether the file was deleted.

NOTE:

If you erase a file by mistake, it is difficult to restore it. Utility programs that contain an "unerase" feature are available for purchase. One example is The Norton Utilities by Peter Norton (Santa Monica, CA).

TYPE

The TYPE command is used to review the contents of a standard ASCII (text) file. An example of this file type is the standard AutoCAD screen menu, ACAD.MNU. Other examples include the AutoCAD help file ACAD.HLP, an AUTOEXEC.BAT file, and any .LSP (AutoLISP) file. Let's use the TYPE command with one of these files.

1　Display the contents of the ACAD.HLP file using the TYPE command. Note the example here. (ACAD.HLP must be contained in your current directory.)

C>TYPE ACAD.HLP (press **RETURN**)

CTRL S will stop the scrolling of the information. Press any key to resume scrolling. Press CTRL C to cancel.

2　Experiment with the TYPE command by displaying the contents of other ASCII files.

DISKCOPY

The DISKCOPY command allows you to produce a "carbon copy" of an entire diskette. This command is used only for copying diskettes. If a hard disk drive letter (such as E) is specified, an error message is displayed.

____NOTE:____

The DOS file called DISKCOPY.COM must be resident in your computer before entering the DISKCOPY command, just as you need the FORMAT.COM file before you can format a new diskette.

> 1 Enter the DISKCOPY command to make a copy of a diskette. Follow the instructions given by the computer. Note the example below.

C>DISKCOPY A: A: (press RETURN)

The above example will copy everything from the first diskette you place in drive A to the second diskette you place in drive A. When the copying process is complete, the two diskettes will be identical.

____CAUTION:____

The DISKCOPY command will erase everything presently on the target diskette as it copies new information onto it. Therefore be sure the target diskette is either blank or contains files you no longer need.

CHKDSK

The CHKDSK command allows you to check for bad sectors or damaged disks.

____NOTE:____

The CHKDSK.COM file must be resident in your computer before the CHKDSK command will work.

> 1 Enter the CHKDSK command. Note the example below.

C>CHKDSK (press RETURN)

This entry will provide information on drive C. You will receive information similar to the following:

```
29913088 bytes total disk space
   57344 bytes in 4 hidden files
   96256 bytes in 41 directories
18919424 bytes in 1167 user files
10840064 bytes available on disk

  655360 bytes total memory
  560192 bytes free
```

If your disk does not pass inspection, the computer will tell you what's wrong with it.

CHKDSK can also be used with the /F option as in: C>CHKDSK /F. This option creates files of lost clusters on your disk. These files can then be deleted to create additional free space on your disk.

In summary, the DIR, COPY, REN, DEL, and TYPE commands are available at any time when the DOS prompt is on your screen. The FORMAT, DISKCOPY, and CHKDSK commands, however, require specific files resident in the computer before these commands can be used. Those file names are FORMAT.COM, DISKCOPY.COM, and CHKDSK.COM, and they are part of the DOS set of files.

Appendix G: Using Your Hard Disk

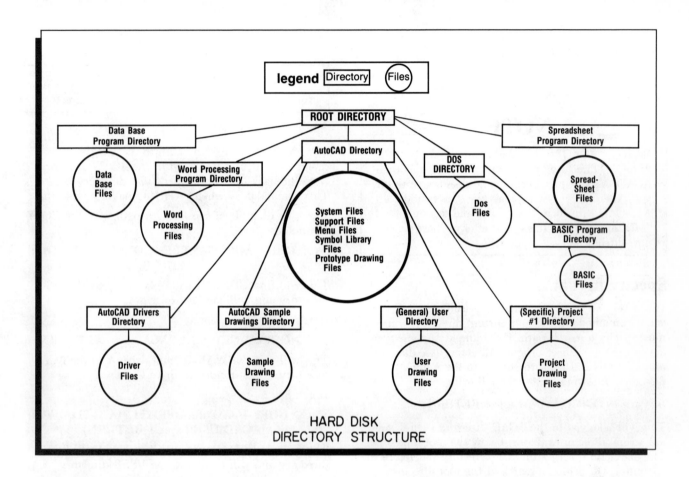

HARD DISK
DIRECTORY STRUCTURE

Hard Disk Organization

A directory is a collection of related files. The diagram below shows a recommended directory structure for your hard disk. Notice that all the other directories (sometimes called subdirectories) grow from the root directory, like branches on a tree. That's why it is called a tree-structured directory system. Also note the AutoCAD directory and the files and directories contained within it.

It is important to have a tree structure similar to the one here. The benefits of such a structure include proper categorization of files, faster retrieval of those files, and better overall organization of your system.

Strive to keep the AutoCAD directory clean of user drawing files. Store in the AutoCAD directory only the files illustrated above; otherwise it will grow too large and cumbersome to effectively use. User drawing files can be stored in a subdirectory within the AutoCAD directory, as shown above. You may even want to devote subdirectories to AutoLISP files, menu files, symbol libraries, and prototype drawings. In any case,

attempt to keep directories small (*i.e.*, fewer than 75 files).

Store all backup files on a separate disk or tape backup system. That way, if files are lost or damaged or if your hard disk crashes, you will have a copy of your files.

To create and use a directory system such as the one in the diagram, you need to use the DOS commands CD, MD, and RD.

CD

The CD (Change Directory) command allows you to change to a different directory. For instance, if you are currently in the root directory (\), you can move to the AutoCAD directory (\ACAD) by entering CD ACAD at the command prompt. In this example, ACAD is the name of the AutoCAD directory.

1 Obtain the DOS prompt (*e.g.*, C:\> or C>).

② Enter CD ACAD in upper- or lowercase letters. Note the example here:

C>CD ACAD (press **RETURN**)

___ NOTE: ___

Replace "ACAD" with the name given to your AutoCAD directory (such as R10) if it is different than ACAD. Also, if the CD command does not work for you, then your system may not yet contain an AutoCAD directory. If so, go to the section called "MD" and return to this section after you have created new directories.

Specifying Paths

Whenever you want to change to a (sub)directory that is not contained within your current directory, you must specify a search path. For example, suppose you are in the spreadsheet program directory (see diagram on page 505) and want to change to the AutoCAD directory. You would enter the following:

C>CD \ACAD (press **RETURN**)

This will take you to the ACAD directory even if you are several directories (levels) below the root directory. The backslash specifies the root directory. Therefore the computer will begin its search at the root directory.

The backslash can also be specified by itself in conjunction with the CD command. This changes to the root directory from any other directory. For example:

C>CD ** (press **RETURN)

Suppose you don't need to go back to the root directory but just want to move up one directory level. Here's how to do it.

C>CD ..

The two periods specify the parent directory of the current directory. For example, if you are currently in the Drivers directory (see diagram on page 505), the above entry will take you to the AutoCAD directory.

You can go through several directory levels in one step. For instance, if you need to change to the SAMPLES directory (Sample Drawing files), you can do this in one step even if you are currently in the root directory. The path specification would look like this:

C>CD \ACAD\SAMPLES (press **RETURN**)

___ NOTE: ___

The backslash preceding ACAD is not necessary unless you are in a directory other than the root directory.

The above entry gives the path to the SAMPLES directory, which is contained in the ACAD directory. Note the backslash between the two directory names. This is mandatory when specifying paths such as this.

Here's an example of specifying a path with the COPY command:

C>COPY \ACAD\SAMPLES\COLUMBIA.DWG A: (press **RETURN**)

This will find COLUMBIA.DWG in the SAMPLES directory and will copy it to drive A.

Here's another example:

C>COPY A:NEW.MNU \ACAD (press **RETURN**)

This will copy NEW.MNU from drive A to the ACAD directory, which resides on drive C.

Here's one more example:

C>COPY \ACAD\SAMPLES\CHAIR-3D.DWG \ACAD\USER (press **RETURN**)

This will find CHAIR-3D.DWG in the SAMPLES directory and will copy it to the USER directory.

DOS Prompt

Your computer can be configured to display the current directory at the DOS prompt. This is recommended because it helps you monitor your current directory. DOS commands work the same whether or not your computer is configured this way.

If your current directory is the root directory, the DOS prompt may look like this:

C:\>

If your current directory is ACAD, the DOS prompt may look like this:

C:\ACAD>

If you are in a directory within ACAD such as the SAMPLES directory, your prompt may look like this:

C:\ACAD\SAMPLES>

To configure your computer so that the DOS prompt displays the current directory, enter **PROMPT=PG** at the DOS prompt. This entry can be made automatic by including it in an AUTOEXEC.BAT file. See the following appendix for details on how to create an AUTOEXEC.BAT file.

MD

The MD (Make Directory) command allows you to create new directories. Though it works on floppy diskettes, the MD command is intended for use in establishing directories on your hard disk. Quickly read through the following steps, including the hint, before you execute the steps.

1 If you are not in the root directory, enter **CD **.

2 Enter **MD WP**. (WP is short for word processor.)

You have just created a new directory named WP.

3 Enter **DIR**.

You should see the new WP directory.

4 Enter **CD WP**.

Your current directory should now be WP. To prove it, ...

5 ...enter **DIR**.

Let's create a new directory inside the WP directory.

1 Enter **MD USER**.

2 Enter **DIR** to see if USER is present.

3 Enter **CD USER**.

Your current directory should be USER.

4 Enter **CD ..** to move up to the WP directory.

5 Enter **DIR** to see if you are in fact in WP.

The new USER directory should appear as an item in WP.

HINT:

Since the MD command will create directories on a floppy diskette too, you may want to practice the MD command on a floppy diskette. This will avoid disruption of your hard disk as you learn to create new directories.

If you choose to practice on a floppy diskette, set your default drive to the drive containing the floppy diskette. For example, type A: and press RETURN. When you are finished, enter C: to return to the C drive. (Hard disk drives are usually the C drive.)

RD

The RD (Remove Directory) command is as simple as the MD command.

1 If your current directory is not WP, change to the WP directory using the CD command.

2 Enter **RD USER**.

3 Enter **DIR** to see if the USER directory has been removed from WP.

4 Enter **CD ..** to move to WP's parent directory, which in this case is the root directory. This is necessary because you cannot remove a directory while it is the current directory.

5 Enter **RD WP**.

6 Enter **DIR**.

The WP directory should be gone.

NOTE:

You cannot remove directories unless they are empty. "Empty" directories contain no files or directories other than the . and .. directories. For example, suppose USER contained several drawing files and a directory named OFFICES. You would have to specify the USER directory and delete the drawing files using DEL or ERASE (see Appendix F). You would also have to remove the OFFICES directory using RD. (OFFICES, too, would have to be empty before you could remove it.) Finally, you could specify the WP directory and remove USER.

Appendix H: Loading AutoCAD for Optimum Performance

This appendix describes alternatives for loading AutoCAD. It also provides ideas for enhancing AutoCAD's performance. AUTOEXEC.BAT and other batch files, the CONFIG.SYS file, buffers, files, and several DOS batch commands are discussed too.

NOTE:

Installation of the AutoCAD software should be complete prior to using this appendix. See the *AutoCAD Installation and Performance Guide* for details on installing AutoCAD. When creating your hard disk directories, see Appendix G for instructions.

Loading AutoCAD

1 Using the CD command, change to the directory containing the AutoCAD system files. (This directory is often named ACAD, but it may be named something else, such as R10.)

HINT:

See Appendix G if you do not know how to use the CD (Change Directory) command.

2 Type **ACAD** and press **RETURN**.

The AutoCAD Main Menu should appear on your screen. (See Unit 1 for information on the Main Menu and for steps in accessing the Drawing Editor.)

Automatic Loading of AutoCAD

The contents of an AUTOEXEC.BAT file are executed step-by-step, automatically, when your computer is turned on or when it is restarted. Use of an AUTOEXEC.BAT file can therefore provide automatic loading of AutoCAD. Here is an example of a simple AUTOEXEC.BAT file.

DATE
TIME
CD ACAD
ACAD

If your computer contains a clock/calendar, the DATE and TIME can be omitted and substituted with the command required by your clock/calendar.

Here are the steps for creating an AUTOEXEC.BAT file with the above contents. Be sure you are in the **root** directory before you begin.

1 At the DOS prompt (*e.g.*, C>), type **COPY CON:AUTOEXEC.BAT** and press **RETURN**. (Use upper- or lowercase letters.)

NOTE:

DOS treats upper- and lowercase letters identically. The examples here are in uppercase letters simply for readability and consistency.

2 Type **DATE** and press **RETURN**.

3 Type **TIME** and press **RETURN**.

4 Type **CD ACAD** and press **RETURN**.

5 Type **ACAD** and press **RETURN**.

6 Press the **F6** function key and press **RETURN**.

The creation of the AUTOEXEC.BAT file is now complete.

7 Restart your computer system by pressing **CTRL ALT DEL** simultaneously, or turn your computer off and then on.

Powerful AUTOEXEC.BAT Files

Here is another example of an AUTOEXEC.BAT file. As you can see, it contains many more DOS functions and, consequently, is more powerful than the one described earlier. (Storing this file will erase the one you created previously.)

1 At the DOS prompt, enter **COPY CON:AUTOEXEC.BAT** and press **RETURN**.

HINT:

You may choose to create the file using a text editor, such as EDLIN, or a word processor.

② Enter the following. Be sure to press **RETURN** after each line.

```
ECHO OFF
DATE
TIME
SET ACADFREERAM=20
PROMPT=$P$G
PATH C:\;C:\DOS
SET LISPHEAP=39000
SET LISPSTACK=5000
ECHO ON
CLS
DIR/W
PAUSE: Press CTRL C to EXIT to DOS
   root directory, or ...
CD ACAD
CLS
ACAD
```

③ Press the **F6** function key and **RETURN**.

As discussed earlier, the components in an AUTOEXEC.BAT file are executed automatically when the computer is started. Let's take a close look at some of these components.

"ECHO OFF" prevents the computer from echoing the text to the screen during the execution of AUTOEXEC.BAT. The functions following it, therefore, will be invisible to the user.

"SET ACADFREERAM=20" reserves 20 kilobytes (20,000 bytes) of random access memory (RAM) for a working storage area. The default size of this area is 24 kilobytes, but often you can get by with less. By setting the ACADFREERAM lower, you leave more memory for AutoCAD to use in other ways. On the other hand, if you set the ACADFREERAM variable too small, AutoCAD may abort with the message "OUT OF RAM." This can be very inconvenient if you're in the process of creating a complex drawing. Only through experimentation will you determine the optimum amount for your device configuration and command usage. The minimum value to which you can set ACADFREERAM is 5 and the maximum is 30.

"PROMPT=PG" displays the current directory in the DOS prompt. For example, if your current directory is ACAD, your DOS prompt would look like this: C:\ACAD . (See Appendix G, the section titled "DOS Prompt," for more information.)

PATH C:\;C:\DOS" sets the default search path. This provides the computer with one or more directories to search in case it cannot locate a file in the current directory. In the previous example, the computer will first search the current directory. Then it will look in the root directory and then in the DOS directory. Generally, you should keep the search path short. Otherwise, the computer will spend unnecessary search time.

"SET LISPHEAP=39000" sets the heap to 39,000 bytes. The heap is an area of RAM set aside for storage of all AutoLISP functions and variables. The more elaborate the AutoLISP program, the greater the heap and stack requirements. The total of the two areas cannot exceed 45,000 bytes. The default size for heap is 40,000; for stack 3000.

"SET LISPSTACK=5000" sets the stack to 5,000 bytes, as you might have guessed. The stack is also an area of memory set aside by AutoLISP. Stack holds function arguments and partial results; the deeper you "nest" functions, the more stack space is used. (A knowledge of AutoLISP programming may be required to understand AutoLISP terminology such as this.)

"ECHO ON" allows the display of text on the screen. Thus, what follows in the batch file will display.

"CLS" clears the display screen.

"DIR/W" will automatically display the root directory on the screen in wide format.

"PAUSE" is a DOS subcommand that temporarily stops the computer. In other words, it suspends the system processing. It also displays the message "Strike a key when ready...". In this particular example, PAUSE is used not only to stop the computer, but also to display another message, "Press CTRL C to EXIT to DOS directory or...". If you choose to press CTRL C, the batch process terminates and you exit to the DOS root directory. Or, if you want to continue, you can strike a key when ready and the AUTOEXEC.BAT file continues.

"CD ACAD" is used to change to the ACAD directory.

"CLS" clears the screen once more.

509

"ACAD" starts AutoCAD, and then you're off and running! All of this may seem as though it could consume a lot if time, but it doesn't; it's quite fast.

Batch Files

Your computer system can contain only one AUTOEXEC.BAT file. However, numerous other batch files (with a BAT file extension) can exist. A batch file contains one or more commands that DOS executes one at a time. Batch files are ASCII text files and are created using the procedure described earlier. A text editor or word processer is recommended for creating lengthy batch files.

You may want to include many of the previously described functions in a batch file other than AUTOEXEC.BAT, particularly if you use your computer for applications other than AutoCAD.

Listed here are the steps and the functions you may choose to include in a batch file named START.BAT. It would be appropriate to include the remaining functions, such as PROMPT=PG, in an AUTOEXEC.BAT file.

1 Enter **CD \ACAD** to set ACAD as your current directory. (*Your* main AutoCAD directory may be named something other than ACAD.)

2 Type **COPY CON:START.BAT** and press **RETURN** to begin the creation of the batch file.

3 Enter the following and press **RETURN** after each entry.

    SET ACADFREERAM=20
    SET LISPHEAP=39000
    SET LISPSTACK=5000
    EXTLISP
    ACAD

4 Press the **F6** function key and press **RETURN**.

The creation of your START.BAT file is now complete.

NOTE:

EXTLISP invokes the EXTLISP.EXE program if it is present. This loads *Extended AutoLISP* if 512 KB of extended memory are available.

5 Start the START.BAT file by entering **START** at the DOS prompt.

The batch file should execute and the AutoCAD Main Menu should appear.

CONFIG.SYS

When your computer is started, DOS automatically looks for the CONFIG.SYS file. This is an ASCII text file which contains important configuration parameters. If the file does not exist, DOS assumes default values for the configuration parameters.

There are parameters you can specify in this file that can have a significant effect on AutoCAD's performance. To edit an existing CONFIG.SYS file, use a word processor or text editor (such as EDLIN).

Let's use the COPY CON method for creating a CONFIG.SYS file. In the file, let's include two items which can improve the performance of AutoCAD: buffers and files.

1 While in the root directory, type **COPY CON:CONFIG.SYS** at the DOS prompt (C>) and press **RETURN**.

2 Type **BUFFERS=20** and press **RETURN**.

3 Type **FILES=20** and press **RETURN**.

4 Press the **F6** function key and press **RETURN**.

Now when you start your system, DOS will set these parameters.

Buffers

Buffers are used to set aside system memory (RAM) for improved disk performance by AutoCAD. If no buffers are specified, the default is 2 buffers. The more buffers you allocate, the more likely it is that an area to be read from disk has recently been read and is still in one of the memory buffers. The result is improved speed.

However, if there are too many buffers, the time DOS spends searching through the buffers can become significant. Also, each configured buffer reduces the amount of memory available for programs, such as AutoCAD, by 528 bytes. A value between 10 and 35 is recommended as a starting point. Only through experimentation will you determine the optimum setting. The buffers value is stored in the CONFIG.SYS file as explained in the above section.

Files

DOS places a limit on the number of files a program can have open at once. AutoCAD often needs to access several files (such as program overlays, AutoLISP functions, and text fonts) simultaneously, and it can sometimes exceed the DOS limit on open files. When this occurs, AutoCAD closes a few of the nonessential open files temporarily. The overhead involved with opening and closing files can degrade performance. Increasing the value of "files" in the CONFIG.SYS file will increase the DOS open-files limit. The default value is 8. A value of 20 is recommended as a starting point.

Virtual Disk

A virtual disk, also referred to as a VDISK or RAM disk, reserves some or all extended memory (if it exists) for AutoCAD use. This reserved area in extended memory is used to emulate a very fast disk drive and therefore minimize disk access time. The virtual disk enables you to temporarily store part or all of AutoCAD in fast memory.

The procedures for configuring a virtual disk depend on your specific hardware and software. However, most involve a *device=vdisk.sys* statement in the CONFIG.SYS file. It is possible to include more than one such statement in your CONFIG.SYS file to create more than one virtual disk.

PC DOS versions 3.0 and above are supplied with a *vdisk.sys* driver that can reserve any amount of memory for use as a virtual disk. If your computer contains floppy disk drives A and B and a hard disk drive C the statement *device=vdisk.sys 1500 /e* reserves 1.5 megabytes of extended memory for use as drive D.

The overlay (OVL) files are the best files to place on a virtual disk because AutoCAD accesses these files frequently. If your virtual disk is not large enough to contain all overlay files, the most strategic files to copy to a virtual disk are ACAD0.OVL, ACAD.OVL, ACAD2.OVL, ACAD3.OVL, and ACADVS.OVL. Only through experimentation will you determine the optimum size of your virtual disk.

The virtual disk does not remain intact after the computer is turned off or is restarted. Therefore, the virtual disk must be created each time you start AutoCAD. A batch file enables you to automatically copy AutoCAD's overlay files to the virtual disk (drive D) prior to starting AutoCAD.

Include PATH D:\ in the batch file or in the AUTOEXEC.BAT file so that AutoCAD looks for the overlay files in virtual disk drive D. Also, be sure these overlay files are not stored in the main AutoCAD directory; otherwise AutoCAD will use them instead of the ones copied to the virtual disk.

The configuration files ACADDS.OVL, ACADDG.OVL, ACADPL.OVL, ACADPP.OVL, and ACAD.CFG must be placed together on the same directory. Also, the ACADCFG environment variable must be set to reflect their location. (See Chapter 4 of the AutoCAD *Installation & Performance Guide* for additional details.)

Example of Virtual Disk Setup

Provided here are examples contained in the AUTOEXEC.BAT, CONFIG.SYS, and START.BAT files. They establish a virtual disk for use with AutoCAD on a Compaq Deskpro 386/25.

Contained in the CONFIG.SYS file is the following statement:

device=c:\dos\vdisk.sys 1024 /e

This statement causes the computer to look in the \DOS directory and find the VDISK.SYS file. The "1024 /e" portion of the statement creates a 1-megabyte virtual disk drive D.

Contained in the AUTOEXEC.BAT file is

PATH d:\;c:\dos

This instructs the computer *and* AutoCAD to look in drive D when they cannot find files in the default disk directory. If the file is not located in drive D, the computer and AutoCAD will search in the C:\DOS directory.

Contained in the START.BAT file is

set acadcfg=c:\acad\ovl
copy c:\acad\ovl\ *.* d:

The first statement instructs AutoCAD to store the configuration files, when created, in C:\ACAD\OVL. This is the permanent location of ACAD.CFG and all AutoCAD overlay files. The second statement copies all files contained in C:\ACAD\OVL to virtual disk drive D. The files include the following:

ACAD.CFG
ACAD.OVL
ACAD0.OVL
ACAD2.OVL

ACAD3.OVL
ACADL.OVL
ACADM.OVL
ACADVS.OVL
ACADPL.OVL
ACADPP.OVL
ACADDG.OVL
ACADDS.OVL

I/O Page Space

AutoCAD writes and reads temporary files to and from memory as a drawing file is created. The memory used for this purpose is call I/O page space.

AutoCAD first uses available conventional memory for I/O page space. When this relatively small space is depleted, AutoCAD will page information to disk, but this causes short delays as you use AutoCAD.

If extended and/or expanded memory is present, AutoCAD will automatically use this memory instead of paging files to disk. AutoCAD will recognize up to 4 megabytes of extended and/or expanded memory for I/O page space. Only through experimentation will you determine the optimum amount of memory to set aside for I/O page space.

Use the ACADXMEM environment variable to dedicate a specific portion of extended memory for AutoCAD I/O page space. (See Chapter 4 of the AutoCAD *Installation & Performance Guide* for details.)

Appendix I: Apple® Macintosh® II Version of AutoCAD

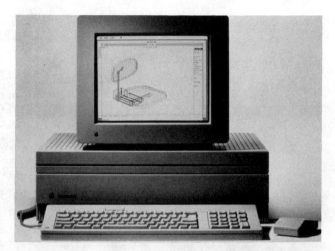

Courtesy of Apple Computer, Inc.

AutoCAD has been installed on this Apple Macintosh II computer.

AutoCAD is available for the Apple Macintosh II computer. It functions similarly to the PC/MS-DOS version of AutoCAD. However, the Mac II version also contains several features consistent with standard Macintosh applications. These features are discussed in this appendix.

Windowing

The Macintosh computer allows you to easily open and close viewing windows. Each window is like a minidisplay. Clicking the mouse pointer onto a window activates that window. If the window is partially covered by another window, clicking onto it will reveal the entire window.

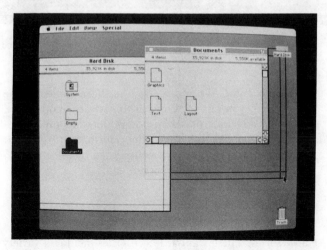

Courtesy of Apple Computer, Inc.

Windows are a feature of the Macintosh II.

The Macintosh enables you to easily increase and decrease the size of each window, drag the window to a new location, and close the window at the click of the mouse button. In addition, the Macintosh lets you scroll the information inside the window, vertically and horizontally, so that you may view information that extends beyond the window.

The Macintosh lets you move and resize the AutoCAD Drawing Editor, too. And when you close an editing session with the END Command, AutoCAD remembers your window configuration.

Multifinder

Under Apple Macintosh's MultiFinder operating system, you can open more than one application at one time. For instance, AutoCAD may be opened in one window, a word processor in another, a publishing program in yet another, and so on.

Clicking the mouse pointer onto the window containing one of the open programs, such as AutoCAD, makes it the active program.

Running AutoCAD under MultiFinder also makes it easy to paste (insert) AutoCAD drawings and portions of drawings into other packages using the Clipboard. (The Clipboard is discussed later in this appendix.)

Single-Button Mouse

AutoCAD supports Apple's single-button mouse. A single click is interpreted as a point pick or menu selection. A double click is equivalent to pressing RETURN unless ✱✱✱AUX1 found in the ACAD.MNU file is modified.

Tear-Off, Pull-Down Menus

In a process similar to locking onto and dragging windows about the screen, you can "tear off" and drag each of AutoCAD's pull-down menus to a new location. A torn-off menu remains open and active. You can then use the menu or close it if you wish. Up to ten torn-off menus can be active at one time.

File Dialogue Box

Consistent with other Macintosh applications, AutoCAD provides a Macintosh-style file dialogue box that enables you to easily store drawing documents (files). The file dialogue box also lets you choose the proper folder (directory) for document storage by picking the small box found near the top. (See p. 515.)

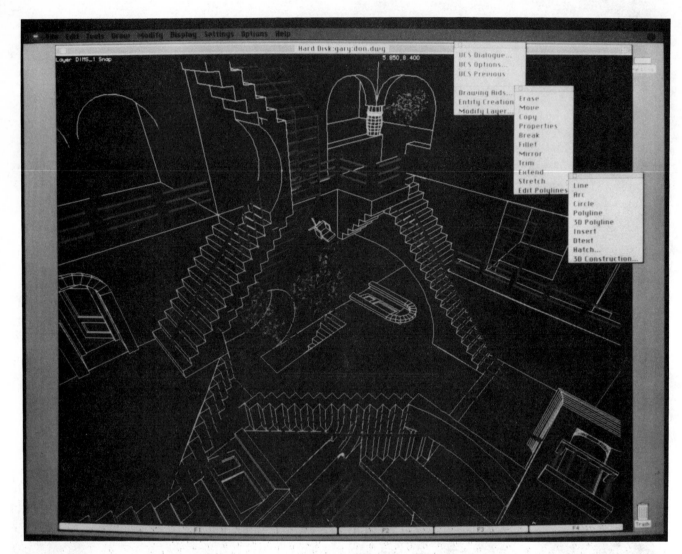

On the Macintosh II, you can tear off and drag AutoCAD's pull-down menus.

Courtesy of Apple Computer, Inc.

Clipboard

AutoCAD supports the Macintosh Clipboard feature. The Macintosh enables you to easily copy information, both text and graphics, into the Macintosh Clipboard. With the AutoCAD SELECT command, you identify the information you want to copy to the Clipboard. You then pick the Copy command found in the Edit pull-down menu. This copies the selected information into the Clipboard.

Once the AutoCAD information has been copied to the Clipboard, you have the option to activate another program such as a presentation graphics or publishing package. You can then insert the information from the Clipboard into it. This is accomplished by selecting Paste from the Edit pull-down menu.

Desk Accessories

AutoCAD also supports the use of the Macintosh desk accessories. These standard accessories include a variety

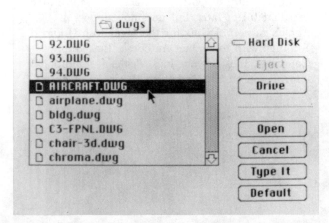

Courtesy of Apple Computer, Inc.

The file dialogue box makes it easy to store drawings.

of utilities, such as the Alarm Clock and Calculator. These accessories can be displayed and active as you work with AutoCAD.

Another desk accessory, the Control Panel, lets you control sound, color, mouse movement, and a range of other Macintosh functions.

F1-F4 Auxiliary Buttons

At the bottom of the Drawing Editor is a narrow rectangular area containing four buttons labeled F1 through F4. Clicking on the F1 button issues a RETURN; F2 displays the Tools pull-down menu, including the Object Snap modes; F3 issues a Cancel (CTRL C); and F4 toggles Snap mode on and off. These four functions are tied directly to ✳✳✳AUX1 found in ACAD.MNU.

Macintosh keyboard functions such as CTRL G (Grid on/off) and CTRL T (Tablet on/off) are the same as the MS-DOS keyboard functions.

File Portability

AutoCAD binary files (.DWG, .FLM, .MNX, .SHX, .SLD) are fully transportable to and from the Mac II and other computing platforms that run AutoCAD, regardless of operating system and machine type. No file translation is necessary.

AutoCAD ASCII support files (.HLP, .LIN, .MNU, .PAT, .SLD, .SHP) can also be moved to and from the Mac II and other computing platforms without modification.

Other Features and Requirements

Like the PC/MS-DOS version of AutoCAD, AutoLISP programming language is embedded and fully supported in the Mac II version of AutoCAD.

AutoCAD on the Mac II fully supports the range of 3D surfacing capabilities, including tabulated cylinders, ruled surfaces, surfaces of revolution, Coons patches, and 3D surface patches with up to 256 × 256 vertices. User Coordinate Systems (UCSs), the dynamic view facility, and multiple viewports are also available.

The industry-standard Drawing Interchange File (DXF) and Initial Graphics Exchange Specification (IGES) translation formats allow you to translate AutoCAD Mac II files to and from other CAD software such as VersaCAD.

AutoCAD requires a Macintosh II or IIx computer with at least five megabytes of system memory (RAM), Macintosh OS 6.0.2 or later, an Apple-compatible color or monochrome display, and a minimum of four megabytes of hard disk space. An Apple mouse can be used with AutoCAD, but it is not required.

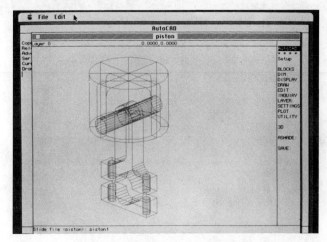

Courtesy of Apple Computer, Inc.

AutoCAD on the Mac II includes the full range of 3D capabilities.

AutoCAD on the Mac II supports the Apple ImageWriter and LaserWriter printers and a wide range of third-party printers compatible with the Print Manager protocol. AutoCAD on the Mac II also allows you to use third-party graphics boards and monitors that support Quickdraw and a range of digitizers and plotters.

AutoCAD fully supports the Macintosh MultiFinder, Version 6.0.1 or later, but does not support A/UX— Apple's version of Unix for the Macintosh II and IIx. You may wish to contact Autodesk, Inc., Apple Computer, Inc., or your local dealer for additional information on the Macintosh II version of AutoCAD.

Appendix J: Reconfiguring AutoCAD

This appendix covers the procedure for configuring the AutoCAD software to work with different types of hardware components. For instance, if you want to change from using a mouse to using a digitizer, you must tell AutoCAD about the new device. Otherwise, the device will not work. Also, when you first install the AutoCAD software, you must step through the entire configuration procedure.

Reconfiguring AutoCAD

1 Load AutoCAD and bring up the Main Menu.

2 Select menu item 5, "Configure AutoCAD."

Your screen should look similar to the following.

```
Current AutoCAD configuration

  Video display:      IBM Video Graphics Array

  Digitizer:          Mouse Systems Mouse
    Port: Asynchronous Communications Adapter COM1
          at address 3F8 (hex)

  Plotter:            Houston Instrument DMP-62MP
    Port: Asynchronous Communications Adapter COM1
          at address 3F8 (hex)

  Printer Plotter:    TI 800 model 855

Press RETURN to continue:
```

3 Press **RETURN**.

You should receive the Configuration Menu as shown below.

```
Configuration menu

  0.  Exit to Main Menu
  1.  Show current configuration
  2.  Allow detailed configuration
  3.  Configure video display
  4.  Configure digitizer
  5.  Configure plotter
  6.  Configure printer plotter
  7.  Configure system console
  8.  Configure operating parameters

Enter selection <0>:
```

Let's proceed through the configuration process by first reconfiguring the plotter.

4 Select menu item 5, "Configure plotter."

5 Respond to the next step with a Yes—you do want a different one.

"Enter drive or directory containing the Plotter device drivers:" may appear. If so, . . .

6 . . . enter the name of the directory (such as DRIVERS) containing the device drivers, or enter the letter of the diskette drive (such as A:) containing the plotter device drivers.

HINT:

The device drivers required here may be contained in a directory with the name DRIVERS (or a similar name). If not, locate the diskette shipped with AutoCAD marked "Driver" and place it in the open drive. In either case, you must specify the location of the plotter device drivers.

Once you specify the location of the plotter device drivers, a list of them should appear.

```
Available plotters:

  1.  None
  2.  ADI plotter
  3.  Alpha Merics
  4.  Calcomp 906/907/PCI
  5.  Canon Laser Printer LPB-8
  6.  Cordata Laser Printer
  7.  Gould Colorwriter
  8.  Hewlett-Packard
  9.  Houston Instrument
  10. IBM 7300 Series
  11. IBM Personal Pageprinter
  12. IOLINE LP 3700
  13. Imagen 8/300
  14. Nicolet ZETA 822 (obsolete)
  15. PostScript devices
  16. Roland DG
  17. Sweet-P
  18. Western Graphtec

Select device number or ? to repeat list <9>:
```

7 Choose one of the plotter options by entering its number.

8 Continue by answering each question until you are able to return to the Configuration Menu.

9   Experiment with each of the other configuration options. Particularly give attention to menu item 8, "Configure operating parameters."

10   Last, select menu item 1 to check your current configuration.

If the current configuration is not correct according to your hardware, make the appropriate change(s).

11   Select menu task 0, "Exit to Main Menu." Save your configuration changes ONLY if you had intended for them to be changed.

12   When you're finished, try the new configuration (if you saved it) by bringing up the Drawing Editor and by plotting.

Appendix K: Contents of Prototype Drawing ACAD.DWG

This appendix lists the general contents of the standard AutoCAD prototype drawing named ACAD.DWG. This information is important because it contains the default modes and settings of all new drawings, unless you choose to use a prototype drawing of your own.

Status of ACAD.DWG

```
STATUS
0 entities in ACAD
Limits are            X:      0.0000      12.0000        (Off)
                      Y:      0.0000       9.0000
Drawing uses          *Nothing*
Display shows         X:     -0.0000      14.7213
                      Y:      0.0000      10.6620
Insertion base is     X:      0.0000   Y:      0.0000   Z:      0.0000
Snap resolution is    X:      1.0000   Y:      1.0000
Grid spacing is       X:      0.0000   Y:      0.0000

Current layer: 0
Current color: BYLAYER--7 (white)
Current linetype: BYLAYER--CONTINUOUS
Current elevation:      0.0000        thickness:      0.0000
Axis off Fill on Grid off Ortho off Qtext off Snap off Tablet off
Object snap modes: None
Free RAM: 12278 bytes    Free disk: 10725376 bytes
I/O page space: 130K bytes
```

Layer Listing of ACAD.DWG

```
      Layer name(s) for listing <*>:

      Layer name          State        Color          Linetype
      ------------------  --------   -------------   -------------
      0                   On         7 (white)       CONTINUOUS

      Current layer: 0
```

Text Styles in ACAD.DWG

```
   Text styles:

   Style name: STANDARD        Font file: TXT
      Height: 0.0000    Width factor: 1.00   Obliquing angle: 0
      Generation: Normal
```

DIM Status of ACAD.DWG

```
DIMALT      Off                     Alternate units selected
DIMALTD     2                       Alternate unit decimal places
DIMALTF     25.4000                 Alternate unit scale factor
DIMAPOST                            Default suffix for alternate text
DIMASO      On                      Create associative dimensions
DIMASZ      0.1800                  Arrow size
DIMBLK                              Arrow block name
DIMBLK1                             First arrow block name
DIMBLK2                             Second arrow block name
DIMCEN      0.0900                  Center mark size
DIMDLE      0.0000                  Dimension line extension
DIMDLI      0.3800                  Dimension line increment for continuation
DIMEXE      0.1800                  Extension above dimension line
DIMEXO      0.0625                  Extension line origin offset
DIMLFAC     1.0000                  Linear unit scale factor
DIMLIM      Off                     Generate dimension limits
DIMPOST                             Default suffix for dimension text
DIMRND      0.0000                  Rounding value
DIMSAH      Off                     Separate arrow blocks
DIMSCALE    1.0000                  Overall scale factor
-- Press RETURN for more --
DIMSE1      Off                     Suppress the first extension line
DIMSE2      Off                     Suppress the second extension line
DIMSHO      Off                     Update dimensions while dragging
DIMSOXD     Off                     Suppress outside extension dimension
DIMTAD      Off                     Place text above the dimension line
DIMTIH      On                      Text inside extensions is horizontal
DIMTIX      Off                     Place text inside extensions
DIMTM       0.0000                  Minus tolerance
DIMTOFL     Off                     Force line inside extension lines
DIMTOH      On                      Text outside extensions is horizontal
DIMTOL      Off                     Generate dimension tolerances
DIMTP       0.0000                  Plus tolerance
DIMTSZ      0.0000                  Tick size
DIMTVP      0.0000                  Text vertical position
DIMTXT      0.1800                  Text height
DIMZIN      0                       Zero suppression
```

Plot Settings in ACAD.DWG

(Yours may differ somewhat depending on your hardware configuration.)

```
Specify the part of the drawing to be plotted by entering:
Display, Extents, Limits, View, or Window <D>:

Plot will NOT be written to a selected file
Sizes are in Inches
Plot origin is at (0.00,0.00)
Plotting area is 34.80 wide by 22.80 high (MAX size)
Plot is NOT rotated 90 degrees
Pen width is 0.010
Area fill will NOT be adjusted for pen width
Hidden lines will NOT be removed
Plot will be scaled to fit available area
```

Entity Color	Pen No.	Line Type	Pen Speed	Entity Color	Pen No.	Line Type	Pen Speed
1 (red)	1	0	32	9	1	0	32
2 (yellow)	1	0	32	10	1	0	32
3 (green)	1	0	32	11	1	0	32
4 (cyan)	1	0	32	12	1	0	32
5 (blue)	1	0	32	13	1	0	32
6 (magenta)	1	0	32	14	1	0	32
7 (white)	1	0	32	15	1	0	32
8	1	0	32				

Other Modes and Values in ACAD.DWG

APERTURE	10 pixels
Attributes	Visibility controlled individually, entry of values during INSERT permitted (using prompts rather than dialogue box)
AXIS	Off, spacing (0.0,0.0)
BASE	Insertion base point (0.0,0.0,0,0)
BLIPMODE	On
CHAMFER	Distance 0.0
COLOR	Current entity color "BYLAYER"
Coordinate display	Updated on point entry
LIMITS	Off, drawing limits (0.0,0.0) to (12.0,9.0)
LINETYPE	Current entity linetype "BYLAYER", no loaded linetypes other than "CONTINUOUS"
LTSCALE	1.0
MENU	"acad"
MIRROR	Text mirrored same as other entities
Object selection	Pick box size 3 pixels
ORTHO	Off
OSNAP	None
PLINE	Line-width 0.0
POINT	Display mode 0, size 0.00
QTEXT	Off
REGENAUTO	On
SKETCH	Record increment 0.10, producing lines
SNAP	Off, spacing (1.0, 1.0)
SNAP/GRID	Standard style, base point (0.0,0.0), rotation 0.0 degrees
Spline curves	Frame off, segments 8, spline type = cubic
STYLE	Only defined text style is "STANDARD", using font "txt" with variable height, width factor 1.0, horizontal orientation, and no special modes.
Surfaces	6 tabulations in M and N directions, 6 segments for smoothing in U and V directions, smooth surface type = cubic B-spline
TABLET	Off
TEXT	Style "STANDARD", height 0.20, rotation 0.0 degrees
TIME	User elapsed timer on.
TRACE	Width 0.05
UCS	Current UCS same as World, origin at World (0,0,0), auto plan view off, coordinate system icon on (at origin).
UNITS (linear)	Decimal, 4 decimal places
UNITS (angular)	Decimal degrees, 0 decimal places, angle 0 direction is to the right, angles increase counterclockwise
Viewing modes	One active viewport, plan view, perspective off, target point (0,0,0), front and back clipping off, lens length 50 mm, twist angle 0.0, fast zoom on, circle zoom percent 100, WORLDVIEW 0
ZOOM	To drawing limits

Of course, you can modify the ACAD prototype drawing to achieve whatever initial conditions you like. To do this, simply edit ACAD.DWG, set the values and modes you prefer, and save your updated version with the END command.

ACAD.DWG is the *default* prototype drawing. When reconfiguring AutoCAD (Appendix J), you can choose a different prototype drawing to be the default. As described in Units 20 and 21, you can also specify an explicit prototype when creating a new drawing via Main Menu item 1. To do this, type the name of your new drawing followed by the equal sign and the name of the prototype drawing.

Example:

Enter NAME of drawing: **STAIRD=PROTO1**

It is also possible to create a new drawing without any prototype drawing.

Example:

Enter NAME of drawing: **ENGINE=**

In this case, AutoCAD will use the default values of ACAD.DWG shown on the first few pages of this appendix.

System Variables

The following is a list of AutoCAD system variables. The list was generated using the SETVAR command and ? option. These variables can be examined and many can be changed with the SETVAR command and AutoLISP's GETVAR and SETVAR functions.

Some of the variables are saved in the drawing file while others are saved in AutoCAD's ACAD.CFG (general configuration file). For more information, see Appendix A, section A.7, of the *AutoCAD Reference Manual*.

ACADPREFIX	" "
ACADVER	"10 c2"
AFLAGS	0
ANGBASE	0
ANGDIR	0
APERTURE	10
AREA	0.0000
ATTDIA	0
ATTMODE	1
ATTREQ	1
AUNITS	0
AUPREC	0
AXISMODE	0
AXISUNIT	0.0000,0.0000
BACKZ	0.0000
BLIPMODE	1
CDATE	19881227.174418628
CECOLOR	"BYLAYER"
CELTYPE	"BYLAYER"
CHAMFERA	0.0000
CHAMFERB	0.0000
CLAYER	"0"
CMDECHO	1
COORDS	0
CVPORT	1
DATE	2447523.73946933
DISTANCE	0.0000
DRAGMODE	2
DRAGP1	10
DRAGP2	25
DWGNAME	"ACAD"
DWGPREFIX	"C:\R10\"
ELEVATION	0.0000
EXPERT	0
EXTMAX	$-1.0000E+20,-1.0000E+20,$ $-1.0000E+20$
EXTMIN	$1.0000E+20,1.0000E+20,$ $1.0000E+20$
FILLETRAD	0.0000
FILLMODE	1
FLATLAND	0
FRONTZ	0.0000
GRIDMODE	0
GRIDUNIT	0.0000,0.0000
HANDLES	0
HIGHLIGHT	1
INSBASE	0.0000,0.0000,0.0000
LASTANGLE	0
LASTPOINT	0.0000,0.0000,0.0000
LASTPT3D	0.0000,0.0000,0.0000
LENSLENGTH	50.0000
LIMCHECK	0
LIMMAX	12.0000,9.0000
LIMMIN	0.0000,0.0000
LTSCALE	1.0000
LUNITS	2
LUPREC	4
MENUECHO	0
MENUNAME	"acad"
MIRRTEXT	1
ORTHOMODE	0
OSMODE	0
PDMODE	0
PDSIZE	0.0000

PERIMETER	0.0000	TEXTEVAL	0
PICKBOX	3	TEXTSIZE	0.2000
POPUPS	1	TEXTSTYLE	"STANDARD"
QTEXTMODE	0	THICKNESS	0.0000
REGENMODE	1	TRACEWID	0.0500
SCREENSIZE	572.0000, 414.0000	UCSFOLLOW	0
SKETCHINC	0.1000	UCSICON	1
SKPOLY	0	UCSNAME	" "
SNAPANG	0	UCSORG	0.0000,0.0000,0.0000
SNAPBASE	0.0000,0.0000	UCSXDIR	1.0000,0.0000,0.0000
SNAPISOPAIR	0	UCSYDIR	0.0000,1.0000,0.0000
SNAPMODE	0	VIEWCTR	7.3607,5.3310,0.0000
SNAPSTYL	0	VIEWDIR	0.0000,0.0000,1.0000
SNAPUNIT	1.0000,1.0000	VIEWMODE	0
SPLFRAME	0	VIEWSIZE	10.6620
SPLINESEGS	8	VIEWTWIST	0
SPLINETYPE	6	VPOINTX	0.0000
SURFTAB1	6	VPOINTY	0.0000
SURFTAB2	6	VPOINTZ	1.0000
SURFTYPE	6	VSMAX	14.7213,10.6620,0.0000
SURFU	6	VSMIN	−0.0000,0.0000,0.0000
SURFV	6	WORLDUCS	1
TARGET	0.0000,0.0000,0.0000	WORLDVIEW	1
TDCREATE	2447441.86872986		
TDINDWG	0.00344884		
TDUPDATE	2447441.86886725		
TDUSRTIMER	0.00351817		
TEMPPREFIX	" "		

The dimensioning variables are excluded from this list since they are printed earlier in this appendix.

Appendix L: Paper-Scale-Limits Sample Relationships

	SHEET SIZE (X × Y)	Approximate DRAWING AREA (X × Y)	SCALE	UPPER RIGHT LIMIT (X,Y) (LOWER LEFT LIMIT IS 0,0)
ARCHITECT'S SCALE	A: 12″ × 9″ B: 18″ × 12″ C: 24″ × 18″ D: 36″ × 24″ E: 48″ × 36″	10″ × 8″ 16″ × 11″ 22″ × 16″ 34″ × 22″ 46″ × 34″	⅛″ = 1′ ½″ = 1′ ¼″ = 1′ 3″ = 1′ 1″ = 1′	80′,64′ 32′,22′ 88′,64′ 11.3′,7.3′ 46′,34′
CIVIL ENGINEER'S SCALE	A: 12″ × 9″ B: 18″ × 12″ C: 24″ × 18″ D: 36″ × 24″ E: 48″ × 36″	10″ × 8″ 16″ × 11″ 22″ × 16″ 34″ × 22″ 46″ × 34″	1″ = 200′ 1″ = 50′ 1″ = 10′ 1″ = 300′ 1″ = 20′	2000′,1600′ 800′,550′ 220′,160′ 10,200′,6600′ 920′,680′
MECHANICAL ENGINEER'S SCALE	A: 11″ × 8½″ B: 17″ × 11″ C: 22″ × 17″ D: 34″ × 22″ E: 44″ × 34″	9″ × 7″ 15″ × 10″ 20″ × 15″ 32″ × 20″ 42″ × 32″	1″ = 2″ 2″ = 1″ 1″ = 1″ 1″ = 1.5″ 3″ = 1″	18″,14″ 7.5″,5″ 20″,15″ 48″,30″ 14″,10.6″
METRIC SCALE	A: 279 mm × 216 mm (11″ × 8½″) B: 432 mm × 279 mm (17″ × 11″) C: 55.9 cm × 43.2 cm (22″ × 17″) D: 86.4 cm × 55.9 cm (34″ × 22″) E: 111.8 cm × 86.4 cm (44″ × 34″)	229 mm × 178 mm (9″ × 7″) 381 mm × 254 mm (15″ × 10″) 50.8 cm × 38.1 cm (20″ × 15″) 81.3 cm × 50.8 cm (32″ × 20″) 106.7 cm × 81.3 cm (42″ × 32″)	1 mm = 5 mm 1 mm = 20 mm 1 cm = 10 cm 2 cm = 1 cm 1 cm = 2 cm	1145, 890 7620, 5080 508, 381 40.5, 25.5 213, 163

NOTE: 1″ = 25.4 mm

Appendix M: Decimal-Fraction Equivalents and Inch-Millimeter Conversion Table

1/2	1/4	1/8	1/16	1/32	1/64	Decimals	Millimeters
					1	.015625	.396875
				1		.031250	.793750
					3	.046875	1.190625
			1			.062500	1.587500
					5	.078125	1.984375
				3		.093750	2.381250
					7	.109375	2.778125
		1				.125000	3.175000
					9	.140625	3.571875
				5		.156250	3.968750
					11	.171875	4.365625
			3			.187500	4.762500
					13	.203125	5.159375
				7		.218750	5.556250
					15	.234375	5.953125
	1					.250000	6.350000
					17	.265625	6.746875
				9		.281250	7.143750
					19	.296875	7.540625
			5			.312500	7.937500
					21	.328125	8.334375
				11		.343750	8.731250
					23	.359375	9.128125
		3				.375000	9.525000
					25	.390625	9.921875
				13		.406250	10.318750
					27	.421875	10.715625
			7			.437500	11.112500
					29	.453125	11.509375
				15		.468750	11.906250
					31	.484375	12.303125
1						.500000	12.700000
					33	.515625	13.096875
				17		.531250	13.493750
					35	.546875	13.890625
			9			.562500	14.287500
					37	.578125	14.684375
				19		.593750	15.081250
					39	.609375	15.478125
		5				.625000	15.875000
					41	.640625	16.271875
				21		.656250	16.668750
					43	.671875	17.065625
			11			.687500	17.462500
					45	.703125	17.859375
				23		.718750	18.256250
					47	.734375	18.653125
	3					.750000	19.050000
					49	.765625	19.446875
				25		.781250	19.843750
					51	.796875	20.240625
			13			.812500	20.637500
					53	.828125	21.034375
				27		.843750	21.431250
					55	.859375	21.828125
		7				.875000	22.225000
					57	.890625	22.621875
				29		.906250	23.018750
					59	.921875	23.415625
			15			.937500	23.812500
					61	.953125	24.209375
				31		.968750	24.606250
					63	.984375	25.003125
1						1.000000	25.400000

Appendix N: Standard Linetypes

A standard library of linetypes is supplied with AutoCAD, in a file named ACAD.LIN. The linetypes contained in it are illustrated below.

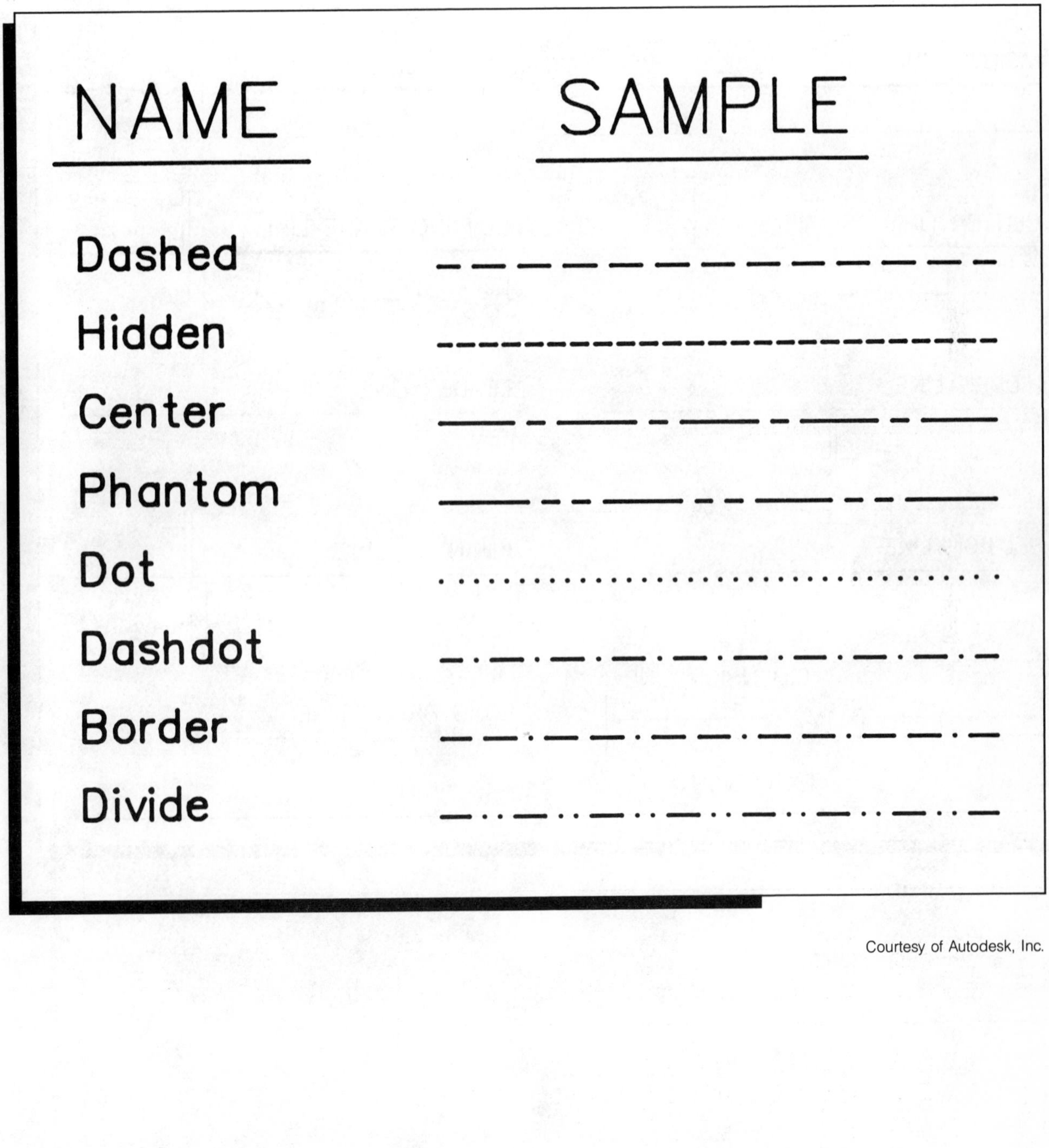

NAME	SAMPLE
Dashed	-- -- -- -- -- -- -- -- -- -- -- --
Hidden	- - - - - - - - - - - - - - - - - - - -
Center	—— — —— — —— — —— — ——
Phantom	—— — — —— — — —— — —
Dot	··································
Dashdot	—·—·—·—·—·—·—·—·—·
Border	—— —— · —— —— · —— —— ·
Divide	—— · · —— · · —— · · —— · ·

Courtesy of Autodesk, Inc.

ANSI Y14.2 line conventions, which differ slightly from
the standard linetypes supplied with AutoCAD, are
shown below.

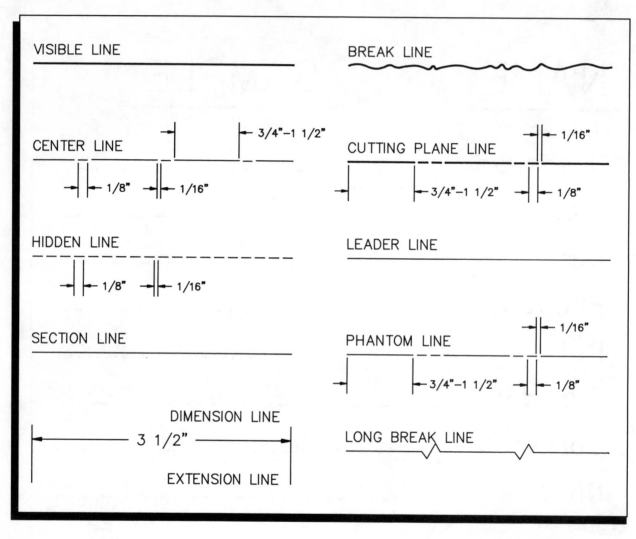

Appendix O: Standard Text Fonts

AutoCAD is supplied with several text fonts. You can use the STYLE command to apply expansion, compression, or obliquing to any of these fonts, thereby tailoring the characters to your needs. (See Unit 19.) You can draw characters of any desired height using any of the fonts.

The fonts supplied with AutoCAD are the following:

TXT
This is the standard AutoCAD text font. It is very simple and will generate quickly on the screen.

MONOTXT
This is identical to the TXT font but is monospaced, whereas TXT is proportionally spaced.

SIMPLEX
This is a "simplex" Roman font drawn by means of many short line segments. It produces smoother-looking characters than those of the TXT font but takes longer to generate on the screen.

COMPLEX
This is a "complex" Roman font with short line segments and multiple strokes, forming smooth characters with varying thickness. COMPLEX consumes even more time during screen regenerations.

ITALIC
This is a true Italic font. It also takes considerable time to generate on the screen.

ROMANS
Simplex Roman font (single stroke, sans serif)

SCRIPTS
Simplex script font (single stroke)

GREEKS
Simplex Greek font (single stroke, sans serif)

ROMAND
Duplex Roman font (double stroke, sans serif)

ROMANC
Complex Roman font (double stroke, serif)

ITALICC
Complex Italic font (double stroke, serif)

SCRIPTC
Complex script font (double stroke)

GREEKC
Complex Greek font (double stroke, serif)

CYRILLIC
Cyrillic—alphabetical

CYRILTLC
Cyrillic—Transliteration

ROMANT
Triplex Roman font (triple stroke, serif)

ITALICT
Triplex Italic font (triple stroke, serif)

GOTHICE
Gothic English

GOTHICG
Gothic German

GOTHICI
Gothic Italian

SYASTRO
Astronomical symbols

SYMAP
Mapping symbols

SYMATH
Mathematical symbols

SYMETEO
Meteorological symbols

SYMUSIC
Music symbols

Samples of 24 fonts are shown in this appendix. (The MONOTXT font is not shown; its characters are the same as those in the TXT font.)

With the exception of MONOTXT, each font's characters are proportionally spaced. Hence, the space needed for the letter "i" is narrower than that for the letter "m."

Each font resides in a separate disk file with the name <font>.SHX. This is the "compiled" form of the font, for direct use by AutoCAD. Another file named <font>.SHP is supplied as well for some of the fonts. This file contains the symbolic description of the font's characters and is not normally needed by AutoCAD. The ".SHP" files are provided as examples for those users who might want to define their own text fonts. If you wish to do this, see Appendix B of the *AutoCAD Reference Manual*.

!"#$%&'()*+,-./01234567
89:;<=>?@ABCDEFGHIJKLMN0
PQRSTUVWXYZ[\]^_'abcdefg
hijklmnopqrstuvwxyz{|}~°±ø´

TXT font

!@#$%~&*()_+{}|:"<>?
1234567890-=[]\;',./
ABXΔEΦΓHIϑKΛMNOΠΘΡΣΤΥΩΞΨZ
αβχδεφγηιϑκλμνοπϖρστυ∈ωξψζ

GREEKS font

!"#$%&'()*+,-./01234567
89:;<=>?@ABCDEFGHIJKLMNO
PQRSTUVWXYZ[\]^_'abcdefg
hijklmnopqrstuvwxyz{|}~°±ø

SIMPLEX font

!@#$%~&*()_+{}|:"<>?
1234567890-=[]\;',./
ABCDEFGHIJKLMNOPQRSTUVWXYZ
abcdefghijklmnopqrstuvwxyz

ROMAND font

!"#$%&'()*+,-./01234567
89:;<=>?@ABCDEFGHIJKLMNO
PQRSTUVWXYZ[\]^_'abcdefg
hijklmnopqrstuvwxyz{|}~°±ø

COMPLEX font

!@#$%~&*()_+{}|:"<>?
1234567890-=[]\;',./
ABCDEFGHIJKLMNOPQRSTUVWXYZ
abcdefghijklmnopqrstuvwxyz

ROMANC font

!"#$%&'()+,-./01234567*
89:;<=>?@ABCDEFGHIJKLMNO
PQRSTUVWXYZ[\]^_'abcdefg
hijklmnopqrstuvwxyz{|}~°±ø

ITALIC font

!@#$%~&()_+{}|:"<>?*
1234567890-=[]\;',./
ABCDEFGHIJKLMNOPQRSTUVWXYZ
abcdefghijklmnopqrstuvwxyz

ITALICC font

!"#$%&'()*+,-./01234567
89:;<=>?@ABCDEFGHIJKLMNO
PQRSTUVWXYZ[\]^_'abcdefg
hijklmnopqrstuvwxyz{|}~

ROMANS font

!@#$%~&*()_+{}|:"<>?
1234567890-=[]\;',./
ABCDEFGHIJKLMNOPQRSTUVWXYZ
abcdefghijklmnopqrstuvwxyz

SCRIPTC font

!"#$%&'()*+,-./01234567
89:;<=>?@ABCDEFGHIJKLMNO
PQRSTUVWXYZ[\]^_'abcdefg
hijklmnopqrstuvwxyz{|}~

SCRIPTS font

!@#$%~&*()_+{}|:"<>?
1234567890-=[]\;',./
ABXΔEΦΓHIϑKΛMNOΠΘΡΣΤΥΩΞΨZ
αβχδεφγηιϑκλμνοπϖρστυ∈ωξψζ

GREEKC font

!@#$%Э&*()Ю+ъьы:"юя?
1234567890−=ЪЬЫ;',./
АБВГДЕЖЗИЙКЛМНОПРСТУФХЦЧШЩ
абвгдежзийклмнопрстуфхцчшщ

CYRILLIC font

!@#$%Ю&*()Э+ъьы:"юя?
1234567890−=ЬЪЫ;',./
АБЧДЕФГХИЩКЛМНОПЦРСТУВШЖЙЗ
абчдефгхищклмнопцрстувшжйз

CYRILTLC font

!@#$%^&*()_+{}|:"<>?
1234567890−=[]\;',./
ABCDEFGHIJKLMNOPQRSTUVWXYZ
abcdefghijklmnopqrstuvwxyz

ROMANT font

!@#$%^&*()_+{}|:"<>?
1234567890−=[]\;',./
ABCDEFGHIJKLMNOPQRSTUVWXYZ
abcdefghijklmnopqrstuvwxyz

ITALICT font

!@#$%^&*()_+{}|:"<>?
1234567890−=[]\;',./
ABCDEFGHIJKLMNOPQRSTUVWXYZ
abcdefghijklmnopqrstuvwxyz

GOTHICE font

!@#$%^&*()_+{}|:"<>?
1234567890−=[]\;',./
ABCDEFGHIJKLMNOPQRSTUVWXYZ
abcdefghijklmnopqrstuvwxyz

GOTHICG font

!@#$%^&*()_+{}|:"<>?
1234567890−=[]\;',./
ABCDEFGHIJKLMNOPQRSTUVWXYZ
abcdefghijklmnopqrstuvwxyz

GOTHICI font

!@#$%^&*()_+{}|:"<>?
1234567890−=[]\;',./

SYASTRO font

!@#$%^&*()_+{}|:"<>?
1234567890−=[]\;',./

SYMAP font

!@#$%^&*()_+{}|:"<>?
1234567890−=[]\;',./

SYMATH font

!@#$%^&*()_+{}|:"<>?
1234567890−=[]\;',./

SYMETEO font

!@#$%^&*()_+{}|:"<>?
1234567890−=[]\;',./

SYMUSIC font

Appendix P: Standard Hatch Patterns

Shown here are the standard hatch patterns supplied in the file ACAD.PAT.

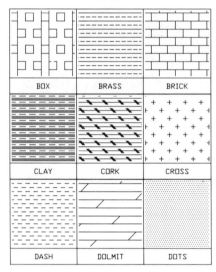

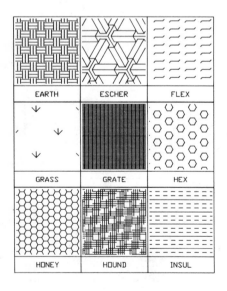

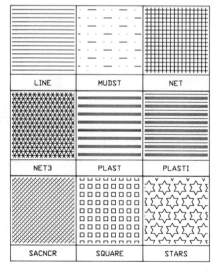

Courtesy of Autodesk, Inc.

Appendix Q: Authorized AutoCAD Training Centers

Authorized AutoCAD Training Centers (ATCs™) offer courses in AutoCAD®, AutoCAD AEC®, AutoSketch®, AutoShade™, and other Autodesk products. For more information, call the ATC nearest you. To learn of recent additions to the list, call 1-800-445-5415.

CENTER	ADDRESS	CITY	ST	ZIP	PHONE	CONTACT/CLASS INFO
USA						
Southern Arkansas University	SAU Tech. Station	Camden	AR	71701	(501) 574-4505	Gary Oden
University of Arkansas	School of Eng. Tech./2801 S. University	Little Rock	AR	72204	(501) 569-8200	Michael Stewart
CAD Institute	4100 E. Broadway, Suite 150	Phoenix	AZ	85040	(602) 437-0405	Don Brown
Bakersfield College A.T.C.	1801 Panorama Drive	Bakersfield	CA	93305	(805) 395-4224/4094	Bob Funk
Clovis Vocational Center	1450 Herndon Ave.	Clovis	CA	93612	(209) 299-0978	Bill Carmichael
College of the Redwoods	7351 Tompkins Hill Road	Eureka	CA	95501	(707) 443-8411 X600	Robert Vojtek
VCP CAD Productions	1970 Broadway, Suite 320	Oakland	CA	94612	(415) 832-2153	Kathleen Martin
MTI College	2011 W. Chapman Ave.	Orange	CA	92668	(714) 532-4320	Kathy Barrett
Sacramento City College	Academy Trng. Ctr., 3835 Freeport	Sacramento	CA	95822	(916) 447-0743	Bob Schropp
Muir Technical College	10981 San Diego Mission Rd., Suite 10	San Diego	CA	92108	(619) 528-2100	Doug Williams
San Francisco State Univ/Eng. Div.	1600 Holloway	San Francisco	CA	94132	(415) 338-1205	Marci Manderscheid
Copper Connection/VIA Tech. Ctr.	3375 Scott Blvd. Suite 240	Santa Clara	CA	95054	(408) 970-9838	Mary Sugden
SPOCAD LA Ed. Ctr.	15445 Ventura Blvd.	Sherman Oaks	CA	91403	(818) 986-7275	Larry Howe
Ventura Community College	4667 Telegraph Road	Ventura	CA	93003	(805) 654-6459	Robert Tholl
Professional Training Center	Denver Inst Tech 7350 N. Broadway	Denver	CO	80221	(303) 426-1900	Robert Fox
Thames Valley State Tech College	574 New London Turnpike	Norwich	CT	06360	(203) 886-0177	Raymond Hasse
Delaware Tech. & Comm. College	1832 N. DuPont Pkwy.	Dover	DE	19901	(302) 736-5438	Daniel Houghtaling
Univ. of Miami	Dep't. of Civil & Arch. Eng., Box 248294	Coral Gables	FL	33124	(305) 284-3391	Mehrad Soltani
Florida Community College	101 West State Street	Jacksonville	FL	32202	(904) 633-8289	C.T. Wezernak
Gulf Coast Comm. College	5230 West Hwy 98	Panama City	FL	32401	(904) 769-1551	Robert Jones
St. Augustine Tech. Ctr.	Collins Ave. at Del Monte Dr.	St. Augustine	FL	32084	(904) 824-4401	Thomas Marsh
New England Institute of Technology	1126 53rd Court	West Palm Beach	FL	33407	(407) 842-8324	Noel Shevak
West Georgia Tech. Institute	303 Fort Dr.	La Grange	GA	30240	(404) 882-2518	Jerry Gray
Gwinnett Tech. Institute	1250 Atkinson Rd.	Lawrenceville	GA	30246	(404) 962-7580	Walter Lawrence
Moultrie Tech.	P.O. Box 520, Industrial Way	Moultrie	GA	31776	(912) 985-8409	Jack Bridwell
Advanced Software Learning Center	205 Marketplace, Suite 204	Roswell	GA	30076	(404) 641-0864	Ann Gabriel
Savannah Tech AutoCAD Trng Ctr	5717 White Bluff Road	Savannah	GA	31499	(912) 352-9969	Jack Parr
Kapiolani Community College	4303 Diamond Head Road	Honolulu	HI	96816	(808) 734-9211	Walea L. Constantinau
CIM Technologies/Iowa State U.	1515 Center	Ames	IA	50011	(515) 296-9914	Clark Gaff
Iowa Western Comm. Coll.	2700 College Rd., Box 4C	Council Bluffs	IA	51502	(712) 325-3403	Joe Henry
Hamilton Tech. College	425 E. 59th St.	Davenport	IA	52807	(319) 386-2213	John Jebens
Southeastern Comm. College	1015 S. Gear Ave.	W. Burlington	IA	52655	(319) 752-2731	Bill Bloomberg
Hawkeye Institute of Technology	1501 E. Orange Road	Waterloo	IA	50704-8015	(319) 296-2320 X342	Bill Roe
Idaho Falls Center for Higher Ed	1776 Science Ctr Dr, Box 778	Idaho Falls	ID	83402	(208) 526-1388	Marvin Eld
Parkland College	2400 W. Bradley Ave.	Champaign	IL	61821	(217) 351-2225	John Leap
Morrison Institute of Technology	P.O. Box 410, 1/4 Mile South Hwy. 78	Morrison	IL	61270	(815) 772-7218 X20	Richard Parkinson
Moraine Valley Community College	10900 South 88th Ave.	Palos Hills	IL	60465	(312) 371-2210 X309	J.C. Malitzke
Triton College/Adv. Technology Ctr	2000 5th Avenue	River Grove	IL	60171	(312) 456-0300 X583	Kim Cannon
CAD Design Systems, Inc.	1305 Remington Road, Suite D	Schaumburg	IL	60195	(312) 882-0114	Mehlinae Douglas
Lincoln Land Community College	Business Ind Dev Ctr/Shepherd Road	Springfield	IL	62794	(217) 786-2208	Gene Beenenga
University of Evansville	1800 Lincoln Avenue (UETAC)	Evansville	IN	47722	(812) 479-2652/2899	Ronald Devaisher
Indiana Vo-Tech College	3800 N. Anthony Blvd.	Fort Wayne	IN	46805	(219) 482-9171 X278	Ron Leigh
Purdue University/Calumet	2233 171st Street	Hammond	IN	46323-2094	(219) 989-2525	C. David Rose
Indiana Vo-Tech College	1315 E. Washington St.	Indianapolis	IN	46206	(317) 269-9233	Jim A. McFarland
Western Kentucky University	Dept. of Ind. and Eng. Tech.	Bowling Green	KY	42101	(502) 745-5323	George Roberts
University of Louisville	209 J.B. Speed Bldg., Rm. 209	Louisville	KY	40292	(502) 588-7908	Robert A. Matthews
Louisiana Productivity Center/USL	241 E. Lewis St., P.O. Box 44172	Lafayette	LA	70504	(318) 231-6422	Kendall Alton
Univ. of New Orleans/ATAC	POLC 226 Carondelet	New Orleans	LA	70130	(504) 523-6859	Jane Purdhomme

CENTER	ADDRESS	CITY	ST	ZIP	PHONE	CONTACT/CLASS INFO
Wentworth Institute of Technology	550 Huntington Av., Civ. Eng. Bldg 23	Boston	MA	02115	(617) 442-9010 X371	Anthony DeRosa
A-CAD Training Center	11 Lakeside Ofc. Park E, 607 North Ave.	Wakefield	MA	01880	(617) 245-4223	Andy Wood
Cantonsville Comm. College	800 S. Rolling Rd.	Baltimore	MD	21228	(301) 455-4110 X110	Tom Siegel
Advanced Tech. Ctr.-OCC	2900 Featherstone Rd.	Auburn Hills	MI	48057	(313) 853-4312	Bill Rose
Lake Michigan College	277 E. Napier Ave.	Benton Harbor	MI	49022	(616) 927-3571	Steve Huycke
Henry Ford Comm. College	5101 Evergreen Rd.	Dearborn	MI	48128	(313) 845-9637	John Nagohostan
GMI Engineering & Mgmt. Inst.	1700 West Third Avenue	Flint	MI	48504-4898	(313) 762-9866 X5842	Jim Barnes
Grand Rapids Junior College/OT	3310 Eagle Park Dr. NE	Grand Rapids	MI	49505	(616) 456-4274	Frank Conner
Hennepin Tech. Inst./E. Prairie Campus	9200 Flying Cloud Drive	Eden Prairie	MN	55347	(612) 944-2222	Dale Sheveland
Thief River Falls Tech Institute	Highway One, East	Thief River Falls	MN	56701	(218) 681-5424 X27	John D. Stewart
Northeast Metro Technical Inst.	3300 Century Ave. North	White Bear Lake	MN	55110	(218) 681-5424 X27	Dave Colby
Missouri Southern State College	Newman & Duquesne Roads	Joplin	MO	64801	(417) 625-9351	Francis Bartholet
Longview Community College	500 Longview Road Science & Tech Bldg	Lee's Summit	MO	64063	(816) 763-7777 X213	Philip G. Hubbard
Linn Technical College	Highway 50 East	Linn	MO	65051	(314) 897-3603	Ralph Keener
St. Louis Community College	Forest Park Campus/5600 Oakland	St. Louis	MO	63110	(314) 644-9291	Jerry Craig
Hinds Comm. College	Gibbes Hall	Raymond	MS	39154	(601) 857-8261	Joe Meador
Northern Montana College	Brockman Center	Havre	MT	59501	(406) 265-4157	Greg Kegel
Southeast Community College	Milford Campus RR2 Box D	Milford	NE	68405	(402) 761-2131 X218	Larry L. Shaw
Metropolitan Tech. Comm. College	P.O. Box 3777	Omaha	NE	68103-0777	(402) 289-1211	Bob Dunker
Wayne State College	200 East 10th	Wayne	NE	68787	(402) 375-2200	Dennis Linster
Camden County College	Little Gloucester Rd., Box 200	Blackwood	NJ	08012	(609) 227-7200	James Hudgings
The CAD Training Ctr.	2 Ethel Rd., Suite 201C	Edison	NJ	08817	(201) 248-8775	Caryn Heffner
San Juan College	4601 College Blvd.	Farmington	NM	87401	(505) 326-3311	Judith Wooderson
Russell Sage College ICET	140 New Scotland Ave.	Albany	NY	12208	(518) 445-1707	Mark Chevalier
SUNY College of Tech. at Farmingdale	Lupton Hall	Farmingdale	NY	11735	(516) 420-2108	Francis Meyer
New York University	11West 42nd Street, Rm. 400	New York	NY	10036	(212) 790-1344	Andrea M. Cohen
Pratt Institute of Technology	295 Lafayette St., Second Floor	New York	NY	10012	(212) 925-8481	Karen Miletsky
Rochester Institute of Technology	33 North Fitzhugh Street	Rochester	NY	14614-1269	(716) 475-5079	Charles Layne
Syracuse University	Ctr Comp Educ & Trng/610 E. Fayette	Syracuse	NY	13244-6020	(315) 423-3291	Norma S. Feldman
Grumman Data Systems Institute	250 Crossways Park Drive	Woodbury	NY	11797	(516) 364-2055	Ralph Ceraso
University of Akron	AutoCAD Training Center	Akron	OH	44325	(216) 375-6690	Ken Klika
Cincinnati Tech. College	3520 Central Parkway	Cincinnati	OH	45223	(513) 569-1752	Cliff Schulte
Franklin University	201 S. Grant Avenue	Columbus	OH	43215	(614) 224-6237 X257	Pete Bates
Sinclair Community College	444 W Third Street	Dayton	OH	45402	(513) 226-3061	Dan Brazelton
Loraine Cty. Comm. College	Advance Tech. Ctr., 1005 N. Abbe Rd.	Elyria	OH	44035	(216) 365-4191	James Ustar
Kent State Univ/Tuscarawas Campus	University Drive, N.E.	New Philadelphia	OH	44663	(216) 339-3391	Kamal Bichara
Owens Technical College	Caller #10,000, Oregon Road	Toledo	OH	43699	(419) 666-0580	Dave Winters
Muskingum Area Tech Trng & Consulting	1555 Newark Road	Zanesville	OH	43701	(614) 454-2501 X321	Jeff Gibbs
Oklahoma City Community College	7777 S May Ave	Oklahoma City	OK	73159	(405) 682-1611 X336	Doug H. Gregory
University of Oregon	Continuation Center, 1553 Moss St.	Eugene	OR	97403	(503) 686-3537	Paul Katz
Clackamas Community College	19600 S. Molalla Ave.	Oregon City	OR	97045	(503) 657-8400 X379	Terry Shumaker
American Institute of Design	1616 Orthodox Street	Philadelphia	PA	19124	(215) 288-8200	Peter Klein
Community College of Alleghany Cty	Neville Tech. Ctr., 5800 Grand Ave.	Pittsburgh	PA	15225	(412) 269-4900	James Kushner
University of Scranton	Monroe Avenue	Scranton	PA	18510	(717) 961-7508-09	J. Connolly
Williamsport Area Comm. College	Ind. Tech. Div., 1005 W. Third	Williamsport	PA	17701-5799	(717) 326-3761	William Thompson
Lancaster County Vo-Tech	1730 Hans Herr Drive, Box 527	Willow Street	PA	17584	(717) 464-3359	Katharine Walker
New England Institute of Technology	2500 Post Road	Warwick	RI	02886	(401) 467-7744	Steven Kitchin
Greenville Technical College	P.O. Box 5616, Station B	Greenville	SC	29606	(803) 242-3170	Vicki Kraeling
Trident Technical College	7000 Rivers Avenue/P.O. Box 10367	N. Charleston	SC	29411	(803) 572-6369	Alan Kalameja
Chattanooga St Ctr for Productivity	4501 Amnicola Highway	Chattanooga	TN	37406	(615) 697-4411	Stephen Reed
Pellissippi State Tech. Comm. College	10915 Hardin Valley Rd, Box 22990	Knoxville	TN	37933-0990	(615) 694-6671/6477	Donnia M. Tabor
Mid-SO Microcomputer Resource Ctr	5983 Macon Cove	Memphis	TN	38134	(901) 377-4277	Lisa Hadley

CENTER	ADDRESS	CITY	ST	ZIP	PHONE	CONTACT/CLASS INFO
University of Texas, Arlington	Mechanical Engineering Box 19023	Arlington	TX	76019	(817) 273-2561	Kent Lawrence
University of Texas, El Paso	Center for Professional Development	El Paso	TX	79968-0540	(915) 747-5187	Lee Nelson
CAD/CAM Centre, Inc.	1003 Wirt, Suite 104	Houston	TX	77055	(713) 467-4994	Cal Avery
Houston Comm. College	4310 Dunlavy	Houston	TX	77006	(713) 868-0787	Larry Brillhart
Univ. of Houston-Downtown	CAD Inst.- One Main St.	Houston	TX	77002	(713) 221-8032	Robert Rhea
C & Z Systems	4315 Lake Shore Drive, Suite J	Waco	TX	76710	(817) 776-7336	Roger Clark
Salt Lake Comm. College	4600 S. Redwood Rd.	Salt Lake City	UT	84130-0808	(801) 967-4326	John Anjewierden
Old Dominion University	School of Engineering MET-DPT	Norfolk	VA	23508	(804) 440-3765	Moustafa R. Moustafa
Vermont Technical College	AutoCAD Training Center	Randolph Center	VT	05061	(802) 728-3391 X86	Henry J. Swiatek
Everett Comm. College/App. Tech.	2333 Seaway Blvd.	Everett	WA	98203	(206) 355-2745 X214	Ronald L. Torrence
SPOCAD Hanford	8300 Gage Blvd, Suite #405	Kennewick	WA	99258	(509) 783-2365	Gary Hordemann
Boeing Computer Serv. Educ. & Train.	P.O. Box 24346 MS 9A-23	Seattle	WA	98124	(206) 575-7400	Janet Wilson
ITT Technical Institute	N. 1050 Argonne Rd.	Spokane	WA	99212-2610	(509) 926-2900	Michael J. Kelly
SPOCAD Educational Center	East 502 Boone Ave.	Spokane	WA	99258	(509) 484-6812	Gary Hordemann
Fox Valley Technical College	1825 N. Bluemound Drive	Appleton	WI	54913-2277	(414) 735-5762	Karen Alesch
University of Wisconsin-Milwaukee	2033 E. Hartford Ave.	Milwaukee	WI	53211	(414) 229-5239	Mark Roth
Putnam County Vo-Tech Center	Rt. 62 P.O. Box 530	Eleanor	WV	25070	(304) 586-2127	Leo E. Arbaugh Jr.
CANADA						
Southern Alberta Inst of Technology	1301 16th Ave NW	Calgary, Alberta		T2M0L4	(403) 284-8054	Wally Baumback
Alberta School of Drafting	6025-86 Street	Edmonton, Alberta		T6E2X4	(403) 468-3248	Ron Coward
Medicine Hat College/Comm Educ.	299 College Drive SE	Medicine Hat, Alberta		T1A3Y6	(403) 529-3847	Robert Melenchuck
British Columbia Inst. of Tech.	3700 Willingdon Ave.	Burnaby, B.C.		V5G3H2	(604) 432-8339	Phillip Dollan
Cariboo College	P.O. Box 3010	Kamloops, B.C.		V2C5N3	(604) 828-5048	Gene Turney
Kwantlen College/Newton Campus	13468 77th Avenue	Surrey, B.C.		V3T5H8	(604) 591-1111 X275	Gunar Capan
Cirrus Enterprises Inc.	3542 Blanchard St.	Victoria, B.C.		V8X1W3	(604) 386-8844	Warren Brown
Marine Institute	Ridge Rd., P.O. Box 4920	St. John's, N.F.		A1C5R3	(709) 778-0200	Mike Davison
Nova Scotia CAD/CAM Centre	1360 Barrington St., P.O. Box 1000	Halifax, Nova Scotia		B3J2X4	(902) 429-8300	Gary Bustin
Georgian College of Appl Arts & Tech	1 Georgian Drive	Barrie, Ontario		L4M3X9	(705) 728-1951 X340	P.A. Graydon
Sheridan College CAD Centre	Box 7500, McGlaughlin Rd.	Brampton, Ontario		L6V1G6	(416) 459-7533	Sally Ornar
Conestoga College	400 Collier Macmillan Dr.	Cambridge, Ontario		N1R7H7	(519) 740-3320	Brian Naylor
Ontario CAD/CAM Center	400 Collier Macmillan Dr.	Cambridge, Ontario		N1R7H7	(519) 622-3100	Louise Opie
Fanshawe College of Appl. Arts & Tech.	520 First St. Bay 20	London, Ontario		N6V3C6	(519) 452-4436	Mike Westmoreland
Sir Sanford Fleming College	743 Monaghan Rd.	Peterborough		K9J5K2	(705) 876-1611	Peter Brockenshire
Cegep de Levis-Lauzon	205 Mgr Bourget	Lauzon, Quebec		G6V6Z9	(418) 833-1965	Pierre Samson
Vanier College CAD/CAM Institute	425 de Maisonneuve Blvd W, #1100	Montreal, Quebec		H3A3G5	(514) 281-9807	Chris Erikkson
St. Henri	4115 rue Saint-Jacques	Montreal, Quebec		H4C1J3	(514) 596-5954	Georges Assal
University of Regina	Faculty of Engineering	Regina, SK		S4S0A2	(306) 585-4709	Kelly Waldal
HONG KONG						
Hong Kong Productivity Council	13F Winglung Bank Bldg., 45 Desvoeux Rd.	Central			(852) 3-7235656	H.K. Man
INDIA						
Datapro Information Technology	201 Embassy Centre, Nariman Pt.	Bombay		400 021	(91) 23-25-20	A.D. Narula
Coimbatore Inst. of Tech.	VRET Training Ctr.	Coimbatore		641 014	(91) 87-40-71	M. Guruswamy
Indian Inst. of Tech.	201 Northern Lab I	Kanpur		208 016	(91) 24-52-26	S.G. Dhande
CADD Centre	340/342 Triplicane High Rd.	Madras		600 005	(91) 84-34-59	V. Sathya Moorthy
ISRAEL						
Israel Inst. of Productivity	Kiryat Hamelaha 4 Shvil Hameretz	Tel Aviv		PO 33010	(972) 3-821192	Jacob Levy
MALAYSIA						
Universiti Teknologi Malaysia	Jalan Semarak, 54100	Kuala Lumpur			(03) 2929033-4411	Azmi Abdullah
MEXICO						
CRT Mexico	Rio Timber 68-404	Mexico D.F.		06500	(52) 5-528-7769	Gabriel Meyassed

CENTER	ADDRESS	CITY	ST	ZIP	PHONE	CONTACT/CLASS INFO
NEW ZEALAND						
Aukland Tech. Inst.	Private Bag	Aukland			(64) 9-773-570	G.H.E. Vervcort
Christchurch Polytechnic	P.O. Box 22-095	Christchurch			(64) 3-798-150	F.D. McAven
Waikato Polytechnic	Private Bag	Hamilton			(64) 71-392-500	John McGarva
Central Inst. of Tech.	Somme Road	Heretaunga			(04) 277-089	A.T. Packer
Carrington Polytechnic	Carrington Road	Mt. Albert		Aukland 3	(64) 9-869-106	Joe Doherty
Taranaki Polytechnic	Bell Street	New Plymouth			(64) 67-88059	Dave Robinson
SINGAPORE						
Brown Boveri Gov't. Trng. Ctr.	15 Kallang Junction	Singapore		1233	(65) 296-7833	Walter Seiner
Singapore Polytechnic	500 Dover Rd.	Singapore		0513	(65) 772-1160	Jack Koh
SOUTH AFRICA						
The AutoCAD Centre	P.O. Box 7	Halfway House		1685	(27) 805-1702/1764	Roberta Sandenbergh
SOUTH KOREA						
New Industry Mgt. Academy	#521 Chang-Kang Bldg., 18-1 Dowha-Dong	Mapo-gu	Seoul		(822) 784-5292/3	Se-hoon Kong
TAIWAN R.O.C.						
China Productivity Ctr./Kaohsiung	6th Floor, 21 Wu-Fu 3 Rd.	Kaohsiung			(886) 7201-9804	Jin-Wei Chou
China Productivity Ctr./Taichung	250-3 Kuokwang Rd.	Taichung		40226	(886) 4287-0040	Shichang Chiao
China Productivity Ctr.	2nd Fl., 340 Tun Hua N. Rd.	Taipei		10592	(886) 2713-7731	Brad C.S. Wu
WEST MALAYSIA						

Autodesk Area Educational Representatives

Autodesk has designated a group of Area Educational Representatives, selected authorized AutoCAD dealers, to provide special consultational services and product pricing to educational institutions. If you are at an educational institution and are interested in purchasing AutoCAD, call 1-800-445-5415 and ask for the Area Educational Representative nearest you.

Appendix R: Standard Screen Menu

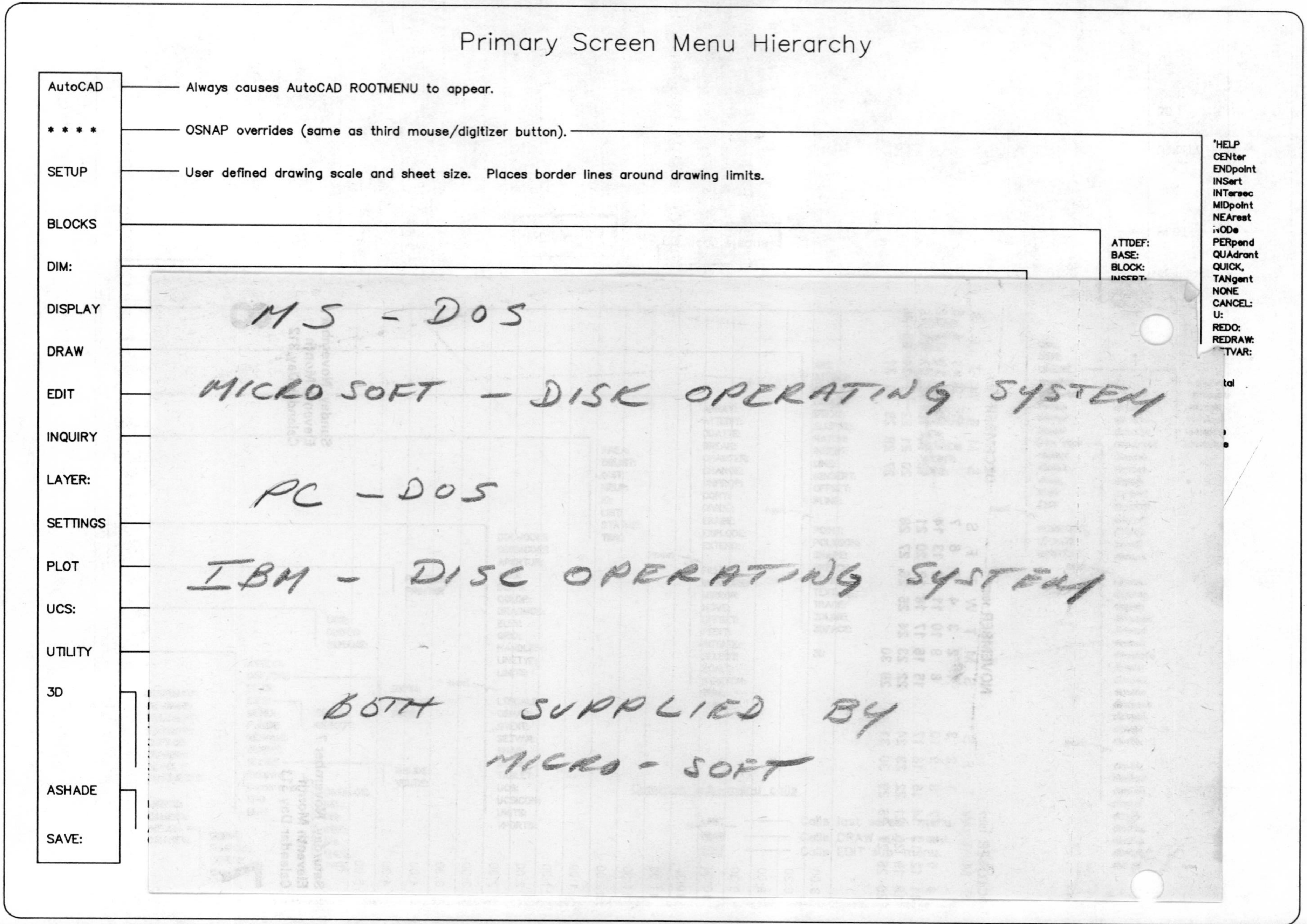

Primary Screen Menu Hierarchy
AutoCAD
Always causes AutoCAD ROOTMENU to appear.
* * * *
OSNAP overrides (same as third mouse/digitizer button).
SETUP
User defined drawing scale and sheet size. Places border lines around drawing limits.
BLOCKS
DIM:
DISPLAY
DRAW
EDIT
INQUIRY
LAYER:
SETTINGS
PLOT
UCS:
UTILITY
3D
ASHADE
SAVE:
ATTDEF:
BASE:
BLOCK:
'HELP
CENter
ENDpoint
INSert
INTersec
MIDpoint
NEArest
PERpend
QUAdrant
QUICK,
TANgent
NONE
CANCEL:
U:
REDO:
REDRAW:
MS - DOS
MICRO SOFT - DISK OPERATING SYSTEM
PC - DOS
IBM - DISC OPERATING SYSTEM
BOTH SUPPLIED BY
MICRO - SOFT

Appendix S: Pull-Down Menus

Menu Bar and Pull-Down Menus

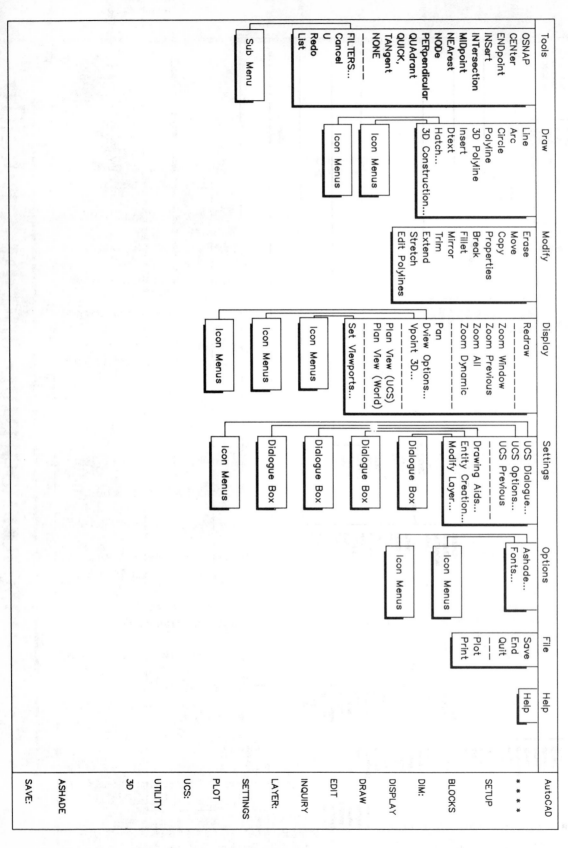

Tools	Draw	Modify	Display	Settings	Options	File	Help
OSNAP	Line	Erase	Redraw	UCS Dialogue...	Ashade...	Save	Help
CENter	Arc	Move	Zoom Window	UCS Options...	Fonts...	End	
ENDpoint	Circle	Copy	Zoom Previous	UCS Previous		———	
INSert	Polyline	Properties	Zoom All	———————		Quit	
INTersection	3D Polyline	Break	Zoom Dynamic	Drawing Aids...		———	
MIDpoint	Insert	Fillet	———————	Entity Creation...		Plot	
NEArest	Dtext	Mirror	Pan	Modify Layer...		Print	
NODe	Hatch...	Trim	Dview Options...				
PERpendicular	3D Construction...	Extend	Vpoint 3D...				
QUAdrant		Stretch	———————				
QUICK,		Edit Polylines	Plan View (UCS)				
TANgent			Plan View (World)				
NONE			Set Viewports...				
———————							
FILTERS...							
Cancel							
U							
Redo							
List							

Sub Menu

Icon Menus

Icon Menus

Icon Menus

Icon Menus

Icon Menus

Dialogue Box

Dialogue Box

Dialogue Box

Dialogue Box

Icon Menus

Icon Menus

Icon Menus

AutoCAD
* * * *
SETUP
BLOCKS
DIM:
DISPLAY
DRAW
EDIT
INQUIRY
LAYER:
SETTINGS
PLOT
UCS:
UTILITY
3D
ASHADE
SAVE:

Trademarks

ACAD, Advanced User Interface, ATC, AutoShade, and DXF are trademarks of Autodesk, Inc.

Acad Partner is a registered trademark of Chase Systems.

AcadPLUS is a registered trademark of Cad Design Systems, Inc.

Apollo is a registered trademark of Apollo Computer, Inc.

Apple, AppleTalk, LaserWriter, and Macintosh are registered trademarks of Apple Computer, Inc.

AppleCD SC, AppleFax, and A/UX are trademarks of Apple Computer, Inc.

Artist XJ10 is a trademark of Control Systems.

AutoCAD, Autodesk, AutoLISP, and AutoCAD AEC are registered trademarks of Autodesk, Inc.

AutoFasteners is a trademark of SPOCAD.

AutoMusic is a trademark of SPOCAD.

BASIC is a registered trademark of the Trustees of Dartmouth College.

CAMM-3 is produced by Roland DG.

Color Digital Imager IV is a trademark of Bell & Howell.

Complete Postprocessor is a registered trademark of NC Microproducts, Inc.

Cray is a registered trademark of Cray Research, Inc.

Cyber 205 is a trademark of Control Data Corporation.

dBASE II and dBASE III are registered trademarks of Ashton-Tate.

Deskpro 386 is a trademark of Compaq Computer Corporation.

Ethernet is a registered trademark of Xerox Corporation.

FixturePro is a trademark of Jergens Inc.

HIPAD Plus and Houston Instrument are trademarks of AMETEK, Inc.

IBM 4300, PC-DOS, IBM PC, IBM PC/AT, and IBM Personal System/2 are registered trademarks of International Business Machines Corporation.

Intel 8087, 8088, 80286, 80287, 80386, and 80387 are trademarks of Intel Corporation.

Kurta is a registered trademark of Kurta Corporation.

LADS is a product of Birmingham Computer Consulting.

LANDCADD is a trademark of LANDCADD, Inc.

Lotus 1-2-3 is a trademark of Lotus Development Corp.

Microsoft and MS-DOS are registered trademarks of Microsoft Corporation.

MicroVAX II is a trademark of Digital Equipment Corp.

Motorola 68020, 68030, 68881, and 68882 are products of Motorola.

MSC/pal 2 is a trademark of MacNeal Schwendler Corp.

NC-Auto-Code is a registered trademark of Kramer Consulting, Inc.

NC Programmer is a registered trademark of NC Microproducts.

NICAM is a trademark of Numeridex.

OMNI 800 is a registered trademark of Texas Instruments Inc.

OrthoCAD is a trademark of TAD.

Plotmaster is a trademark of CalComp.

POSTSCRIPT is a registered trademark of Adobe Systems, Inc.

Reflex is a trademark of Borland/Analytica, Inc.

SCAN-CAD is a trademark of Houston Instrument.

SmartCAM is a trademark of Point Control Co.

Sun is a trademark of Sun Microsystems, Inc.

Supersap is a trademark of Algor Interactive Systems.

Synthesis is a trademark of Synthesis, Inc.

Tektronix is a registered trademark of Tektronix, Inc.

10CAD Plus is a trademark of ACS Telecom.

Tool Designer's Assistant is a trademark of Carr Lane Manufacturing Company.

Trainer CNC Bridgeport Retrofit is a product of Cardinal Engineering.

UNIX is a registered trademark of AT&T Information Systems.

VAX 8600, MicroVAX II, and VAXstation 2000 are trademarks of Digital Equipment Corp.

Volkswriter is a registered trademark of Lifetree Software Inc.

WordPerfect is a registered trademark of Satellite Software International.

Index